DISC

MORE GOLD IN YOUR ATTIC

Books by Van Allen Bradley

MUSIC FOR THE MILLIONS
GOLD IN YOUR ATTIC
MORE GOLD IN YOUR ATTIC

More
Gold in your Attic

VAN ALLEN BRADLEY

FLEET PUBLISHING CORPORATION

NEW YORK

Library of Congress Catalog Card Number: 61-15017
Printed in the United States of America

DEDICATION

To the members of the Antiquarian Booksellers
Association of America,
for constructive criticism and help.

ACKNOWLEDGMENTS

AMONG THE MANY to whom I owe special thanks for help with the column, "Gold in Your Attic," and with this book, my wife naturally comes to mind first. To Patricia, then, for, among other attributes, forbearance. To my newspaper readers and to the readers of *Gold in Your Attic* for their loyalty. To my research and secretarial assistants, Clementine Kucera and Edna Luehr, for exceptional service. And finally to the booksellers, collectors, and plain booklovers who made the work on this book a possibility and a pleasure: especially Wright Howes, Kenneth Nebenzahl, Owen Davies, Paul Schopflin, Donald La Chance, Peter Decker, Howard S. Mott, Philip Roskie, Harold Tribolet, Jacob Blanck, Sol M. Malkin, Dr. Stanley Pargellis, the Rev. Don Norman, W. A. Stewart, Wendell W. Goodpasture, Adolph Kroch, Richard Harwell, Louis Silver, Everett D. Graff, Ralph Newman, Ben Gabriel, Peggy McNee, Harold Graves, John Carter, and George Charney. An extra-special word of thanks also to my publisher, S. George Little, without whose faith and support neither the column nor the book could have had an existence.

A precious mouldering pleasure 'tis
To meet an Antique Book
In just the Dress his Century wore
A privilege I think

His venerable Hand to take
And warming in our own
A passage back or two to make
To Times when he was young

His quaint opinions to inspect
His thought to ascertain
On Themes concern our mutual mind
The Literature of Man

—Emily Dickinson

I believe that today more than ever a book should be sought after if it has only *one* great page in it: we must search for fragments, splinters, toenails, anything that has ore in it, anything that is capable of resuscitating the body and soul.
—Henry Miller, from *Tropic of Cancer*

CONTENTS

PART ONE

PART TWO

PART THREE

PART ONE

FOUR GOLDEN YEARS OF
BOOK HUNTING

A SHORT TIME AFTER this book appears in the bookstores this fall, the newspaper column "Gold in Your Attic," on which it is based, will be observing its fourth birthday. In its relatively brief life, the column has attracted a surprisingly large number of loyal followers. It has met with a warm response among booklovers new and old. For many it has opened up new paths to the joys of book collecting. For others it has shown the way to a literary hobby that is profitable monetarily and otherwise. And for at least a few, newcomers to the rare book trade, it has meant new careers as book scouts and booksellers. Over these four years it has been an instrument for locating many rare and valuable books, pamphlets, maps, and other literary materials and for turning those materials into cash for their owners. Thus it has channeled into the hands of dealers, libraries, and private collectors many items that otherwise might have remained lost and forgotten. Not the least of its modest achievements have been the several fairly important bibliographical discoveries it has helped to make,

13

particularly in the field of Western Americana. The most notable and satisfying of these was the discovery of not only the first, but also the *second,* complete copy of a famous Western guidebook for which Americana specialists had hunted in vain for half a century.

Of all the pleasant things that have happened through the column, none has afforded more reward than the continuously heavy flow of mail from its readers, over the sustained period of its appearance in American and Canadian newspapers. It is one of my genuine regrets that the volume of this correspondence has been so large as to make it physically impossible for me, even with the help of two trained assistants, to answer in person all the thousands of readers who have written in response to the column, as well as to my first book, *Gold in Your Attic,* which appeared in 1958. To all those who have written, I offer this personal assurance that their letters have in every case been read by me personally and that all have been cordially received. In every case where it seemed that a reader had an exceptional "find" on his hands, I have endeavored to reply, either personally or in the newspaper column. There is at all times a bulging back file of these inquiries awaiting processing. In the meantime, it is my hope that this second compilation of featured books from the column, along with its supplemental Price Index, will serve, as did its 1958 predecessor, to answer many of the questions that have so far had to remain unanswered.

Looking back over the last four years, I think that perhaps the greatest of all the satisfactions in writing the column and the first book has been the awareness I have gained of what these efforts have meant to so many readers hungry for information about the glamorous, sometimes mysterious world of old and rare books. For example, there is the woman in Winnetka, Illinois, who wrote to me, "Thank you so much for this fascinating column. You have made me look at my bookshelves with a completely new interest. And though I have several items which you say are valuable, I don't want to sell them now, for I've fallen in love with these old books all over again."

And the woman on a rural route in Maryland who wrote in to say, simply, "I have been reading your book *Gold in Your Attic,* and it is so very interesting. I have begun buying books again." Then there was the wealthy Texas publisher, an ardent student of his state's history and the owner of a substantial private library, who wrote to say, "I am amazed," when his newspaper began running the column. He had suddenly discovered that many of the books in his library were worth many times what he paid for them. One of the best letters of all came from a retired couple in Florida, who wrote, "Thank you so very much for giving us this wonderful new hobby and a new interest in life."

Among many letters have been a number from men and women who were prompted by the column or the first book, to take up book hunting as a livelihood. There was, for example, the amusing case of the woman in Williams Bay, Wisconsin, who read *Gold in Your Attic* at a sitting and rushed out to buy books right and left, at auction and elsewhere, without ever having digested what she had read about the identifying "points" of first editions, the importance of condition, *et cetera.* She "confessed" her unbusinesslike approach to a highly specialized business in an hilarious advertisement in Antiquarian Bookman that titillated the entire rare book trade—and, as a result, promptly sold her entire stock of books, at a profit, to a well-known Chicago dealer who took his own truck up to Wisconsin and hauled the books away! Later, somewhat chastened by her shaky first plunge into antiquarian book-selling, she wrote to me that she was making a second start with proper caution and happily using *Gold in Your Attic* as a guide. And just a day before the writing of these lines I had a letter from a Long Island reader of the column who has successfully launched her own mail order bookstore after a trial run of advertising in the book trade media.

My pangs of regret at not being able to answer all my correspondents in person are eased somewhat by the knowledge that a great many readers know that such a task is almost impossible to cope with. A housewife in New Haven, Connecticut, put it this way in her amusing letter: "I suppose by now you have been swamped with letters and lists of books so you could pull your hair out." My answer was, "Yes!"

Most of all I would like to thank all the hundreds of readers—laymen as well as professional bookmen—who have written to praise the first book so generously. No one is more aware than I am of the faults that that book had, yet the complaints have been astonishingly few. Those from laymen received so far can still be counted on the fingers of one hand, and three of these four resulted not from any dissatisfaction with the material presented but from an inability to locate a purchaser for books. The fourth complaint grew out of a misinterpretation of an item in the text and was satisfactorily answered by cor-respondence.

Librarians, collectors, and the book trade in general

have been especially kind to *Gold in Your Attic*. The complaints from dealers have been somewhat more numerous than those from laymen, as I had expected, but in only two instances have booksellers shown me any outright hostility. That is all the more surprising when one stops to think that what I have really being doing is "giving away" many of the "secrets" of the rare book trade and showing the public at large the true values of rare books. It is a credit to the integrity of the American rare book dealer that by and large he does not deliberately seek to make his business the dark mystery it has often seemed to be. The simple fact is that the whole field of bibliography and book prices is so complex that few booksellers have ever had the time to try to make it understandable to the layman. My experience has been that most of the nation's rare bookmen, and especially the able members of the Antiquarian Booksellers Association of America, have welcomed the steps I have taken, however faltering, to bring to the general public a wider basic understanding of the values of old and rare books.

Of the bookseller complaints that I have received, most can be placed in one of three categories: The protests that certain prices I have quoted are too high, that some of my readers have made pests of themselves by offering worthless books for sale, and that certain entries in *Gold in Your Attic* contained inaccuracies.

The first type of protest was expected, for the simple reason that no two dealers see a book alike. There is a wide range of prices prevailing among the various dealers, coast to coast, on almost any specific title you may name. What I have tried to do in the column and in the books based on it is to strike an average and to reflect the general range of the book market. The most difficult part of this task lies in the "blind spot" offered by the question of interpretation of "condition" as it may apply to different copies of the same book. There is no fixed price on any book that is out of print and rare, so the tendency of dealers is to price books at what the traffic will bear. The prices, in other words, are dictated by the laws of supply and demand. Further, there is no fixed agreement among booksellers generally as to what is meant by "good" condition, or even "fine" condition. The only absolute in the trade so far as condition is concerned is the term "mint," which means an absolutely pristine book, just as it came from the binder. One dealer may price a "fine" copy of a book at $75 while another catalogues the same book, also "fine," at $125. But since each dealer may think of "fine" in different terms, there is no possible way, without actually comparing the two books side by side, to determine which book is "fine" and which is priced correctly.

In this connection, I think the most interesting bookseller complaint about prices in the "Gold in Your Attic" column came from Boston. A bookman who shall remain unidentified sent a postcard to my Boston newspaper outlet to accuse me of publishing "erroneous and misleading information" concerning the rare first edition, first issue, of Mark Twain's *The Adventures of Tom Sawyer,* which I had said was worth up to $750, and possibly more, in fine condition. After offering to oblige me with a "free lecture" on the value of American first editions, this gentleman cited as being closer to the real value a $100 price on "Tom" from the 1958 edition of the auction record book, *American Book-Prices Current.* Of course, he was wholly mistaken. For *he did not note* at the same time that the book that sold for $100 at auction was a "recased" copy with "cover stains" and was NOT in fine condition.

In reply to him, I simply called attention to this omission, and its obvious unfairness, and in addition named the two specific authorities for my own price quotation. They happened to be, for the record, the leading American authority on Mark Twain's first editions, Franklin J. Meine of Chicago, and the well-known Eastern bookseller, Howard S. Mott.

Among the dealer complaints in the second category—protesting the pests—the loudest came, strangely enough, from a veteran bookseller of the Midwest who had picked up several quite rare items from my readers, including a Mormon pamphlet which he later sold to a noted Americana collector. While I respect this dealer's position and understand his annoyance at having to answer so many fruitless letters (he is an able, conscientious man), I believe that the number of my readers who rush madly to bookstores with worthless junk after reading the column is a small minority. From the beginning I have sought to emphasize the necessity for book owners to first determine what they have before offering it for sale. I have also striven to underline the importance of condition as it affects book prices. This effort to educate the general public in the field of old books and their values will continue, for I am convinced that it is an endeavor beneficial to the antiquarian trade rather than harmful. The mail from the many dealers around the country who have obtained excellent material from readers confirms that belief. For the sales are substantial and have several times run into the four figures for individual rarities.

Finally, to those dealers who have taken the time to report—usually with grace and with an obvious interest in helping along the good work—on the inevitable errors that have upon occasion crept into the column, my sincere thanks. Wherever possible I have taken steps to correct the slips (some are corrected in the present volume). I shall continue to welcome the cooperation of all bookmen in reducing error to a minimum in the dissemination of rare book information.

My friendly relationship with dealers on the whole has been one of the warmest satisfactions of the entire experience of writing the column. For it has led me to believe that with very few exceptions the really knowledgeable and fair-minded bookseller welcomes the educational effort I have undertaken. The few who have opposed my column have doubtless acted in the sincere belief that it is a harmful influence on their trade. I cannot believe, however, that any dealer of reputation and fairness is really opposed to letting the public in on the true values of old books.

It would be impossible in the brief space allotted to this chapter for me to discuss in detail even a small number of the rare and valuable books that have been unearthed by my readers since 1957. But for the record, here are a few:

A wealthy Midwestern collector purchased and presented to a leading Americana collection a previously unrecorded edition of John Disturnell's *The Traveller's Guide Through the State of Illinois,* with a separate folding map in color, published in New York in 1858. A syndicate of dealers joined to purchase the most important single discovery, the hitherto unrecorded first edition of P. L. Platt's and Nelson Slater's *The Traveller's Guide, Across the Plains,* published in Chicago in 1852. Until this copy was turned up by a reader in the state of Washington, nobody had ever seen a complete copy of the first edition. The only copy previously known, in the library of the collector, Thomas Winthrop Streeter, lacked the first 16 pages, including the title page, and bibliographers had assumed the book was published in 1854. They had been looking for the book for half a century. It is one of the superstitions of the rare book trade that whenever a long-sought book is found, another copy, or sometimes several, will turn up in quick succession. Sure enough, a few months after the first copy of the Platt and Slater was found, a *second* perfect copy was located in the hands of a California reader. Both these copies sold for substantial figures which, for the moment, must remain undisclosed.

A South Dakota minister turned up one day with a copy of the rare first edition of Augusta Jane Evans Wilson's *Macaria*, the paperbound novel which was the *Gone with the Wind* of the Confederacy. It found a resting place in Chicago's famous Newberry Library.

A Chicago dealer paid a Massachusetts reader $1,800 for a 32-page paperbound book entitled *Guide to the New Gold Region of Western Kansas and Nebraska*. I later saw this copy catalogued at $2,800, which speaks well, I think, for the fair-mindedness of this particular dealer. His payment was higher in relation to retail value than is commonly current in the trade, where a 100% markup is the universal standard. The same dealer also bought a copy of the rare Overton Johnson and William H. Winter narrative *Route Across the Rocky Mountains*. A well-known New York dealer paid a four-figure price for a copy of Lansford W. Hastings' *The Emigrants' Guide to Oregon and California*.

Other sales made by readers from every section of the country have included the first editions of Mark Twain's *The Adventures of Tom Sawyer* and *Adventures of Huckleberry Finn,* Stephen Crane's *The Red Badge of Courage,* Nathaniel Hawthorne's *The Scarlet Letter,* L. Frank Baum's *The Wonderful Wizard of Oz,* and hundreds of other rarities of major and minor degree. There doubtless also were a great many more sales of major collector's items about which no report has come to me from either dealers or readers, along with innumerable other sales of lesser works.

In the years ahead, we look forward to a steady succession of new surprises. And that is what makes the column such a satisfying adventure. Who knows? Maybe some day one of the *Gold in Your Attic* readers will turn up one of the great unfindable rarities—a first edition of *Murders in the Rue Morgue,* an undiscovered Gutenberg Bible, or a Bay Psalm Book. The challenge is always there.

COLLECTORS ARE A CURIOUS BREED

IT HAS ALWAYS BEEN REMARKED ABOUT the newspaper profession that it is a place where you meet "so many interesting people." And this has surely been true of the many
contacts I have had with booklovers through my rare book
column. For the collector is almost always a man possessed,
a "curious breed of cat," as one has put it. Such is the
range of collecting that there are always new frontiers,
new fields to develop, long-lost avenues to explore, exciting
adventures waiting around every bend of the endless paths
through the vast and myriad groves of the world's great
books that make up what Emily Dickinson calls the Literature of Man.

There is, for example, my longtime friend, Franklin J.
Meine, the Mark Twain authority and a specialist in
American humor whose great collection was acquired a
few years ago for the University of Illinois Library. Like
every collector, Mr. Meine has a few special interests that
drive him well-nigh to distraction, engaging almost every
waking hour. One of these is his vision of a phantom book
that may have once belonged to George W. Harris, the

nineteenth century American storyteller who wrote *Sut Lovingood's Yarns.* But let Mr. Meine tell his story:

"In 1869," he wrote to me a short while ago, "Harris became ill on a train while returning from Lynchburg, Virginia, to Knoxville, Tennessee, and died without regaining consciousness. The account of his death in the Knoxville Press and Messenger for December 15, 1869, contained the following: 'We recollect reading in a Lynchburg paper, of Thursday last, that Capt. Harris was in that city, looking well and hearty, and in high spirits, having completed arrangements, during his stay in Richmond, for the publication of his later writings of the famous Sut Lovingood letters.' Other accounts of his death agree that he had made arrangements for the publication of another book. Prof. George F. Mellen, an authority of this period who published several articles on George W. Harris in the Knoxville Sentinel in 1911, gives the name of this projected work as *High Times and Hard Times.*

"The 'manuscript' seems never to have been published. As to whether it was turned over to the publisher or was still in the possession of Harris, is not known. The daughter of Harris' wife (his stepdaughter) made the statement that the 'manuscript' was in her possession at one time. But it seems never to have been published.

"This manuscript may have been in the form of a *scrapbook of newspaper clippings,* i.e., newspaper printings of Harris' stories which he had contributed to the papers. Often a writer would do this: cut out his stories at the time they appeared in the papers and paste them in a scrapbook with a view to future publication.

"My search for this phantom book is a long shot, of course, but funnier things have happened. This one has been bothering me for 25 years. My thought is that Harris might have made a deal with some job printer in Richmond or Lynchburg for a local printing which might not have been more than 500 copies. As you know, this was often done with local Americana. Also, in view of the fact that the Sut Lovingood stories were often considered so vulgar or coarse that chances for survival would be slim. Anyway, this is my story, and you might get a clue."

If any reader has a *High Times and Hard Times* (or the scrapbook of it), Mr. Meine will be glad to hear from you. His address is 1422 North La Salle Street, Chicago 10, Illinois.

Then there is the New York advertising executive, Ralph D. Gardner, the Horatio Alger collector who has also become a good friend of mine and has perhaps the best Alger collection in America. Mr. Gardner's special distraction is finding a first edition copy of Alger's anonymous story *Timothy Crump's Ward,* published by Loring of Boston in 1866. Just to show you the nature of Mr. Gardner's pleasurable obsessions, I quote from a letter I received from him the other day:

"I have been offered $100 for my copy of Alger's *Dan the Detective* but, of course, I do not wish to sell it. It was originally serialized in Street & Smith's New York Weekly in 1880. However, the 'first edition' is considered to be the hard cover volume published in 1884 by G. W. Carleton & Co., New York. This is a great rarity, and I know of only two other copies of *Dan,* whereas I know of at least seven first edition copies of *Ragged Dick.*"

Mr. Gardner also discusses another Alger book, *The Western Boy,* also published by Carleton, and comments: "Until I found my copy and advised other serious Alger collectors that the first edition has the Carleton imprint, it was believed that this book was first published by J. S. Ogilvie and Co., New York. Like *Dan the Detective, The Western Boy* was first serialized in Street & Smith's New York Weekly, in 1873. The story was then brought out by Carleton in book form in 1878. After what probably was a very limited printing, this story was retitled *Tom the Bootblack* and, with this new title, became one of Alger's best-known works. It is my personal belief that it was Ogilvie who first published it under the *re-issue* title but, after years of searching, I have not been able to come up with a copy of the Ogilvie book. I do not know the cash value of the Carleton *Western Boy,* but I believe it could bring only slightly less than *Dan the Detective.*

"There is no question in my mind but that the Horatio Alger stories published by G. W. Carleton (there were three altogether; *The Train Boy*—1883—which completes the Carleton trio, is also on the hard-to-get-list) are among the rarest of Algers. Certainly they are *much* harder to find than most of the better-known A. K. Loring editions. Between 1867 and 1880 Loring published some 36 original Alger titles, including *Ragged Dick* and the rarest, *Timothy Crump's Ward.*"

If any reader has a first edition of *Timothy Crump's Ward,* Mr. Gardner will be glad to hear from him. His address is 745 Fifth Avenue, New York 22, New York. For a stamped envelope, he will send you his "want list."

A man more successful in one of his obsessions than either Messrs. Meine and Gardner is Ben P. P. Moseley of Boston, Massachusetts. I heard about Mr. Moseley through an Eastern bookseller, P. E. Rothenburger, who told me that he was the proud possessor of the first edition of a famous novel, the three-decker *All but Lost*, by G. A. Henty.

"In the first place," Mr. Moseley wrote to me, "I started reading Henty books somewhere around 1890. I know it was before I could read myself, as my Aunt had to read to me. Most of my early books came from a collector named Brown in Boston and he had some connections with London.

"Regarding *All but Lost*, Mr. Rothenburger can tell you more than I can as I obtained the book through him. Mr. Goodspeed [a Boston dealer] told me that there had not been one in an auction for 34 years. As to price, if I remember correctly, I paid $1,200 for the book, which, of course, was an ungodly sum. It was a chance that came once in a lifetime, and besides it made my collection complete."

These stories of three bookmen's quests, while fascinating in their own way, are not more so than the bookish fervor of the distinguished elderly gentleman, a machine tool operator by profession, who came into my office one day to tell his astonishing story.

In manner and appearance he seemed, with his Swiss accent, his obvious education, and his excellent command of the English language, more like a professor of literature than a worker in a factory. He bore with him a special sorrow, and as he told me about it great tears appeared in his eyes and rolled down across his craggy cheeks and over the drooping firleaves of his mustache.

It seems that he was a lifelong bibliophile, wed to a shrew and a book-hater, and life was one continuing hell in which he tried to save enough out of his lunch money to buy the books he wanted and smuggle them into his house. Now he was reduced to selling some of his collector's items to buy others that he wanted.

In his pocket he had a Bernard Shaw letter, which I promptly bought and later donated to a literary auction for Poetry magazine. (It brought $35.) In his arms was a rare Colorado book on railroading, for which I managed with a telephone call to find a buyer at a decent price.

My last collector in this little gallery is an aging Texan who several times has taken the time to write to me long letters about his literary pursuit, which is the loving care and restoration of ancient volumes. There are several famous hand binders around the country who are experts at restoring and revivifying old paper, but few of them are willing to share their secrets. My Texan, Fred W. Dibble from the little town of Reagan, has described his methods in detail, and I pass them along for the benefit of other booklovers:

"Some 10 or 12 years ago I had several books I valued and which would soon be utterly worn out, and beyond reclamation, if something were not done for them. I had to study what I would do in such cases. I first studied rebinding. But in some of the books the pages were badly foxed and rusty. I did research along that line. In rebinding I had to largely dismantle the book. I then ran each piece of paper through a bleaching solution which removes the rust or foxing and leaves the paper as white as it was originally. This requires a minimum of seven, and preferably nine, submersions and washings, and paper 100 years or older has to be handled very carefully. It requires a great deal of care to avoid at least a few tears, although it can be done after practice. The solutions to be used can be very easily made up yourself.

"You need three shallow trays (I use baking pans about one-half a yard square and two inches deep which I have enameled with white enamel). Fill one of these trays with a potassium permanganate solution, one with water, and the third with a sodium meta-bisulphite solution. The solution strengths are the same: one part of potassium permanganate to 16 parts of water and one part of sodium meta-bisulphite to 16 parts of water. This is pretty close to a saturated solution (chemical formulas $KMnO_4$ and $Na_2S_2O_5$).

"Wet the paper to be bleached by immersing in plain water until thoroughly soaked. This is done so that the first chemical will permeate the paper quickly and evenly. Then place the paper in the solution of potassium permanganate bath for no more than 30 seconds. Wash out the paper in plain water three times. After washing, submerge the paper (which comes from the permanganate a sort of liver color) in the solution of sodium meta-bisulphite. It is very striking to see the discoloration fade out and the paper assume its original whiteness. As soon as it is white, wash out the remaining chemical in the paper in three plain water baths. If it appears that the bleaching is not what it should be it simply means that one of the solutions is losing strength. If I am in the middle of the process and this occurs, I usually add a small amount of bisulphite first. This usually produces the desired result. A test may be made thus: Get a few crystals on the end of a knife blade and shake in the solution so that it will settle over a place as yet most discolored, or resistant to the bisulphite. The paper will probably whiten almost instantly. The bisulphite will deteriorate after a time.

"I use two gallon glass jugs to hold my solutions. After

one using I pour the chemicals back into the jug for sub-sequent use. The permanganate reacts with the rust in the paper (the rust is a fungus) to produce a sludge which settles to the bottom. This does not affect the operation except to weaken the solution. I have filtered off the sludge, using an ordinary paper towel folded, as in a chemical laboratory. Weaker solutions may be used, but such will require a little longer in the bath. In using per-manganate your fingers will become brown, but when put in the bisulphite solution the brown will disappear. The solutions have never irritated my skin. The potassium per-manganate may be had at almost any drug store. There is small demand for the sodium meta-bisulphite. However, I order both from a wholesale chemical sales house in Houston. The cost is not high."

Mr. Dibble also tells me about "a very efficient means of repairing tears" in the pages of an old book. This is the use of a rather thick solution of cellulose acetate, which he applies to a tear, working it in with a flat knife blade. He says it makes the paper at the tear even stronger than it was in the beginning.

"The cellulose acetate solution," he writes, "is very easy to make. The difficulty will be in securing the amorphous cellulose acetate. I had to order a 500-gram bottle from Houston, although 50 grams is enough to last quite a while. I make up my solution in a small glass jar the size of a paste jar. I put in the cellulose acetate and add the acetone, which can be obtained at any drug store. It dis-solves rather slowly. When dissolved, if too thick, add a little more acetone until the solution is about the thick-ness of a maple syrup. I apply with a small brush or with the tip of my knife blade. Of course, I see to it that the torn edges match perfectly."

Such is the tedious way of a true bookman with the pages of his treasures.

Yes, indeed, the collector is a curious cat.

EXACTLY HOW YOU CAN SELL
YOUR OLD BOOKS

IT IS EASY ENOUGH to answer questions from readers about individual books that are known or suspected to be scarce or rare and for which full information has been supplied. The most discouraging type of question comes, however, from the reader who submits a long list of miscellaneous books, usually recording only the author and title, and asks, "Where can I sell my old books? List enclosed. Please mark value of each book on margin and return to me."

In the first place, I am not engaged in appraising books, which is a job usually done by a bookseller or a bookseller's assistant, for a fee. I do answer certain "selected questions," as my column states every week, but these choices must be confined to those books which are of some value and of some interest to a wide range of readers. It would be an impossible task—even with a staff of 50 people helping me—to supply accurate information on all the titles about which readers write.

In the second place, nobody can even begin to suggest a probable price for any rare book unless the questioner provides him with certain essentials: the author's name, the title of the book, the place of publication (from the title page), the date of publication (from the title page), the copyright date (from the reverse of the title page), a description of the binding, and a fair description of the book's condition. Even then, it should be emphasized, no absolute price figure can be given—only a rough estimate. The final decision on the exact value of the book will still have to be based on a personal examination of the copy in question.

The questions that I receive in the mail—"How can I tell the value of an old book?" and "Do I have any valuable books on this list?"—are the same questions that are most frequently asked of the second-hand or rare bookseller. For that reason, I shall try to explain in this chapter just how a bookseller looks at the usual book collection and in the course of this explanation endeavor as best I can to offer concrete suggestions on exactly how anyone can realize the best prices for books he may have to offer.

Let us first consider the rare book dealer. Many a reader has mistakenly assumed that every second-hand book dealer knows about and handles rare books, but such is not the case. There are many men and women operating second-hand bookstores who would not know a Gutenberg Bible if it spoke to them, and there are book scouts who make a comfortable living profiting by their mistakes. The better second-hand stores, even if they do not specialize in rarities, pay decent prices for ordinary books if they are in condition for resale. It is when the book owner suspects that he has something out of the ordinary, or a rarity, that he should begin to think of the specialized knowledge and experience of the dealer.

How does one select a qualified rare book dealer with whom to do business? There are several ways. One is by searching the local telephone book and carefully reading the classified advertisements to see which dealers profess to be rare book specialists. Another is to determine, if possible, which dealers in town are members of the Antiquarian Booksellers Association of America. Ask the dealers themselves. (The ABAA at one time published a national list of members which it distributed free for the asking. It discontinued the free distribution of this list some time ago because of the extraordinary demand for it that came from "Gold in Your Attic" readers; there simply was too much clerical work involved in mailing it and, besides, the ABAA reported, too many readers neglected the courtesy of enclosing a stamped, self-addressed envelope in requesting the list.) A third method of locating dealers is to consult the annual publication, *American Book-Prices Current,* which is in the reference rooms at most large libraries. It contains the advertisements of most of the nation's leading rare book specialists.

Even after one has compiled a list of possible dealer prospects, there is another consideration that should be made, and that is whether the material you have is exactly in a specific dealer's line. Why this is an important consideration has been best described, I think, in a letter I had some time ago from Donald La Chance, an Evanston, Illinois, specialist in rare and scholarly books and autographs.

"I have enjoyed *Gold in Your Attic,*" he wrote, "and have sold copies to other book dealers and to those who have written in with long lists of books to know what they are worth. If I may make a suggestion pertaining to values and what a dealer should pay [you may indeed, sir!], I think that it should be pointed out that all book dealers (antiquarian) do not handle the same types of books. If a person brings in a book that obviously is a collector's item, but of a type for which he has no immediate or potential market, he would not feel that he could offer the same price as a dealer who specializes in the field which the book covers. . . . As with retail customers there is the right client for the right book, and if the person wants to get the most for his 'find,' it is up to him to make the rounds or accept an average offer, which might possibly be below one half of, let us say, an auction record. He must also understand that an auction price is the highest price any dealer or collector offered for the item at that time."

(It should be explained here that I have, in my column, pointed out from time to time that prices of books sold at book auctions, which are chiefly attended by book dealers, tend by and large to be wholesale prices and that dealers frequently mark these up 50% to 100%.)

"Auction and dealer prices," Mr. La Chance continues, "can be a very general guide at best. Just because a dealer lists a book for $100 in his catalogue, it doesn't necessarily mean that that was the price at which it was sold (he even may still have it gathering dust on his shelf)."

(This is not the place to debate with Mr. La Chance over the influence of auction and catalogue prices. I should point out, however, that the matter of *over-priced* and *unsold* copies has been fully considered and accounted for in both this book and its predecessor. My view of auction prices is identical with that stated by the well-known West Coast bookseller, Philip Roskie, whose two volumes of *The Bookman's Bible* are widely used for pricing books in the antiquarian book trade.)

Let us return now to the question of the rare book dealer. After we have made our choice, how shall we approach him? Certainly not with a long list of poorly described titles. Then where shall we begin?

The first thing to do is to weed out the obviously unsaleable material—the broken, mutilated, and defective books. Unless they are of great antiquity or of known interest, the best thing to do is to forget about them; or give them to anyone who will take them off your hands. (I still can't bring myself to burn a book, no matter how mangled!)

Next, eliminate the "collected works" of Shakespeare, Dickens, Milton, Byron, Balzac, Cooper, *et cetera, ad infinitum, unless* they are in good condition and handsomely bound. If they are in good to fine condition, the second-hand or rare book dealer *may* be interested, but do not expect a fancy price. Most of the "collected works" that are cluttering up the bookshelves of American homes today are commercially of very little value, since they are in plentiful supply. They were sold around the turn of the century as furniture and the proper things to buy.

Third, forget about trying to sell the old family Bible *unless* it happens to be of known value or *unless* it happened to have belonged to a very important person and is therefore valuable for its association. The chances are $999\frac{1}{2}$ out of 1,000 that any Bible you may have is commercially worthless. If you still have doubts, consult a specialist dealer in old Bibles.

Fourth, weed out all the obvious reprint books—and especially the cheaply printed novels published by such houses as A. L. Burt, the Henneberry Co., Grosset & Dunlap, and other large reprint publishers. What you should be looking for is first editions, since there is not a reprint in a carload that is worth much more than a dime at the wholesale level. As a general rule, the way to tell a reprint from a first edition is to examine both the title page and the copyright page and compare them. Most reprint books have no date on the title page, although there are some exceptions. In such exceptions, a title page date later than the copyright date almost always indicates a later printing. On the other hand, if the date on the title page and the date on the copyright page are the same, you *may* have a first edition. But again there are exceptions, and if you are in any doubt you may have to study the book further. Sometimes a book bears a line stating that it is a first edition. In other cases, it may be necessary to take the book to a bookseller or to consult a librarian or a bibliography of the author's work to determine if it is a first edition or simply a reprint.

Now that you are well along toward eliminating the books that are obviously of no great value, what next?

You should begin to sort your books by category; i.e., into separate groups, such as Fiction, History, Poetry, Western Americana, Science, Medicine, *et cetera*. You can then begin a further process of eliminating unlikely books. In this category of poor prospects, you may generally lump together books of sermons, old theological books, "gift" books, and special editions of old authors who were popular half a century or a century ago but are never heard of or even considered as enduring writers today. Add to these such items as old dictionaries, old medical books, old cookbooks, and old textbooks of all kinds, unless they happen to be American textbooks published in the years prior to about 1830. Into the unlikely category you may also place such items as nineteenth century almanacs, except the Davy Crockett series and Commodore Rollingpin almanacs; bound volumes of magazines, except for the Civil War issues of Harper's, perhaps, or issues of the National Geographic of 1910 or earlier; most foreign language books, unless they are of known value or are dated in the seventeenth century or earlier; most of the popular mystery and detective novels; most popular Western fiction, and most anthologies, either prose or poetry.

Having eliminated most of the obvious reprints among your books and most of the unlikely duds, what is the next thing to look for? The answer is: Books that have some importance—either because of the subject matter or because of the author. The first editions of all authors of literary distinction and importance are valuable and are likely to increase in value so long as there are booklovers and collectors. Obviously, then, the next step, insofar as the poetry and fiction titles in your collection are concerned, is to eliminate the items of no great consequence as literature. If you have a general knowledge of literary values, this should present no great difficulty. If you need assistance in choosing the important authors from the unimportant ones, ask a knowledgeable friend. Another way of determining which authors are important is to consult a good standard encyclopedia. Still another is to read the catalogues of dealers in rare poetry and fiction and see what they are offering. You will also find brief lists of important authors of current collecting interest in the opening chapter of the first of my own series of books, *Gold in Your Attic,* which should be available at your public library or at any good bookstore.

After you have narrowed down your fiction and poetry

groups, you will want to determine what the possibilities are among your nonfiction titles. Again, the matter of the first edition is of prime importance in every category, for it is almost always the first edition, the earliest form of an important work in any category, that is sought by the collector and is therefore saleable immediately to a dealer. And again, the books that are most wanted are those that are of some degree of importance in their field. It is practicable here only to suggest a few among the multitude of subjects and types of books that are of interest to the collector. Any color-plate book may have value. Any early American book of the eighteenth century is a possibility. Any first edition by a person well known in some special field of human endeavor is a potentially valuable book. So is any early county or city history or any first directory of a city. Early books about the West and its exploration are especially valuable in the current Americana market. Gold Rush material and emigrant guides have brought extraordinarily high prices in recent years. Children's books by well-known authors are frequently valuable in the first edition. Sporting books, books of travel and exploration, nature books, fine press books, and limited editions of all kinds are to be seriously considered.

For other possibilities, consult the brief list of Americana suggestions offered in the first chapter of *Gold in Your Attic*. And, finally, study the "Price Index and Guide" in that book and in this present volume for clues to the *types* of books that have demonstrated their monetary value. Then look at your own books for similarities of theme or pattern or authorship.

After you have done all these things, you should have

whittled down your possibilities to a relatively small number of books to be considered. What then?

There are two courses open to you. One is to attempt to sell your books directly to collectors. The other is to attempt to sell them to dealers. In either case, you should have some general idea of the worth of your books. That, I am afraid, is going to have to be up to your own diligence and ingenuity—unless, of course, you want to pay for an appraisal, which is never worthwhile for the small home library. (Again, I must point out that appraisals are made for a fee; no book dealer is going to tell you, free of charge, what your books are worth. He will tell you if you also agree to sell them to him, but not otherwise. And this is a fair position for him to take, in view of the fact that he has spent a lifetime acquiring his knowledge; he is in the same position as the physician who dispenses advice and is paid for what he knows.)

Suppose you decide to sell directly to collectors. Then you will need to do two more things. You will need, first of all, to determine *exactly* what you have by carefully researching each book through the bibliographical resources that are available to you at any large public library. Ask your librarian for help. As you satisfy yourself that each book is a book of importance and is a first edition, or perhaps another edition of some importance, you must then seek to determine its proper retail price level. Here again there is no better place to turn than to the public library, where you will usually find available at least a few of the necessary tools for this job. In addition to *More Gold in Your Attic*, with its "Price Index and Guide," you will want to consult the similarly indexed material in its predecessor, *Gold in Your Attic*, as well as the several reference works suggested in that book. In the prefatory notes to the "Price Index and Guide" in Part Three of the present volume, I have mentioned two other reference books of particular value in seeking price information. As you gain experience in sleuthing out book values, you will also learn to use the auction record book, *American Book-Prices Current,* mentioned several times in this text, always keeping in mind that auction prices are generally representative of the wholesale level of the rare book trade. As the final, and ultimately the best, guide to retail prices, you should obtain as many current bookseller catalogues as possible and study the prices and descriptions. In this way, you should be able to solve a great many pricing problems. One good way to obtain rare book catalogues is to watch the advertisements in the classified section of the New York Times Book Review for offerings of catalogues by rare book dealers.

Now that you have determined the general price level of the titles you have to offer, you must decide where these prices fit in relation to the condition of your individual books. If a bookseller lists a William Faulkner novel in "fine" condition at $25 and your copy can only be described as "good," then you must reduce your price accordingly. Every individual book must be analyzed in this manner, and unless you do this, you may void the possibility of a satisfactory sale.

Now that your books have all been priced, you still have the problem of finding a buyer. If the books you have are of sufficient importance, the problem will not be difficult. One good place to start looking for a buyer is among your friends and neighbors. If you have a book of importance in the field of medicine, ask your own physician for the names of doctors who are interested in old medical books. If you have a Willa Cather first edition, ask your librarian if there are Cather experts or collectors in your community. Consult them on possible markets. If you have an early book on the raising of pheasants and know it to be a book of importance and value, ask your local nature club or conservation group where the collectors are. *The clubs and organizations that cater to any special field of human interest or endeavor are good sources of leads to book buyers and collectors.* If you have a book of outstanding importance and value, consult your own librarian; he may want it for his own institution, even if he has to find a wealthy patron to get it out of your hands. There may be a private library or a college library that is interested. There is no end to the markets if you have resourcefulness in finding them.

But what, you ask, am I going to do if I don't want to go to all this trouble? The answer is obvious: You will have to take half price or less for your books and sell to a dealer—if you can find one who is interested. If you have pursued your price searches carefully, there is no need to let any dealer take advantage of you. Be firm in your knowledge and hold your ground, and if your book is really important you will be able to sell it in time for a price that is fair to all, the dealer included.

Finally, you may ask, how do I go about actually selling to a dealer after I have sorted my books and made at least a rough estimate of their potential value? Shall I ask the dealer to come out and look at them? The answer here is, *No!* No dealer has the time, and none has the inclination, to make a trip to your home unless he knows *in advance* that you have something that is of potential value to him.

Obviously, then, the thing to do is to prepare a list of your most important books for him, describing them accurately and completely. He can then decide whether the trip to your home will be worthwhile. The following form is a recommendation of the ABAA and will bring you the promptest action from a rare book dealer:

AUTHOR:

TITLE:

SIZE (give size of page in inches):

BINDING (full leather, half leather, cloth, paper cover):

PUBLISHER AND PLACE WHERE PUBLISHED:

DATE (if no date on title, give copyright date on reverse of title):

NUMBER OF PAGES AND ILLUSTRATIONS (plain or colored):

CONDITION (inside and out; state if stains and tears are present):

After the dealer has seen this report from you, carefully filled out, he will notify you whether he wants to see the book. (If he is in another city he may ask you to send it in, which you should do by insured parcel post—book rate —or Railway Express prepaid.)

If, after having seen your books, the dealer makes you an offer, you are prepared, if you have properly determined the values of your individual titles, to either accept or reject it. If he offers you 35% to 50% of what you honestly believe the book to be worth at the retail level, you should accept, for that is generally considered fair. (It is my personal belief that no dealer should offer less than 50% of retail value, but some booksellers, citing their high overhead and the gambles inherent in their business, feel otherwise. It is certainly true that, unless a dealer has an immediate prospect of sale, the acquisition of an expensive book, which he may have to hold on his shelves for quite a long time before selling, is always a gamble.)

That is about all there is to the mystery of how to sell your old and rare books. It is admittedly a complicated business and one filled with ifs and buts and blighted hopes, but it also is one of the most absorbing of endeavors. To those who are willing to pursue its intricacies it offers substantial benefits, along with many bookish pleasures.

And if you haven't the time or the inclination to do your own research, or to at least give the overworked bookseller an assist by preparing an understandable list of what you have to offer, the next best thing to do is to give your books to some charity drive or to the Salvation Army. If there are valuable items among them, there is always some conscientious and hungry book scout who has to make a living. Let us earnestly pray that he finds them!

PART TWO

EIGHTY-EIGHT FABULOUS AMERICAN BOOKS AND HOW TO RECOGNIZE THEM

IN THE FOLLOWING SECTION, adapted from the weekly "Gold in Your Attic" column, are brief descriptions of eighty-eight fabulous American books and pamphlets much sought by collectors. All are within the range of possible discovery by the book hunter. Title pages are reproduced as an easy aid in identification, and various clues are offered in the texts of the separate articles. In every case, it should be emphasized that these exact editions—*and not similar editions*—are the ones desired by book collectors. Additional price information and aids to identification may be found in the alphabetical "Price Index and Guide" in Part Three of this book.

THE

VVHOLE

BOOKE OF PSALMES

Faithfully

TRANSLATED *into* ENGLISH

‹ *Metre.*

Whereunto is prefixed a difcourfe de-
claring not only the lawfulnes, but alfo
the neceffity of the heavenly Ordinance
of finging Scripture Pfalmes in
the Churches of
God.

Coll. III.

*Let the word of God dwell plenteoufly in
you, in all wifdome, teaching and exhort-
ing one another in Pfalmes, Himnes, and
fpirituall Songs, finging to the Lord with
grace in your hearts.*

Iames V.

*If any be afflicted, let him pray, and if
any be merry let him fing pfalmes.*

Imprinted

1˙640

1. *The Whole Book of Psalmes* [Bay Psalm Book]

A perfect copy of the Bay Psalm Book, the first book published in the English colonies in America, was sold at auction in New York City in 1947 for $151,000. It was the highest price ever paid for an American rare book.

Even the best authorities have difficulties in estimating prices on such rarities. Almost on the eve of this sensational sale, Colton Storm and Howard Peckham wrote in their book *Invitation to Book Collecting:* "Nobody knows what it is worth today. . . . Probably from $25,000 to $35,-000 would be accepted as an opening bid."

The title page of this rarity, printed by Stephen Daye at Cambridge, Massachusetts Bay, reads as follows:

THE / WHOLE / BOOKE OF PSALMES / Faithfully / TRANSLATED into ENGLISH / Metre. / Whereunto is prefixed a discourse de- / claring not only the lawfullness, but also / the necessity of the heavenly Ordinance / of singing Scripture Psalmes in / the Churches of / God. / Coll. III. / Let the word of God dwell plenteously in / you, in all wisdome, teaching and exhort- / ing one another in Psalmes, Himnes, and / spirituall Songs, singing to the Lord with / grace in your hearts. / James V. / If any be afflicted, let him pray, and if / any be merry let him sing psalmes. / Imprinted / 1640.

There are eleven known copies—five complete, six incomplete.

Spiritual

MILK

FOR

BOSTON BABES

In either ENGLAND.

Drawn out of the
Breasts of both *TESTAMENTS*
for their souls *nourishment.*

But may be of like use to any
Children.

By JOHN COTTON, B. D.
late Teacher to the Church of
Boston *in* New-England.

CAMBRIDG
Printed by *S. G.* for *Hezekiah Usher*
at Boston in *New-England.*
1 6 5 6.

2. *Spiritual Milk for Boston Babes*
By John Cotton

Among our literary inheritances from Puritan New England is a little catechism known as *Spiritual Milk for Boston Babes,* a children's classic of which there is only one known copy.

This priceless rarity, which appeared in 1954-55 in the Pierpont Morgan Library Exhibit of Children's Literature, is the first American edition.

Its title page reads as follows:

Spiritual / MILK / FOR / BOSTON BABES / In either ENGLAND. / Drawn out of the / Breasts of both TESTAMENTS / for their souls nourishment. / But may be of like use to any / Children. / [*rule*] / By JOHN COTTON, B.D. / late Teacher to the Church of / Boston in New-England. / [*rule*] / CAMBRIDG / Printed by S. G. for Hezekiah Usher / at Boston in New-England. / 1656.

If another copy turned up today, it would be worth a small fortune.

Printed in Boston, this thirteen-page work by John Cotton bears a Cambridge imprint, with the "e" missing from Cambridge. The first edition had appeared ten years earlier in London.

MAMUSSE

WUNNEETUPANATAMWE

UP-BIBLUM GOD

NANEESWE

NUKKONE TESTAMENT

KAH WONK

WUSKU TESTAMENT.

Ne quoſhkinnumuk naſhpe Wuttinneumoh *CHRIST*
1.oh aſɔꝏwelit

JOHN ELIOT·

CAMBRIDGE:

Printcuꝏp naſhpe *Samuel Green* kah *Marmaduke Johnſon.*

1 6 6 3.

3. *Mamusse Wunneetupanatamwe Up-Biblum God*
[John Eliot's Bible in the Natick Indian Language]

Few American Bibles are worth much on the collector's market, but a rare exception is the famous Eliot Indian Bible, the first Bible printed in North America.

In 1958, an imperfect copy, with the English title page, but lacking the Indian language title page, brought $20,160 at auction. It established a new record for this historically important work.

The Eliot Bible was the work of the Rev. John Eliot, a missionary who translated the scriptures into Natick, one of the Indian tongues, for distribution among the natives of New England.

The Natick title page reads as follows:

MAMUSSE / WUNNEETUPANATAMWE / UP-BIBLUM GOD / NANEESWE / NUKKONE TESTAMENT / KAH WONK / WUSKU TESTAMENT. / [rule] / Ne quoshkinnumuk nashpe Wuttinneumoh CHRIST / noh asoowetic / JOHN ELIOT. / [rule] / CAMBRIDGE: / Printcuoopnashpe Samuel Green kah Marmaduke Johnson. / 1663.

Even a second edition of the Eliot Bible, published twenty-two years later, is a costly volume. The Chicago Bible Society's copy cost $1,450 when the late Werner Schroeder, a Chicago collector, purchased it for that institution some years ago.

NEHEMIAH
ON THE
VVALL
IN
TROUBLESOM TIMES;
OR,

A Serious and Seasonable Improvement of that great
Example of Magistratical Piety and Prudence, Self-denial
and Tenderness, Fearlesness and Fidelity, unto In-
struction and Encouragement of present and
succeeding Rulers in our Israel.

As it was delivered in a SERMON Preached at
Boston in *N. E. May* 15. 1667. being the
DAY of ELECTION
THERE

By that faithful Servant of Christ,
Mr. *JONATHAN MITCHEL*, late Pastor of
the Church of Christ at *Cambridge*.

Pſ. 78.70. He chose David his servant——He brought him to feed Jacob
his people, and Israel his inheritance. So he fed them according to the integrity of his heart, and guided them by the skilfulness of his hands.
Josh. 7.10. And the Lord said to Joshua, Get thee up; wherefore liest thou thus
upon thy face?
Iſa. 32.1-2.——Princes shall rule in judgement. And a man shall be as an hiding-place
from the wind, and a cover from the tempest; as rivers of water in a dry
place, as the shadow of a great rock in a weary land.

CAMBRIDGE:
Printed by *S. G.* and *M. J.* 1671.

4. *Nehemiah on the Wall in Troublesom Times*
By Jonathan Mitchel

Old religious books generally are lacking in commercial value on the collector's market unless they happen to be first editions of important major works.

Exceptions, however, are the early New England "election sermons," often found unbound. The election day sermon was an official bit of business in Massachusetts from 1663, when the first one appeared, until 1885, when the custom perished.

A typical example of this kind of literature, now treasured as rare Americana, is Jonathan Mitchel's sermon preached in Boston on May 15, 1667. Oddly enough, it was not printed until 1671.

The title page reads, in part, as follows:

NEHEMIAH / ON THE / WALL / IN / TROU-BLESOM TIMES; / [*etc., 10 lines*] / [*rule*] / By that faithful Servant of Christ, / Mr. JONATHAN MITCHEL, late Pastor of / the Church of Christ at Cambridge. / [*rule*] / [*quotations, 8 lines*] / [*rule*] / CAMBRIDGE: / Printed by S. G. and M. J. 1671.

A copy in fine condition should bring $300 to $400 in the rare book market today.

THE AMERICAN
Almanack

For the Year of

Chriſtian ACCOUNT

1731.

Wherein is contained

The Planets daily Motions, their Aſpects, Eclipſes, Lunations, Judgment of the Weather, the Time of the Sun's Riſing and Setting, Moon's Riſing and Setting, Seven Stars Riſing, Southing and Setting, Time of High-Water and Spring-Tides, Fairs, Courts, and Obſervable Days.

Fitted to the Latitude of Forty Degrees North, and a Meridian of Five Hours Weſt from *LONDON*, but may without much Error ſerve from *Newfoundland* to *Carolina*.

By *JOHN JERMAN*, *Philomat.*

When ye ſee a Cloud riſo out of the Weſt, ſtraightway ye ſay there cometh a Shower, and ſo it is : and when yo perceive the South Wind, ye ſay there will be Rain, and it cometh to paſs. · Luke xii. 54.

Philadelphia: Printed and Sold by *B. Franklin* and *H. Meredith*, at the New Printing-Office near the Market.

5. *The American Almanack For . . . 1731*
By John Jerman

Although it is not likely that you will ever find one of the first "Poor Richard" almanacs of 1733 (printed by Benjamin Franklin in 1732 and worth $500 or more), there are dozens of potentially valuable almanac items awaiting discovery.

In general, almanacs printed since the middle of the last century (from 1850 to today) are not likely to be worth much. But it is safe to say that any early American almanac, particularly if it is dated earlier than 1800, is worth its weight in gold—and often many times that. The reason these items are scarce and valuable is that they were usually paperbound and therefore fragile. Most of them have disappeared.

One of the more valuable items, like the "Poor Richard" series, a Franklin product, is the John Jerman almanac of 1731, a copy of which brought $350 at a New York auction in 1954.

Its title page reads, in part, as follows:

THE AMERICAN / Almanack / For the Year of / Christian ACCOUNT / 1731. / [*etc., 11 lines*] / [*rule*] / By JOHN JERMAN, Philomat. / [*rule*] / [*Bible quotation, 4 lines*] / Philadelphia: Printed and Sold by B. Franklin and H. / Meredith, at the New Printing-Office near the Market.

At the same sale, a 1735 "Poor Richard" brought $475 and a 1748 issue $450.

THE

TREATY

HELD WITH THE

INDIANS

OF THE

SIX NATIONS,

AT

PHILADELPHIA,

In *JULY*, 1742.

PHILADELPHIA:

Printed and Sold by B. FRANKLIN, at the New-Printing-
Office, near the Market. M,DCC,XLIII.

6. *The Treaty Held with the Indians of the Six Nations*

When the famed Benjamin Franklin collection formed by Arthur Bloch, Philadelphia book collector, was auctioned in October, 1954, one of the fancier prices was the $900 paid for a Franklin printing of an Indian treaty made in 1742.

The title page of this rarity, dated 1743, reads as follows:

THE / TREATY / HELD WITH THE / INDIANS / OF THE / SIX NATIONS, / AT / PHILADEL-PHIA, / In JULY, 1742. / [*rule*] / [*shield*] / [*rule*] / PHILADELPHIA: / Printed and Sold by B. FRANKLIN, at the New-Printing- / Office, near the Market. M,DCC,XLIII.

Franklin served his apprenticeship from 1718 to 1723 and became a printer in Philadelphia, where his *Poor Richard's Almanack* became a success. Any Franklin printing, including the German language imprints, is worth a premium on the collector's market today.

A
TOKEN
FOR
CHILDREN.
BEING

An Exact Account of the Conver-
fion, Holy and Exemplary Lives
and Joyful Deaths of feveral young
Children.

By JAMES JANEWAY,
Minifter of the Gofpel.

To which is added,
A TOKEN for the CHILDREN
of *NEW-ENGLAND.*
OR,

Some Examples of Children, in whom the
Fear of God was remarkably Budding be-
fore they died, in feveral Parts of *NEW-
ENGLAND.*

Preferv-d and publifhed for the Encouragement of *Piety*
in other Children.

With New Additions.

BOSTON, Printed:
PHILADELPHIA, Re-printed, and fold by
B. FRANKLIN, and D. HALL, MDCCXLIX.

7. *A Token for Children*
By James Janeway

One of the rarest of American rare books is the Benjamin Franklin printing of James Janeway's *A Token for Children*. There is only one copy known.

This priceless item was among the extraordinary books shown in 1954-55 in the Pierpont Morgan Library Exhibit of Children's Literature.

The title page reads, in part, as follows:

A / TOKEN / FOR / CHILDREN. / BEING / An Exact Account of the Conver- / sion, Holy and Exemplary Lives / and Joyful Deaths of several young / Children. / [*rule*] / By JAMES JANE-WAY, / Minister of the Gospel. / [*rule*] / To which is added, / A TOKEN for the CHILDREN / of NEW-ENGLAND. / [*etc., 8 lines*] / [*rule*] / BOS-TON, Printed: / PHILADELPHIA, Re-printed, and sold by / B. Franklin, and D. Hall, MDCCX-LIX.

If another copy of this pious little book should turn up today, the finder could name his own price—and probably get it.

8. *The Holy Bible*
[Aitken's first English Bible to be printed in America]

Almost everybody has an old family Bible—and suspects that it is valuable. The truth is that most old Bibles are

THE

HOLY BIBLE,

Containing the OLD and NEW

TESTAMENTS:

Newly tranflated out of the

ORIGINAL TONGUES;

And with the former

TRANSLATIONS

Diligently compared and revifed.

PHILADELPHIA:

PRINTED AND SOLD BY R. AITKEN, AT POPE's
HEAD, THREE DOORS ABOVE THE COFFEE
HOUSE, IN MARKET STREET.
M.DCC.LXXXII.

worthless, except for the sentimental value that may be attached to them.

For that reason we have written very little about Bibles and their values. Further, the identification and appraisal of Bibles—especially those in German, Latin, and other foreign languages—is a job for the specialist.

Nevertheless, there are a number of old Bibles that bring premium prices when found in good condition. We asked W. A. Stewart, a dealer and Bible collector of Norristown, Pennsylvania, to give us some of the latest news about Bible prices.

One of the items he mentioned specifically is the famous Aitken Bible, printed in Philadelphia in 1782. This was the first English Bible published in America. "A very good copy," said Mr. Stewart, "brings $1,000 today."

The title page reads as follows:

THE / HOLY BIBLE, / Containing the OLD and NEW / TESTAMENTS: / Newly translated out of the / ORIGINAL TONGUES; / And with the former / TRANSLATIONS / Diligently compared and revised. / [rule] / [shield] / [double rule] / PHILADELPIIIA: / PRINTED AND SOLD BY R. AITKEN, AT POPE'S / HEAD, THREE DOORS ABOVE THE COFFEE / HOUSE, IN MARKET STREET. / M.DCC.LXXXII.

Some of the high prices recently obtained for other old Bibles include Tyndale's version of the Pentateuch, 1530-34, $4,200; Matthew's First Bible, 1537, $7,280; the first "Great" Bible, 1539, $7,000; and an incomplete Coverdale Bible, first complete English Bible to be printed, 1535, $2,240.

A
NARRATIVE
OF THE
Strange Principles, Conduct
AND
CHARACTER
Of the People known by the Name of
SHAKERS:
Whose ERRORS have spread in several Parts of
NORTH-AMERICA, but are beginning to diminish,
and ought to be guarded against.

In TWO NUMBERS.

By Amos Taylor.
Late of their Number, and acquainted with them in
five different Governments for ten Months.

NUMBER I.
Wherein their whole Constitution is
laid open, more particularly the Method used by that People in making
their Proselytes.

WORCESTER, (*Massachusetts*) Printed for the
AUTHOR.   MDCCLXXXII.

9. *A Narrative of the Strange Principles, Conduct and Character of the People Known by the Name of Shakers*
By Amos Taylor

While there is little commercial value in most old theological books, the scarcer historical works about American religious beginnings are another matter.

For example, early books about the Shakers are desirable Americana because members of this sect were closely associated with the development of American agriculture and industrial enterprise. The Shakers, who settled at Watervliet, New York, in 1774, constituted the first communistic organization in the United States. The sect has dwindled, and today there are only a handful of members, but interest in its activities continues.

One of the earliest anti-Shaker documents is Amos Taylor's *Narrative*, published in 1782. The title page reads, in part, as follows:

A / NARRATIVE / OF THE / Strange Principles, Conduct / AND / CHARACTER / Of the People known by the Name of / SHAKERS: / [etc., 3 lines] / In TWO NUMBERS. / [rule] / By Amos Taylor. / [etc., 2 lines] / [rule] / NUMBER I. / [etc., 4 lines] / [double rule] / WORCESTER, (Massachusetts) Printed for the / AUTHOR. MDCCLXXXII.

There was no No. 2, and any surviving copies of the first number are worth $100 or more.

THE
HISTORY
OF LITTLE
GOODY TWOSHOES
OTHERWISE CALLED
Mrs. *Margery Twoſhoes.*

WITH

The Means by which ſhe acquired her Learning and Wiſdom, and in Conſequence
thereof her Eſtate.

Set forth at large for the Benefit of thoſe,

Who from a State of Rags and Care,
And having Shoes but half a Pair,
Their Fortune and their Fame would fix,
And gallop in their Coach and Six.

See the original Manuſcript in the VATICAN
at ROME, and the Cuts by MICHAEL
ANGELO ; illuſtrated with the Comments
of our great modern Criticks.

THE FIRST *WORCESTER* EDITION

PRINTED at WORCESTER, *Maſſachuſetts.*
By ISAIAH THOMAS,
And SOLD, Wholeſale and Retail, at his Book
Store. MDCCLXXXVII.

10. *The History of Little Goody Twoshoes*

Among the children's books of the last two centuries, one of the most successful has been *The History of Little Goody Twoshoes,* an almost nauseatingly wholesome moral tale first published by the English publisher John Newbery in 1765.

There is no known copy of the first edition, and there are only two known copies of the second edition of 1766. All the very early editions, both American and British, are in the category of collector's items and therefore scarce and valuable. Typical of the early American printings is the first Worcester edition, published by Isaiah Thomas in 1787. A copy brought $190 at a New York City auction sale a few years ago.

Its title page reads, in part, as follows:

THE / HISTORY / OF LITTLE / GOODY TWO-SHOES / OTHERWISE CALLED / Mrs. Margery Twoshoes. / [*etc., 13 lines*] / [*rule*] / THE FIRST WORCESTER EDITION / [*double rule*] / PRINTED AT WORCESTER, Massachusetts. / By ISAIAH THOMAS, / And SOLD, Wholesale and Retail, at his Book / Store. MDCCLXXXVII.

Among those suspected of being the anonymous creator of Little Goody is Oliver Goldsmith.

11. *The New-York Directory* [1786]
By David Franks

One of the rarest city directories is David Franks' *New-York Directory* of 1786, the first directory of that metropo-

THE
NEW-YORK DIRECTORY,

CONTAINING,

A Valuable and well Calculated ALMANACK;----
Tables of the different COINS, suitable for any
State, and digested in such order, as to render an
Exchange between any of the United States plain
and easy.

LIKEWISE,

1. The names of all the Citizens, their occupations and places of abode.
2. The members in Congress, from what state, and where residing.
3. Grand departments of the United States for adjusting public accounts, and by whom conducted.
4. Members in Senate and Assembly, from what county, and where residing.
5. Judges, Aldermen, and other civil officers, with their places of abode.
6. Public state-offices, and by whom kept.
7. Counsellors at law, and where residing.
8. Ministers of the gospel, where residing, and of what Church.
9. Physicians, Surgeons, and their places of abode.
10. President, Directors, days, and hours of business at the Bank.
11. Professors, &c. of the university of Columbia college.
12. Rates of porterage, as by law established.
13. Arrivals and departures of the mails at the Post-Office.

BY DAVID FRANKS.

NEW-YORK:

Printed by SHEPARD KOLLOCK, corner of Wall
and Water Streets, M,DCC,LXXX,VI.

lis. A copy brought $2,500 at an auction some years ago. Only a few libraries have original copies of this 82-page book. If you found one today, you could just about name your own price.

The title page reads, in part, as follows:

THE / NEW-YORK DIRECTORY, / CONTAIN-ING, / A Valuable and well Calculated ALMA-NACK;— / [etc., 5 lines plus 37 lines double column] / [rule] / BY DAVID FRANKS. / [rule] / [printer's device] / NEW-YORK: / Printed by SHEPARD KOLLOCK, corner of Wall / and Water Streets, M,DCC,LXXX,VI.

Several reprints have been made, but they are of relatively small value. Typical is the facsimile produced in New York in 1909, which sells for about $15 at retail.

12. *The Federalist*

Among the collectors of important American historical documents, the extremely scarce 1788 first edition of *The Federalist* is a prize of four figure value.

There were two kinds of original binding—boards and calf; there were also two kinds of paper used—thick paper and regular book stock of the period. Complete sets of this two-volume treasure on thick paper with the leaves uncut (untrimmed) are extremely scarce.

A thick paper set with some small defects sold recently for $1,200 at auction, and another sold for $1,100, the same price asked by a New York dealer. A rebound set sold for $675 at auction, and in 1955 a fine copy of the second volume brought $1,100 alone. Copies bound in boards have usually brought less than those in calf. Fine

THE

FEDERALIST:

A 'COLLECTION

OF

ESSAYS,

WRITTEN IN FAVOUR OF THE

NEW CONSTITUTION,

AS AGREED UPON BY THE FEDERAL CONVENTION,
SEPTEMBER 17, 1787.

IN TWO VOLUMES.

VOL. I.

NEW YORK:

PRINTED AND SOLD BY J. AND A. M'LEAN,
No. 41, HANOVER-SQUARE.
M,DCC,LXXXVIII.

copies of the regular issue, either in calf or boards, are worth up to $600, and possibly more, according to my records.

The title page of Vol. 1 reads as follows:

THE / FEDERALIST: / A COLLECTION / OF / ESSAYS, / WRITTEN IN FAVOUR OF THE / NEW CONSTITUTION, / AS AGREED UPON BY THE FEDERAL CONVENTION, / SEP-TEMBER 17, 1787. / IN TWO VOLUMES. / VOL. I. / NEW-YORK: / PRINTED AND SOLD BY J. AND A. McLEAN, / No. 41, HANOVER-SQUARE, / M,DCC,LXXXVIII.

The Federalist was the work of Alexander Hamilton, James Madison, and John Hay. Henry Cabot Lodge has pointed out that it was "the first authoritative interpretation of the Constitution." This accounts for its importance in the eyes of collectors.

13. *The Farmer's Almanac . . . 1793*
By Robert B. Thomas

One of the most valuable of early American almanacs is *The Old Farmer's Almanac,* published every year since 1792. A good copy of the first issue is worth up to $100 on the collector's market.

According to Robb Sagendorph of Dublin, New Hampshire, the present publisher, the first edition appeared in Boston as *The Farmer's Almanac* in November, 1792. (The word "Old" was added in the 1830's.)

The title page of the first number reads, in part, as follows:

[Nº. I.]

THE

FARMER's ALMANAC,

CALCULATED ON A NEW AND IMPROVED PLAN,

FOR THE YEAR OF OUR LORD

1793:

Being the first after Leap Year, and seventeenth of the Independence *of* America.

Fitted to the town of BOSTON, but will serve for any of the adjoining States.

Containing, besides the large number of ASTRO-NOMICAL CALCULATIONS and FARMER's CA-LENDAR for every month in the year, as great a vari-ety as are to be found in any other Almanac, *Of* NEW, USEFUL, *and* ENTERTAINING MATTER.

BY ROBERT B. THOMAS.

"While the bright radient fun in centre glows,
The earth, in annual motion round it goes;
At the fame time on its own axis reels,
And gives us change of feafons as it wheels."

Published according to Act of Congrefs.

PRINTED AT THE Apollo Prefs, IN BOSTON,
BY BELKNAP AND HALL,
Sold at their Office, State Street; also, by the *Author*
and M. *Smith*, *Sterling*.
[*Sixpence fingle*, 4*s*. *per dozen*, 40*s*. *per groce*.]

[No.1.] / THE / FARMER'S ALMANAC, / CALCULATED ON A NEW AND IMPROVED PLAN, / FOR THE YEAR OF OUR LORD / 1793: / [*etc., 9 lines*] / [*rule*] / BY ROBERT B. THOMAS. / [*rule*] / [*quotation, 4 lines*] / Published according to Act of Congress. / [*double rule*] / PRINTED AT THE Apollo Press, IN BOSTON, / BY BELKNAP AND HALL, / Sold at their Office; State Street; also, by the Author / and M. Smith, Sterling. / [Sixpence single, 4s. per dozen, 40s. per groce.]

Most almanac collectors try to assemble sets, says Mr. Sagendorph. A complete file is worth $250 to $1,000 at retail, depending on binding and condition.

Even more valuable than the first edition is the first issue off the press for the year 1816. It contained a prediction of "Rain, hail and snow" for July 13. It actually did rain, hail and snow, writes the amazed Mr. Sagendorph. If you find this number, he adds, it is worth a minimum of $150.

And I will back him up with the cash!

14. *American Cookery*
By Amelia Simmons

There are two, or possibly three, copies in existence of the first edition of Amelia Simmons' *American Cookery,* the first American cookbook to be written by an American.

Oxford University Press published in 1958 a $15 facsimile edition that was limited to 800 copies, using the copy owned by the American Antiquarian Society. On the slip case provided for the book, Oxford announced that

AMERICAN COOKERY,

OR THE ART OF DRESSING

VIANDS, FISH, POULTRY and VEGETABLES,

AND THE BEST MODES OF MAKING

PASTES, PUFFS, PIES, TARTS, PUDDINGS, CUSTARDS AND PRESERVES.

AND ALL KINDS OF

CAKES,

FROM THE IMPERIAL PLUMB TO PLAIN CAKE:

ADAPTED TO THIS COUNTRY,

AND ALL GRADES OF LIFE.

By Amelia Simmons,

AN AMERICAN ORPHAN.

PUBLISHED ACCORDING TO ACT OF CONGRESS.

HARTFORD:

PRINTED BY HUDSON & GOODWIN.

FOR THE AUTHOR.

1796.

there are only two known copies of the first edition. This does not agree, however, with Morgan Towne's statement in his book, *Treasures in Truck and Trash,* that a *third* copy was discovered in October, 1948, and placed on sale by a bookseller at $200.

Be that as it may, Amelia's book is one of the supreme rarities among American books and is well worth looking for.

The title page reads as follows:

AMERICAN COOKERY, / OR THE ART OF DRESSING / VIANDS, FISH, POULTRY and VEGETABLES, / AND THE BEST MODES OF MAKING / PASTES, PUFFS, PIES, TARTS, PUDDINGS, / CUSTARDS AND PRESERVES, / AND ALL KINDS OF / CAKES, / FROM THE IMPERIAL PLUMB TO PLAIN CAKE. / ADAPTED TO THIS COUNTRY, / AND ALL GRADES OF LIFE. / [*printer's device*] / By Amelia Simmons, / AN AMERICAN ORPHAN. / [*printer's device*] / PUBLISHED ACCORDING TO ACT OF CONGRESS. / [*double rule*] / HART-FORD: / PRINTED BY HUDSON & GOOD-WIN, / FOR THE AUTHOR. / [*rule*] / 1796.

A paper-covered book of 47 pages, Miss Simmons' pioneering effort was widely reprinted, as well as plagiarized. The first edition appeared in two issues, the second with an errata leaf. [See *Gold in Your Attic,* 1958, index for price listing.]

A

Compendious Dictionary

OF THE

English Language.

In which FIVE THOUSAND Words are added
to the number found in the BEST ENGLISH COMPENDS.;

The ORTHOGRAPHY is, in some instances, corrected ;

The PRONUNCIATION marked by an Accent or other suitable Direction ;

And the DEFINITIONS of many Words amended and improved.

TO WHICH ARE ADDED FOR THE BENEFIT OF THE

MERCHANT, the STUDENT and the TRAVELLER,

I.——TABLES of the MONEYS of most of the commercial Nations in the world, with the value expressed in Sterling and Cents.

II.——TABLES of WEIGHTS and MEASURES, ancient and modern, with the proportion between the several weights used in the principal cities of Europe.

III.——The DIVISIONS of TIME among the Jews, Greeks and Romans, with a Table exhibiting the Roman manner of dating.

IV.——An official List of the POST-OFFICES in the UNITED STATES, with the States and Counties in which they are respectively situated, and the distance of each from the seat of Government.

V.——The NUMBER of INHABITANTS in the United States, with the amount of EXPORTS.

IV.——New and interesting CHRONOLOGICAL TABLES of remarkable Events and Discoveries.

By NOAH WEBSTER, Esq.

From Sidney's Press.

FOR HUDSON & GOODWIN, BOOK-SELLERS, HARTFORD, AND INCREASE COOKE & CO.

BOOK-SELLERS, NEW-HAVEN.

1806.

15. *A Compendious Dictionary of the English Language*
By Noah Webster

Although it was his first great two-volume dictionary, *An American Dictionary of the English Language* (1828), that really established Noah Webster's claim to fame, there was an earlier trial effort in 1806.

This first Webster dictionary is quite as rare as the 1828 masterpiece but is worth somewhat less on the collector's market because it lacked the authority of its great successor. It illustrates the point, often made in my columns, that a book's importance has a great bearing on its price.

The title page of Webster's first effort reads, in part, as follows:

A / Compendious Dictionary / OF THE / English Language. / [*etc., 7 lines plus 21 lines in double column*] / [*double rule*] / By NOAH WEBSTER, Esq. / [*double rule*] / From Sidney's Press. / FOR HUDSON & GOODWIN, BOOK-SELLERS, HARTFORD, AND INCREASE COOKE & CO. / BOOK-SELLERS, NEW-HAVEN. / [*rule*] / 1806.

A copy in fine condition is worth roughly $35 to $50 at retail.

NARRATIVE

OF THE

TRAGICAL DEATH

OF MR.

DARIUS BARBER,

AND HIS

SEVEN CHILDREN,

WHO WERE INHUMANLY BUTCHERED BY THE

INDIANS,

In CAMDEN COUNTY, GEORGIA, JANUARY 26 1813.

To which is added an account of the Captivity and Sufferings of MRS. BARBER, who was carried away a Captive by the SAVAGES, and from whom she fortunately made her escape six weeks afterwards.

☞ It may be a gratification to the reader, to learn that the said tribe of SAVAGES have been since exterminated by the Brave and Intrepid

GEN. JACKSON,

And the Troops under his command.

BOSTON—Printed for DAVID HAZEN—Price 0d.

16. *Narrative of the Tragical Death of Mr. Darius Barber*

Indian "captivities"—the harrowing accounts of early settlers captured by the Indians—are often encountered in collections of Americana, and sometimes they bring high prices.

One of the scarcest of the captivity pamphlets is the dreadful tale of Darius Barber and his seven children, who were slain in Camden County, Georgia, in 1813.

The undated title page bears coffin symbols for the eight dead and reads, in part, as follows:

NARRATIVE / OF THE / TRAGICAL DEATH / OF MR. / DARIUS BARBER, / AND HIS / SEVEN CHILDREN, / WHO WERE INHU-MANLY BUTCHERED BY THE / INDIANS, / IN CAMDEN COUNTY, GEORGIA, JANUARY 26 1813. / [*eight coffin devices*] / [*etc., 9 lines*] / [*printer's device*] / BOSTON—Printed for DAVID HAZEN—Price 0d.

This paperbound rarity was printed in Boston in about 1818. Only a few copies have appeared for sale in recent years. A defective copy brought $130 at auction some time ago. Another was listed by a rare bookseller at $150. Wright Howes states in his book *U. S.-iana* that there are only four perfect copies known. Such a copy ought to be worth $300 or more.

AN

AMERICAN DICTIONARY

OF THE

ENGLISH LANGUAGE;

INTENDED TO EXHIBIT,

I. The origin, affinities and primary signification of English words, as far as they have been ascertained.
II. The genuine orthography and pronunciation of words, according to general usage, or to just principles of analysis.
III. Accurate and discriminating definitions, with numerous authorities and illustrations.

TO WHICH ARE PREFIXED,

AN INTRODUCTORY DISSERTATION

ON THE

ORIGIN, HISTORY AND CONNECTION OF THE

LANGUAGES OF WESTERN ASIA AND OF EUROPE,

AND A CONCISE GRAMMAR

OF THE

ENGLISH LANGUAGE.

BY NOAH WEBSTER, LL. D.

IN TWO VOLUMES.

VOL. I.

He that wishes to be counted among the benefactors of posterity, must add, by his own toil, to the acquisitions of his ancestors.—Rambler.

NEW YORK:
PUBLISHED BY S. CONVERSE.
PRINTED BY HEZEKIAH HOWE—NEW HAVEN.
1828.

17. *An American Dictionary of the English Language*
   By Noah Webster

Noah Webster's first large dictionary of the English language, published in two volumes in 1828, is one of the milestones in American cultural achievement. The result of many years of work and the outgrowth of his *Compendious Dictionary* of 1806, it was instantly accepted as the first really authoritative American dictionary. It set the standard for the Webster dictionaries that followed.

The title page of Vol. 1 reads, in part, as follows:

AN / AMERICAN DICTIONARY / OF THE / ENGLISH LANGUAGE: / [*etc., 12 lines*] / [*double rule*] / BY NOAH WEBSTER, LL.D. / [*double rule*] / IN TWO VOLUMES. / VOL. I. / [*double rule*] / [*quotation*] / [*double rule*] / NEW YORK: / PUBLISHED BY S. CONVERSE. / PRINTED BY HEZEKIAH HOWE—NEW HAVEN / 1828.

There were only 2,500 sets of the first edition published, and they sold for $20 a set. Complete copies are quite scarce today. In good condition, they command as much as $50, and sometimes more, at auction. In rare book shops, they bring up to $100, depending on condition. [See *Gold in Your Attic,* 1958, for price listing.]

THE

CABINET

OF

NATURAL HISTORY

AND

AMERICAN RURAL SPORTS.

WITH ILLUSTRATIONS.

A MONTHLY PUBLICATION.

VOL. I.

Philadelphia:
PUBLISHED BY J. & T. DOUGHTY, S. E. CORNER WALNUT & FOURTH STREETS.

Kessell & M.... , Printers

1830.

18. *The Cabinet of Natural History*

Color-plate books are expensive to produce, and because of this they are generally issued in limited quantities and tend to become scarce and valuable. Such an item is the three-volume *Cabinet of Natural History,* which contains the first colored sporting prints made in America.

This famed collection appeared originally in separate paperbound parts, issued monthly and dated 1830 to 1834. The parts are virtually unobtainable, but the three bound volumes, dated 1830, 1832, and 1833, still turn up from time to time and fetch a fancy price.

The title page of the first volume reads as follows:

THE / CABINET / OF / NATURAL HISTORY / AND / AMERICAN RURAL SPORTS. / [*type decoration*] / WITH ILLUSTRATIONS. / [*rule*] / A MONTHLY PUBLICATION. / [*type decoration*] / VOL. I. / [*double rule*] / Philadelphia: / PUBLISHED BY J. & T. DOUGHTY, S. E. CORNER WALNUT & FOURTH STREETS. / Russell & Mactien, Printers / [*dotted rule*] / 1830.

There are two engraved portraits, 54 colored plates, and three uncolored plates in the three volumes.

In December, 1957, a set brought $300 at a New York book auction. The usual bookseller price is around $750. [See *Gold in Your Attic,* 1958, for price listing.]

EXPERIMENTS

AND

OBSERVATIONS

ON THE

GASTRIC JUICE

AND THE

PHYSIOLOGY OF DIGESTION.

BY WILLIAM BEAUMONT, M. D.

Surgeon in the U. S. Army.

PLATTSBURGH

PRINTED BY F. P. ALLEN.

1833.

19. *Experiments and Observations on the Gastric Juice*
By William Beaumont

An unusual service occasionally rendered to the rare book lover by modern publishers is the publication of facsimile editions of famous works.

Two such works which recently appeared in the bookstores are William Beaumont's *Experiments and Observations on the Gastric Juice,* now available in a Dover paperback, and William Dean Howells' *Life of Abraham Lincoln* (Indiana University Press).

Readers of the first *Gold in Your Attic* book will recall that Beaumont's little medical classic was featured there without the title page. That page, reproduced here from the Dover facsimile, reads as follows:

EXPERIMENTS / AND / OBSERVATIONS / ON THE / GASTRIC JUICE / AND THE / PHYSIOLOGY OF DIGESTION. / [*rule*] / BY WILLIAM BEAUMONT, M.D. / Surgeon in the U. S. Army. / [*rule*] / PLATTSBURGH, / PRINTED BY F. P. ALLEN. / 1833.

A copy of the original edition is worth around $200 in fine condition. [See *Gold in Your Attic,* 1958, for price listing.]

SCIENCE

AND

HEALTH.

BY

MARY BAKER GLOVER.

———

BOSTON:
CHRISTIAN SCIENTIST PUBLISHING COMPANY.
1875.

20. *Science and Health*
By Mary Baker Glover [Eddy]

Its very nature as a Bible supplement has made Mary Baker Eddy's *Science and Health* one of America's most controversial books, and scarcity has made the first edition extremely valuable. There are supposed to exist only 1,000 copies of the original edition. Black cloth is the usual binding, although other colors are on record. The book bears a gold imprint, "Science and Health—Glover," near the top of the spine.

The title page reads as follows:

SCIENCE / AND / HEALTH. / BY / MARY BAKER GLOVER. / [*rule*] / BOSTON: / CHRISTIAN SCIENTIST PUBLISHING COMPANY. / 1875.

The most valuable first issue copies have no index (it was inserted later).

A fine black cloth copy (in mint condition) is currently worth around $750. Other copies have been offered recently by dealers as follows: Less fine, with errata leaf inserted, $250 and $237.50; terra cotta cloth, $200; green cloth, worn and with writing on title pages and other leaves, $300. [See *Gold in Your Attic,* 1958.]

LIFE

OF

MA-KA-TAI-ME-SHE-KIA-KIAK

OR

BLACK HAWK,

EMBRACING THE

TRADITION OF HIS NATION—INDIAN WARS IN WHICH HE HAS
BEEN ENGAGED—CAUSE OF JOINING THE BRITISH IN THEIR
LATE WAR WITH AMERICA, AND ITS HISTORY—DES-
CRIPTION OF THE ROCK-RIVER VILLAGE—MAN-
NERS AND CUSTOMS—ENCROACHMENTS BY
THE WHITES, CONTRARY TO TREATY—
REMOVAL FROM HIS VILLAGE IN 1831.

WITH AN ACCOUNT OF THE CAUSE

AND

GENERAL HISTORY

OF THE

LATE WAR,

HIS SURRENDER AND CONFINEMENT AT
JEFFERSON BARRACKS,

AND

TRAVELS THROUGH THE UNITED STATES.

DICTATED BY HIMSELF.

CINCINNATI:
1833.

21. *Life of Ma-Ka-Tai-Me-She-Kia-Kiak or Black Hawk*

One of the first lessons the students of rare books learns is that books which appear repeatedly in reprint editions are likely to be scarce in first edition form and, therefore, of possible value. For the appearance of a reprint obviously means that some publisher believes the book to be in relatively short supply. If there is enough demand for the book to justify a reprint edition, there is in all likelihood a demand for the first edition also.

One of the books that falls into this category is Black Hawk's famous autobiography, one of the scarcer Midwestern Indian narratives. There have been numerous reprints since this historically important work was first published in 1833, the latest a few years ago by the University of Illinois Press.

The title page of the first edition reads, in part, as follows:

LIFE / OF / MA-KA-TAI-ME-SHE-KIA-KIAK / OR / BLACK HAWK, / [*etc., 17 lines*] / [*rule*] / DICTATED BY HIMSELF. / [*rule*] / CINCINNATI: / 1833.

A good copy, in the original boards, with linen backstrip and paper label, is worth around $100 at retail, occasionally more. [See *Gold in Your Attic*, 1958.]

A

BOOK

OF

COMMANDMENTS,

FOR THE GOVERNMENT OF THE

Church of Christ,

ORGANIZED ACCORDING TO LAW, ON THE

6th of April, 1830.

ZION:

PUBLISHED BY W. W. PHELPS & CO.

....

1833.

22. *A Book of Commandments for the Government of the Church of Christ* [Mormon]

Historical books about the Mormons and the books of early Mormon leaders are often highly valued by collectors. A good example is the uncompleted first edition of Joseph Smith's anonymous *A Book of Commandments,* a copy of which brought £440 ($1,232) at a London auction sale in 1957. About half a dozen of these rarities are known to be in private hands, and there are five recorded in American public libraries.

A Book of Commandments was the second publication of the Church of Jesus Christ of Latter Day Saints. It bears a Zion (Independence, Missouri) imprint. Only five sheets of 32 pages each had been run off in 1833 when an anti-Mormon mob attacked the printing house and halted work on the book. The existing copies are said to be made up from salvaged sheets.

The title page reads as follows:

A / BOOK / OF / COMMANDMENTS, / FOR THE GOVERNMENT OF THE / Church of Christ, / ORGANIZED ACCORDING TO LAW, ON THE / 6th of April, 1830. / [*double rule*] / ZION: / PUBLISHED BY W. W. PHELPS & CO. / [*dotted rule*] / 1833.

Some copies bear a type decoration around the title page; others lack it. [See *Gold in Your Attic,* 1958, for price listing.]

SKETCHES

OF

IOWA AND WISCONSIN,

EMBODYING THE EXPERIENCE OF A RESIDENCE

OF

THREE YEARS

IN THOSE TERRITORIES,

EMBRACING

The General Report of the Canada Delegation, sent to examine the Territory of Iowa, by the Mississippi Emigration Society; descriptive letters from several distinguished individuals who have visited the country; extracts from the Journal of a Trip to the Falls of Saint Anthony; general view of the peculiar advantages presented to emigrants by these Territories, particularly to natives of the middle and eastern States; and to those from Europe, as contrasted with the situation of the Canadas by Lord Durham: with

A MAP

OF THE SURVEYED PART OF

IOWA TERRITORY,

From the official plats, defining all the townships and counties, and being the only Map yet published, exhibiting the location of Iowa City, the permanent seat of Government of that Territory.

BY JOHN PLUMBE, JR.

PRINTED BY
Chambers, Harris & K
ST. LOUIS
1839.

23. *Sketches of Iowa and Wisconsin*
By John Plumbe, Jr.

Books about the American past are always in demand in the collector's market, but Western books have been particularly strong for the last decade. One of the bigger auction sales of materials in this category occurred in December, 1958, at the Parke-Bernet Galleries in New York, where the library of Dr. Lester E. Bauer of Detroit went on the block.

Among the notable items in this sale was John Plumbe, Jr.'s *Sketches of Iowa and Wisconsin*, a paperbound rarity, which brought $725.

The title page reads, in part, as follows:

SKETCHES / OF / IOWA AND WISCONSIN, / EMBODYING THE EXPERIENCE OF A RESI-DENCE / OF / THREE YEARS / IN THOSE TERRITORIES, / [*etc., 19 lines*] / BY JOHN PLUMBE, JR. / [*rule*] / PRINTED BY / Chambers, Harris & Knapp. / ST. LOUIS. / 1839.

Its importance as Americana lies in the fact that Plumbe was an early promoter of an overland railroad from Lake Michigan to the Pacific Coast, and his is the earliest book printed west of the Ohio River to mention such a project. It contains a folding, thin paper map locating Iowa City as the territorial seat of government.

THE
PUBLIC AND GENERAL
STATUTE LAWS
OF THE
STATE OF ILLINOIS:

CONTAINING

ALL THE LAWS PUBLISHED IN THE "REVISED STATUTES" OF 1833, EXCEPT SUCH AS
ARE REPEALED,—TOGETHER WITH ALL THE ACTS OF A GENERAL AND
PUBLIC NATURE, PASSED BY THE NINTH GENERAL
ASSEMBLY, AT THEIR

FIRST SESSION,

COMMENCING

DECEMBER 1, 1834, AND ENDING FEBRUARY 13, 1835;

AND AT THEIR

SECOND SESSION,

COMMENCING

DECEMBER 7, 1835, AND ENDING JANUARY 18, 1836,

AND THOSE PASSED BY THE

TENTH GENERAL ASSEMBLY,

AT THEIR SESSION

COMMENCING DECEMBER 5, 1836, AND ENDING MARCH 6, 1837;

AND AT THEIR

SPECIAL SESSION,

COMMENCING

JULY 10, AND ENDING JULY 22, 1837; WHICH ARE NOT REPEALED:

AND ALSO THE

MILITIA LAW.

———

COMPILED AND

ARRANGED ALPHABETICALLY,

WITH

OCCASIONAL REFERENCES.

————

CHICAGO:
PUBLISHED BY STEPHEN F GALE.
1839.

24. *The Public and General Statute Laws of the State of Illinois* [1839]

Scarcely any phase of history escapes the notice of the Americana collector, and among the materials he finds of special interest are the early statute laws of states and territories.

A good example of these is the compilation of Illinois laws published by Stephen F. Gale in Chicago in 1839. It was a revision of the statutes of 1833.

The wordy title page reads, in part, as follows:

THE / PUBLIC AND GENERAL / STATUTE LAWS / OF THE / STATE OF ILLINOIS: / [*etc., 22 lines*] / [*rule*] / COMPILED AND / ARRANGED ALPHABETICALLY, / WITH / OCCASIONAL REFERENCES. / [*double rule*] / CHICAGO: / PUBLISHED BY STEPHEN F GALE. / 1839.

A copy in good condition retails in the $15 to $25 price range. However, if you are lucky enough to locate one of the very few copies of the *first issue* of 1839, it may be worth $150 or more. In this issue, the printer's credit line "Printed and bound by O. C. B. Carter & Co., Roxbury, Massachusetts" is missing from the title page.

GENERAL DIRECTORY

AND

BUSINESS ADVERTISER

OF THE

CITY OF CHICAGO,

For the Year 1844;

TOGETHER WITH A

HISTORICAL SKETCH

AND

STATISTICAL ACCOUNT,

TO THE PRESENT TIME.

BY J. W. NORRIS.

CHICAGO:
ELLIS & FERGUS, PRINTERS, SALOON BUILDINGS.

1844.

25. *General Directory and Business Advertiser of the City of Chicago*
By J. W. Norris

The first directory of any city is a potential collector's item, because of the classic influences of scarcity and demand. Such a directory is, by its very nature, issued in a limited quantity. And it is certain to be in demand by later generations for its historical and reference value.

An example is James Wellington Norris' 116-page Chicago Directory of 1844, a copy of which recently sold at auction for $475. A year or so before, a defective copy, turned up by a reader of the "Gold in Your Attic" column, was sold to a noted Chicagoan for $250. This rare little book is bound in pink paper covers.

The title page reads as follows:

GENERAL DIRECTORY / AND / BUSINESS ADVERTISER / OF THE / CITY OF CHICAGO, / For the Year 1844; / TOGETHER WITH A / HISTORICAL SKETCH / AND / STATISTICAL ACCOUNT, / TO THE PRESENT TIME. / BY J. W. NORRIS / [seal—City of Chicago] / CHICAGO: / ELLIS & FERGUS, PRINTERS, SALOON BUILDINGS. / 1844

My Chicago reader's copy was an especially notable prize because it was annotated in the handwriting of Robert Fergus, the pioneer Chicago printer and publisher who published it. It would have brought a better price had its cover not been ragged and frayed.

AN

IOWAY GRAMMAR,

ILLUSTRATING

THE PRINCIPLES

OF THE

LANGUAGE

USED BY THE

IOWAY, OTOE AND MISSOURI

INDIANS

⸺••●•⸺

PREPARED AND PRINTED
BY
REV. WM. HAMILTON
AND
REV. S. M. IRVIN.
Under the direction of the Presbyterian B. F. M.

IOWAY AND SAC MISSION PRESS.
1848.

26. *An Ioway Grammar*
By The Rev. William Hamilton and The Rev. S. M. Irvin

When the pioneers went west across the plains, book publishing advanced with them, often through the medium of a rickety hand press stowed away in a covered wagon. The products of these frontier presses were usually issued in small quantities, and some of them have become collector's items.

One such is the Indian grammar issued in 1848 at Wolf Creek, Nebraska, by two Presbyterian preachers who were seeking to convert the natives to Christianity.

The title page reads as follows:

AN / IOWAY GRAMMAR, / ILLUSTRATING / THE PRINCIPLES / OF THE / LANGUAGE / USED BY THE / IOWAY, OTOE AND MIS-SOURI / INDIANS. / [*printer's device*] / PRE-PARED AND PRINTED / BY / REV. WM. HAMILTON / AND / REV. S. M. IRVIN. / Under the direction of the Presbyterian B. F. M. / [*double rule*] / IOWAY AND SAC MISSION PRESS. / 1848.

A few years ago a copy of this rare Western item brought $625 at an auction sale in New York City.

HISTORICAL

AND

STATISTICAL

SKETCHES,

OF

LAKE COUNTY

State of Illinois

—◆—

IN TWO PARTS,

The first consisting of General Observations

The second, gives a minute Review of each
Township, in its order.

—◆—

By ELIJAH M. HAINES.

—◆—

WAUKEGAN, ILL.

PUBLISHED BY E. G. HOWE,

Books and Stationer.

1852.

Geer & Print, Waukegan.

27. *Historical and Statistical Sketches, of*
  Lake County [Illinois]
  By Elijah M. Haines

County histories generally fall into the "mildly scarce" category and are worth a small premium, primarily for their genealogical references. Most of them are sloppily written and compiled. Some of them are important in a larger sense historically, however, and these sometimes bring very high prices, depending on scarcity and demand.

One of the more important ones in the Middle West is Elijah M. Haines' pioneer work on Lake County, Illinois.

The title page of this paperbound rarity reads, in part, as follows:

HISTORICAL / AND / STATISTICAL / SKETCHES, / OF / LAKE COUNTY / State of Illinois / [*decorative rule*] / IN TWO PARTS, [*etc., 3 lines*] / [*decorative rule*] / BY ELIJAH M. HAINES. / [*decorative rule*] / WAUKEGAN, ILL. / PUBLISHED BY E. G. HOWE. / Bookseller and Stationer. / 1852. / Geer's Print, Waukegan.

No copy of Haines' 112-page book has appeared on the auction market in recent years. A fine copy is worth $100 to $150 at retail. (I live in Lake County, and would like to have a copy.)

ANCIENT AND MODERN

MICHILIMACKINAC,

INCLUDING AN ACCOUNT

OF THE

CONTROVERSY BETWEEN MACKINAC

AND THE

MÖRMONS.

MDCCCLIV.

28. *Ancient and Modern Michilimackinac*

Chicago's Newberry Library, one of the world's great rare book repositories, announced the acquisition, not long ago, of one of the seven known copies of an important Mormon pamphlet that every collector in the field would like to own.

This 48-page item, with a drawing of an Indian on the cover, is James Jesse Strang's *Ancient and Modern Michilimackinac,* published in St. James, Michigan, in 1854. The Newberry Library describes it as the only responsible source for the history of the Strangite faction among the Mormons in the middle of the last century.

Its cover title reads as follows:

ANCIENT AND MODERN / MICHILIMACKI-NAC, / INCLUDING AN ACCOUNT / OF THE / CONTROVERSY BETWEEN MACKINAC / AND THE / MORMONS. / [*Indian scene*] / MDCCCLIV.

If another copy of the first issue should turn up today, it should fetch a minimum of $1,000, and probably more, if in almost any complete condition. [Note: There was a second, less valuable, printing also dated 1854, but produced on paper "obviously" of a later date, according to Wright Howes, the Americana authority.]

29. Sears, Roebuck & Co., Consumers Guide: Catalogue No. 105

You will never make a fortune out of that old mail order catalogue the family has handed down, but it could be worth a new hat or a suit of clothes, depending on its age and condition.

Sears, Roebuck & Co. gets thirty to forty letters a year from owners of old catalogues, an officer of the company told me recently. Sometimes, if they need one for the files, they offer $10 to $15 for the copy. In some cases, private collectors have paid up to $50 and more for early mail order catalogues.

The earliest catalogue in the Sears collection is a jewelry number dated 1887-89. (The company began operations in 1886.) The 1897 general catalogue is typical of the period. It has an ornate pictorial cover, with a title that reads, in part, as follows:

SEARS, ROEBUCK AND CO. / INCORPORATED / CHEAPEST SUPPLY HOUSE / ON EARTH / OUR TRADE REACHES AROUND THE WORLD / CONSUMERS GUIDE / CATA- LOGUE / No. 105 / CHICAGO, ILL. U. S. A.

There are several book dealers who specialize in such business Americana as catalogues, old posters, old correspondence, trading cards, etc. They pay roughly half of the expected retail price. Other markets are museums and private buyers.

30. *Davy Crockett's Almanack . . . 1837*

Among the scarcest treasures in the field of Americana is the series of Davy Crockett "Almanacks" issued in Nashville, Tennessee, for the years 1835 to 1841. The 1835 almanac is worth $100 or more in good condition; the others bring somewhat less in the collector's market.

Franklin J. Meine, of Chicago, is one of the few collectors with a complete file of the Nashville almanacs. His collection also includes others published in Boston, New York, and Philadelphia.

The 1837 issue, worth roughly $35 to $50 in good condition, is typical of the Nashville imprints. The cover title of this paperbound rarity reads as follows:

Vol. 1. "Go Ahead!" No. 3. / [*rule*] / Davy Crockett's / 18 ALMANACK, 37 / OF WILD SPORTS IN THE WEST, / Life in the Backwoods, & Sketches of Texas. / [*rule*] / [*portrait*] / [*rule*] / O KENTUCKY! THE HUNTERS OF KENTUCKY!!! / [*rule*] / Nashville, Tennessee. Published by the heirs of Col. Crockett.

This was the first of the Crockett almanacs published after the Colonel's death at the Alamo.

HISTORICAL SKETCHES

OF

KENTUCKY:

EMBRACING

ITS HISTORY, ANTIQUITIES, AND NATURAL CURIOSITIES, GEOGRAPHICAL,
STATISTICAL, AND GEOLOGICAL DESCRIPTIONS;

WITH

ANECDOTES OF PIONEER LIFE,

AND

MORE THAN ONE HUNDRED BIOGRAPHICAL SKETCHES OF DISTINGUISHED
PIONEERS, SOLDIERS, STATESMEN, JURISTS, LAWYERS, DIVINES, ETC.

ILLUSTRATED BY FORTY ENGRAVINGS.

BY LEWIS COLLINS.

PUBLISHED BY
LEWIS COLLINS, MAYSVILLE, KY.;
AND J. A. & U. P. JAMES,
CINCINNATI.
1847.

31. *Historical Sketches of Kentucky*
By Lewis Collins

Because Kentucky was one of the key areas in the Westward expansion of this country in the last century, the historical books of that region are generally popular with collectors.

One of the better historical works of the period is Lewis Collins' *Historical Sketches of Kentucky,* which has been reprinted several times.

The title page of the first edition reads, in part, as follows:

HISTORICAL SKETCHES / OF / KENTUCKY: / FMBRACING / ITS HISTORY, ANTIQUI-TIES, AND NATURAL CURIOSITIES, GEO-GRAPHICAL, / STATISTICAL, AND GEO-LOGICAL DESCRIPTIONS; / [*etc., 5 lines*] / ILLUSTRATED BY FORTY ENGRAVINGS. / BY LEWIS COLLINS. / [*seal—State of Kentucky*] / PUBLISHED BY / LEWIS COLLINS, MAYS-VILLE, KY., / AND J. A. & U. P. JAMES, / CIN-CINNATI. / 1847.

There is a folding map preceding the title page. Fine copies of the first edition are worth around $75 at retail. [See *Gold In Your Attic,* 1958, for price listing.]

CONFEDERATE

RECEIPT BOOK.

A COMPILATION

OF

OVER ONE HUNDRED RECEIPTS,

ADAPTED TO THE TIMES.

WEST & JOHNSTON, RICHMOND.

1863.

G. W. GARY, Printer, 21 Pearl Street.

32. *Confederate Receipt Book*

Artificial oysters, apple pie without apples, and Republican pudding are some of the recipes included in the *Confederate Receipt Book,* a rare Civil War item recently reprinted by the University of Georgia Press.

The first edition of this curious work survives in only five known copies. If another were to turn up today, it would bring at least $35 and perhaps more, in the opinion of Richard B. Harwell, a well-known authority on Confederate books. (I think his estimate is a little low.)

Because of paper scarcities, the original edition was bound in wallpaper. The printed cover title reads:

CONFEDERATE / RECEIPT BOOK. / [*decorative rule*] / A COMPILATION / OF / OVER ONE HUNDRED RECEIPTS, / ADAPTED TO THE TIMES. / [*decorative rule*] / WEST & JOHNSTON, RICHMOND. / 1863. / [*rule*] / G. W. GARY, Printer, 21 Pearl Street.

An even more famous and valuable Confederate item in the same tradition is Francis P. Porcher's *Resources of the Southern Fields and Forests* (Charleston, 1863).

THE

WESTERN MISCELLANY;

OR,

ACCOUNTS

HISTORICAL, BIOGRAPHICAL,

AND

AMUSING.

COMPILED BY G. W. STIPP

XENIA, O.
PRINTED FOR THE COMPILER.

—

1827.

33. *The Western Miscellany*
Compiled by G. W. Stipp

J. Christian Bay, the Chicago bibliophile and collector, told the story, in his *A Handful of Western Books,* of how William Stipp's exceedingly rare book, *The Western Miscellany,* once sold for $1 at a Chicago sale and later came to be valued at $1,000.

According to Dr. Bay, there were "two and nine-tenths" copies of the Stipp item known. One of these copies showed up in December, 1958, in the auction sale of Dr. Lester E. Bauer's library at the Parke-Bernet Galleries in New York. Although defective, it brought $1,000.

The title page of this rarity reads:

THE / WESTERN MISCELLANY, / OR, / AC-COUNTS / HISTORICAL, BIOGRAPHICAL, / AND / AMUSING. / [*rule*] / COMPILED BY G. W. STIPP / [*rule*] / XENIA, O. / PRINTED FOR THE COMPILER. / [*rule*] / 1827.

A note in the Bauer sale catalogue explains that Stipp's compilation is valuable solely because it includes "Bradford's Historical Notes on Kentucky."

ENSAYO HISTORICO

DE LAS

REVOLUCIONES

DE MEGICO,

DESDE 1808 HASTA 1830.

Por D. LORENZO DE ZAVALA.

TOMO SEGUNDO.

NUEVA-YORK,

IMPRENTA DE ELLIOTT Y PALMER,

CALLE DE WILLIAM, No 20.

1832.

34. *Ensayo Histórico de las Revoluciones de Megico*
By Lorenzo de Zavala

In his fascinating book *The Adventures of a Treasure Hunter*, the late Charles P. Everitt attributed much of his financial success in the rare book market to his ability to quickly recognize such words as "Mexico," "Oregon," and "California" on the covers of old books.

Most of the nineteenth century historical works about these areas have acquired some value in the collector's market. A typical rare book of this kind is Lorenzo de Zavala's Spanish language work, *Ensayo Histórico de las Revoluciones de Megico,* published in two volumes in 1831 and 1832.

The title page of the second volume reads as follows:

ENSAYO HISTORICO / DE LAS / REVOLU-CIONES / DE MEGICO, / DESDE 1808 HASTA 1830. / Por. D. LORENZO DE ZAVALA. / [*decorative rule*] / TOMO SEGUNDO. / [*decorative rule*] / NUEVA-YORK. / IMPRENTA DE ELLIOTT Y PALMER, / CALLE DE WILLIAM, NO. 20. / [*rule*] / 1832.

De Zavala's work is primarily of Texas interest. An official in Yucatan, he found himself favoring the American colonies in Texas and was twice exiled by the Mexican government. He was the first vice president of Texas, and Zavala County, Texas, bears his name.

The first volume of *Ensayo Histórico* was published in Paris in 1831. The second volume was published in New York in 1832. A set in good condition is worth $135 to $150 at retail. [See *Gold In Your Attic,* 1958.]

TRIP

TO THE

WEST AND TEXAS.

COMPRISING

A JOURNEY OF EIGHT THOUSAND MILES,

THROUGH

NEW-YORK, MICHIGAN, ILLINOIS, MISSOURI, LOUISIANA AND
TEXAS, IN THE AUTUMN AND WINTER OF
1834—5.

INTERSPERSED WITH ANECDOTES, INCIDENTS
AND OBSERVATIONS.

WITH A BRIEF SKETCH

OF THE

TEXIAN WAR.

BY A. A. PARKER, ESQ.

Second Edition.

CONCORD, N. H.:
PUBLISHED BY WILLIAM WHITE.
BOSTON:
BENJAMIN B. MUSSEY.
1836.

35. *Trip to the West and Texas*
By A. A. Parker

In most cases the first edition of an important book is the valuable one from the collector's standpoint. But A. A. Parker's *Trip to the West and Texas* is an exception to the rule.

Parker was an Easterner who made an eight-thousand mile journey Westward from New York to Texas, via Illinois, Missouri, and Louisiana, in the fall and winter of 1834-35. He recorded his observations in an important little book first published in 1835. In 1836, a second edition appeared. Some copies bore a folding map, and these are more valuable than the first edition copies.

The title page reads as follows:

TRIP / TO THE / WEST AND TEXAS. / COMPRISING / A JOURNEY OF EIGHT THOUSAND MILES, / THROUGH / NEW-YORK, MICHIGAN, ILLINOIS, MISSOURI, LOUISIANA AND / TEXAS, IN THE AUTUMN AND WINTER OF / 1834-5. / INTERSPERSED WITH ANECDOTES, INCIDENTS / AND OBSERVATIONS. / WITH A BRIEF SKETCH / OF THE / TEXIAN WAR. / [*rule*] / BY A. A. PARKER, ESQ. / [*rule*] / Second Edition. / [*rule*] / CONCORD, N. H.: / PUBLISHED BY WILLIAM WHITE. / BOSTON: / BENJAMIN B. MUSSEY. / 1836.

Fine copies of the first edition are worth up to $50 at retail. The second edition copies with map are worth as much as $65 to $75. Without map, the price is around $35.

NARRATIVE

OF THE

ADVENTURES OF

ZENAS LEONARD,

A NATIVE OF CLEARFIELD COUNTY, PA. WHO SPENT FIVE YEARS IN TRAPPING FOR FURS, TRADING WITH THE INDIANS, &c., &c., OF THE ROCKY MOUNTAINS:

WRITTEN BY HIMSELF:

———

PRINTED AND PUBLISHED

BY D. W. MOORE,

CLEARFIELD, PA.

1839.

36. *Narrative of the Adventures of Zenas Leonard*

About $5,000 is generally accepted as a fair retail price for a fine copy of the first edition of Zenas Leonard's famous account of his fur trading adventures among the Indians in the Rocky Mountains in the years 1831-37. The title page of this much-sought Western book reads as follows:

NARRATIVE / OF THE / ADVENTURES OF / ZENAS LEONARD, / A NATIVE OF CLEAR-FIELD COUNTY, PA. WHO SPENT FIVE / YEARS IN TRAPPING FOR FURS, TRADING WITH / THE INDIANS, &c., &c., OF THE / ROCKY MOUNTAINS: / WRITTEN BY HIM-SELF: / [*rule*] / PRINTED AND PUBLISHED / BY D. W. MOORE, / CLEARFIELD, PA. / 1839.

The book is important as an historical record because, as Wright Howes has pointed out in *U.S.-iana*, it is a completely trustworthy account of pioneering adventure.

In 1954 a copy in original cloth, with binding repaired, brought $4,600 at auction. In 1957 another copy appeared in modern morocco binding and brought $2,900. In original condition it would, of course, have brought much more. Prices for other copies in varying condition have ranged in recent years from $600 upward.

NARRATIVE

OF A TOUR

FROM THE STATE OF INDIANA

TO THE

OREGON TERRITORY,

IN THE YEARS 1841-2.

BY JOSEPH WILLIAMS.

CINCINNATI:
PRINTED FOR THE AUTHOR.

J. B. Wilson, Printer.
1843.

37. *Narrative of a Tour from the State of Indiana to the Oregon Territory*
By Joseph Williams

Only a few copies—most of them in libraries—remain of the small paperbound booklet in which the Rev. Joseph Williams, an Indiana Methodist, described his overland trip to Oregon in 1841-42. The last copy of which I have a record sold for $2,000, and the chances are that another copy, if found today, would bring much more.

The Rev. Mr. Williams left Napoleon, Indiana, on April 26, 1841, and reached Oregon in September or October of that year. He began his return east in April of the following year and completed the journey in the fall. Historically important, his 48-page record is a collector's prize.

The title page reads as follows:

NARRATIVE / OF A TOUR / FROM THE STATE OF INDIANA / TO THE / OREGON TERRITORY, / IN THE YEARS 1841-2. / [*rule*] / BY JOSEPH WILLIAMS. / [*rule*] / [*another, longer, rule*] / CINCINNATI: / PRINTED FOR THE AUTHOR. / [*rule*] / J. B. Wilson, Printer. / 1843.

The Williams narrative was reprinted in New York City in 1921 in a limited edition, now worth roughly $15 to $25 at retail.

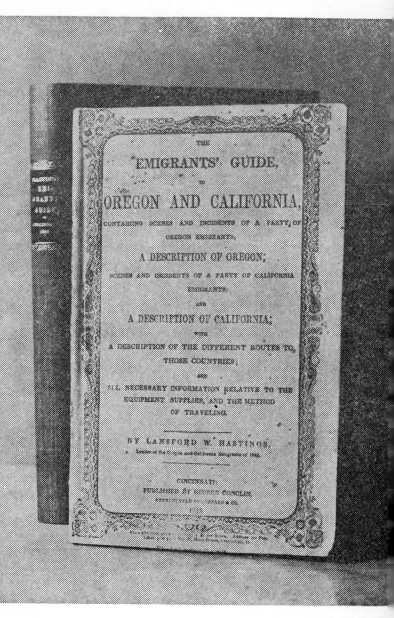

38. *The Emigrants' Guide, to Oregon and California*
By Lansford W. Hastings

Even the experts were jolted in December, 1958, by the manner in which the prices of the scarcer Western items skyrocketed at the sale of Dr. Lester E. Bauer's library of Western Americana.

A top example was Lansford W. Hastings' famous paperbound guidebook, of which there are only a few copies on record. A copy rebound in calf brought $4,700 at the auction, whereas not too many years before a copy could have been bought for as little as $500.

The title page of this 152-page rarity reads, in part, as follows:

THE / EMIGRANTS' GUIDE, / TO / OREGON AND CALIFORNIA, / [*etc., 14 lines*] / [*rule*] / BY LANSFORD W. HASTINGS. / Leader of the Oregon and California Emigrants of 1842. / [*rule*] / CINCINNATI: / PUBLISHED BY GEORGE CONCLIN, / STEREOTYPED BY SHEPARD & CO. / 1845.

The record $4,700 price was established in competitive bidding among leading Western specialist dealers, but many of their colleagues considered it excessively high.

Be that as it may, any new copy of Hastings that turns up in the future will almost certainly wind up in the $3,000 to $4,000 price range. (The copy illustrated here formerly was in the author's collection.) [See *Gold in Your Attic*. 1958.]

THREE YEARS AMONG

THE

INDIANS AND MEXICANS.

BY GEN. THOMAS JAMES,
OF MONROE COUNTY, ILLINOIS.

WATERLOO, ILL.
PRINTED AT THE OFFICE OF THE "WAR EAGLE"

1846.

39. *Three Years Among the Indians and Mexicans*
By Gen. Thomas James

There remain in existence probably no more than ten copies of the first edition of Gen. Thomas James' account of his Western adventures, one of the scarcest of early Illinois imprints.

In it the general told of his experience on the upper Missouri in 1809-10, his expedition to Santa Fe in 1821-22, and his experiences on the prairies in the following year. The actual writing of the book has been attributed to Col. John M. Niles.

The title page of this paperbound rarity reads as follows:

THREE YEARS AMONG / THE / INDIANS AND MEXICANS. / [*double rule*] / BY GEN THOMAS JAMES, / OF MONROE COUNTY, ILLINOIS. / [*double rule*] / WATERLOO, ILL. / PRINTED AT THE OFFICE OF THE "WAR EAGLE." / [*dotted rule*] / 1846.

The last copy offered at an auction, with paper covers supplied, brought $2,600. A fine copy, in original condition, should command even more.

ROUTE

ACROSS THE ROCKY MOUNTAINS,

WITH A

DESCRIPTION OF OREGON AND CALIFORNIA;

THEIR

GEOGRAPHICAL FEATURES, THEIR RESOURCES, SOIL,
CLIMATE, PRODUCTIONS, &c., &c.

BY OVERTON JOHNSON AND WM. H. WINTER,
OF THE EMIGRATION OF 1843.

LAFAYETTE, IND:
JOHN B. SEMANS, PRINTER.
1846.

40. *Route Across the Rocky Mountains*
By Overton Johnson and William H. Winter

Among the book discoveries reported by my readers was a copy of Overton Johnson's and William H. Winter's rare overland narrative, found nestling in a trunk owned by an Indiana housewife.

This rarity, which also happened to be an Indiana imprint, was worth $500 to the finder. Had it been in better condition it might have brought up to $850 or more, according to the price records in my files.

The title page reads as follows:

ROUTE / ACROSS THE ROCKY MOUNTAINS, / WITH A / DESCRIPTION OF OREGON AND CALIFORNIA; / THEIR / GEOGRAPHICAL FEATURES, THEIR RESOURCES, SOIL, / CLIMATE, PRODUCTIONS, &c., &c. / [rule] / BY OVERTON JOHNSON AND WM. H. WINTER, / OF THE EMIGRATION OF 1843. / [rule] / LAFAYETTE, IND: / JOHN B. SEMANS, PRINTER. / 1846.

Johnson was a native of Crawfordsville, Indiana, and attended Wabash College, where he was in Lew Wallace's class, according to the bibliographer Henry R. Wagner. Johnson and Winter made the overland trip to California in 1843.

THE

PRAIRIE FLOWER;

OR,

ADVENTURES IN THE FAR WEST.

BY EMERSON BENNETT.

AUTHOR OF THE "BANDITS OF THE OSAGE," "THE RENEGADE," "MIKE FINK," "KATE CLARENDON," ETC., ETC.

But O, the blooming prairie,
  Here are God's floral bowers,
Of all that he hath made on earth
  The loveliest.   *   *   *
This is the Almighty's garden,
  And the mountains, stars, and sea,
Are nought compared in beauty,
  With God's garden prairie free.

STRATTON & BARNARD:

CINCINNATI AND ST. LOUIS.

1849.

41. *The Prairie Flower*
By Emerson Bennett

Discovery of gold in California a little more than a century ago inspired innumerable books and pamphlets among the fortune hunters, and the best of them are still touched with the magic of gold dust.

One of the scarcer items is Emerson Bennett's 25¢-paperbound narrative, *The Prairie Flower,* which described "the travels of a party of young men from an Eastern city across the Rocky Mountains, thence to California . . ."

The title of this 128-page book reads as follows:

THE / PRAIRIE FLOWER; / OR, / ADVEN-TURES IN THE FAR WEST / BY EMERSON BENNETT. / [*etc., 2 lines*] / [*rule*] / [*quotation—8 line poem*] / [*rule*] / STRATTON & BARNARD: / CINCINNATI AND ST. LOUIS. / 1849.

The Prairie Flower is said to have been printed first in the Cincinnati weekly, The Great West, in 1848, but no copy of that date is known.

A fine copy of the book should bring $200 or more at retail in today's Americana market. It has a recent auction record of $130.

THE

EMIGRANTS' GUIDE

TO

CALIFORNIA,

CONTAINING EVERY POINT OF INFORMATION FOR
THE EMIGRANT—INCLUDING ROUTES, DISTANCES,
WATER, GRASS, TIMBER, CROSSING OF RIVERS,
PASSES, ALTITUDES, WITH A LARGE MAP OF
ROUTES, AND PROFILE OF COUNTRY, &C.,—
WITH FULL DIRECTIONS FOR TESTING AND
ASSAYING GOLD AND OTHER ORES.

BY JOSEPH E. WARE.

PUBLISHED BY J. HALSALL,
No. 124 MAIN STREET,
ST. LOUIS, MO.

42. *The Emigrants' Guide to California*
By Joseph E. Ware

Naming a price on any of the old Gold Rush guide-books is risky business in the current market. The safest thing to say about Joseph E. Ware's famed 1849 *The Emigrants' Guide* is that it is worth $1,000 and up. It is always possible that before this ink is dry somebody will have paid twice that for a copy.

Ware, who hailed from Galena, Illinois, published his guidebook, one of the first of the Gold Rush guides, early in 1849 and died later that year on his way to the gold fields.

The title page reads, in part, as follows:

THE / EMIGRANTS' GUIDE / TO / CALI-FORNIA / [*etc., 7 lines*] / [*rule*] / BY JOSEPH E. WARE. / [*seal—State of Missouri*] / PUB-LISHED BY J. HALSALL, / No. 124 MAIN STREET, / ST. LOUIS, MO.

The book is bound in blue-gray cloth and contains a map of the route to California. On the back of the title page is the date 1849. [See *Gold in Your Attic*, 1958, for price listing.]

43. *California. A Trip Across the Plains.*
By James Abbey

James Abbey's 64-page paperbound record of a trip to California, published in New Albany, Indiana, in 1850, is a prime example of the kind of Western Americana

CALIFORNIA.

A TRIP

ACROSS THE PLAINS,

IN THE SPRING OF 1850,

BEING A DAILY RECORD OF INCIDENTS OF THE TRIP OVER
THE PLAINS, THE DESERT, AND THE MOUNTAINS,
SKETCHES OF THE COUNTRY, DISTANCES FROM
CAMP TO CAMP, ETC.,

AND CONTAINING VALUABLE INFORMATION TO

EMIGRANTS,

AS TO WHERE THEY WILL FIND WOOD, WATER, AND
GRASS AT ALMOST EVERY STEP OF THE JOURNEY.

BY JAMES ABBEY.

PUBLISHED BY
JNO. R. NUNMACHER, CITY BOOKSTORE,
KENT & NORMAN, LEDGER BUILDINGS,
NEW ALBANY, IND.

C. Hagan & Co., Louisville; Wm. H. Moore & Co., Cincinnati; and Lippincott, Grambo & Co., Philadelphia.

1850.

that collectors want. In typical fashion, it combines a narrative of overland adventures with a generous helping of information for others who might want to follow.

The cover title, enclosed in an ornate border, reads as follows:

> CALIFORNIA. / [*decorative rule*] / A TRIP / ACROSS THE PLAINS, / IN THE SPRING OF 1850, / BEING A DAILY RECORD OF THE INCIDENTS OF THE TRIP OVER / THE PLAINS, THE DESERT, AND THE MOUN- TAINS, / SKETCHES OF THE COUNTRY, DISTANCES FROM / CAMP TO CAMP, ETC., / AND CONTAINING VALUABLE INFORMA- TION TO / EMIGRANTS, / AS TO WHERE THEY WILL FIND WOOD, WATER, AND / GRASS AT ALMOST EVERY STEP OF THE JOURNEY. / BY JAMES ABBEY. / [*rule*] / PUB- LISHED BY / JNO. R. NUNMACHER, CITY BOOKSTORE, / KENT & NORMAN, LEDGER BUILDINGS, / NEW ALBANY, IND. / [*etc., 2 lines*] / 1850.

The last copy I saw catalogued was offered by a dealer at $600. In 1954, a copy lacking the back cover brought $550 at auction.

44. *Scenery of the Plains, Mountains and Mines*
By Franklin Langworthy

Prices are still edging upward in the Western book market, even for the minor items. A good example is Franklin Langworthy's overland diary of a trip to Cali-

SCENERY

OF

THE PLAINS, MOUNTAINS AND MINES:

OR

A DIARY KEPT UPON THE OVERLAND ROUTE

TO

CALIFORNIA,

BY WAY OF THE GREAT SALT LAKE:

TRAVELS IN THE CITIES, MINES, AND AGRICULTURAL DISTRICTS
EMBRACING THE RETURN BY

THE PACIFIC OCEAN AND CENTRAL AMERICA,

In the Years 1850, '51, '52 and '53.

BY

FRANKLIN LANGWORTHY.

I speak of things which I have seen and do know, touching men and objects
in a stirring period of my country's history.

OGDENSBURGH:

PUBLISHED BY J. C. SPRAGUE, BOOK-SELLER.

HITCHCOCK & TILLOTSON, PRINTERS.

1855.

fornia and the mining regions, published in 1855. A few years ago good copies could be bought for $35 to $40. Today the retail price is more likely to be in the $60 to $80 range.

The title page of this scarce item reads as follows:

SCENERY / OF / THE PLAINS, MOUNTAINS AND MINES: / OR / A DIARY KEPT UPON THE OVERLAND ROUTE / TO / CALIFOR-NIA, / BY WAY OF THE GREAT SALT LAKE: / TRAVELS IN THE CITIES, MINES, AND AGRICULTURAL DISTRICTS / EMBRAC-ING THE RETURN BY / THE PACIFIC OCEAN AND CENTRAL AMERICA, / In the Years 1850, '51, '52 and '53. / [rule] / BY / FRANK-LIN LANGWORTHY. / [rule] / [quotation, 2 lines] / [rule] / OGDENSBURGH: / PUBLISHED BY J. C. SPRAGUE, BOOK-SELLER. / [rule] / HITCHCOCK & TILLOTSON, PRINTERS. / 1855.

The text is set in double columns of type, which was often the style for the crudely printed books and pamphlets of the period. [See Gold in Your Attic, 1958, for price listing.]

45. Miners & Business Men's Directory

We have referred several times to the Bauer sale of 1958 and the boost it gave to Western Americana prices. Almost a year later, in October, 1959, there occurred an-other great sale of Western books when the library of Dr. Henry W. Plath of Piedmont, California, came to

MINERS & BUSINESS

MEN'S DIRECTORY.

FOR THE

Year Commencing January 1st, 1856.

EMBRACING A

GENERAL DIRECTORY

OF THE

CITIZENS OF TUOLUMNE,

AS ALSO THOSE OF

CALAVERAS, STANISLAUS AND SAN JOAQUIN COUNTIES.

TOGETHER WITH

The Mining Laws of Each District,

DESCRIPTION OF THE DIFFERENT CAMPS,

AND

Other Interesting Statistical Matter.

BY HECKENDORN & WILSON.

COLUMBIA:
PRINTED AT THE CLIPPER OFFICE, FULTON ST., NEAR MAIN
1856.

auction at the Parke-Bernet Galleries in New York City.

California books were especially prominent at this disposal, and many of them established new high records. As in the case of the Bauer sale, dealers and others who strive to keep abreast of the book market (including the author of this book), were hard put to keep up with the general advance of Western materials all along the line.

One example of the prices resulting from the free-handed bidding at this sale is the $1,000 record attained by the very rare Columbia (California) history and directory published in 1856.

The title page of this paperbound rarity reads as follows:

> MINERS & BUSINESS / MEN'S DIRECTORY. / FOR THE / Year Commencing January 1st, 1856. / EMBRACING A / GENERAL DIRECTORY / OF THE / CITIZENS OF TUOLUMNE, / AND PORTIONS OF / CALAVERAS, STANISLAUS AND SAN JOAQUIN COUNTIES. / TOGETHER WITH / The Mining Laws of Each District, / DESCRIPTION OF THE DIFFERENT CAMPS, / AND / Other Interesting Statistical Matter. / [rule] / BY HECKENDORN & WILSON. / [rule] / COLUMBIA: / PRINTED AT THE CLIPPER OFFICE, FULTON ST., NEAR MAIN. / 1856.

According to the catalogue of the sale, this was one of fewer than half a dozen known copies of this directory.

JOURNAL

OF

SAMUEL RUTHERFORD DUNDASS,

FORMERLY

AUDITOR OF JEFFERSON COUNTY, OHIO.

INCLUDING HIS

ENTIRE ROUTE TO CALIFORNIA,

AS A MEMBER OF THE

Steubenville Company bound for San Francisco

IN THE YEAR 1849.

STEUBENVILLE, O.
PRINTED AT CONN'S JOB OFFICE.
1857.

46. *Journal of Samuel Rutherford Dundass*

The discovery of gold in California brought waves of gold hunters, emigrants, and adventurers from every section of America. From these Forty-Niners there came a steady stream of overland narratives, many of them cheaply printed and perishable. Some of these accounts were destined to be highly regarded by historians in later years, and a number of them all but vanished and are eagerly sought today.

Among those who went West in 1849 and provided a valuable record was Samuel Rutherford Dundass, an Ohioan, whose scarce *Journal,* rebound, brought $500 at a recent auction sale.

The title page reads as follows:

JOURNAL / OF / SAMUEL RUTHERFORD DUNDASS, / FORMERLY / AUDITOR OF JEFFERSON COUNTY, OHIO. / INCLUDING HIS / ENTIRE ROUTE TO CALIFORNIA, / AS A MEMBER OF THE / Steubenville Company bound for San Francisco / IN THE YEAR 1849. / [*decorative rule*] / STEUBENVILLE, O. / PRINTED AT CONN'S JOB OFFICE. / 1857.

There were sixty persons in the Steubenville Company of emigrants. They left on March 24, and arrived in California in September.

REID'S TRAMP,

OR, A

JOURNAL OF THE INCIDENTS

OF

TEN MONTHS TRAVEL THROUGH

Texas, New Mexico, Arizona, Sonora, and California.

INCLUDING TOPOGRAPHY, CLIMATE, SOIL, MINERALS, METALS, AND INHABITANTS;

WITH A NOTICE OF

THE GREAT INTER-OCEANIC RAIL ROAD

By JOHN C. REID.

SELMA, ALABAMA.

PRINTED AT THE BOOK AND JOB OFFICE OF JOHN HARDY & CO.

1858.

47. *Reid's Tramp*
By John C. Reid

Collectors seem to have a special fondness for *Reid's Tramp*, perhaps because of the refreshing brevity of its short-title identification as contrasted with most of the long-winded titles of other Western narratives.

Unlike most of the major items in this field, *Reid's Tramp* was published in the South instead of the East or North.

Its full title is as follows:

REID'S TRAMP, / OR, A / JOURNAL OF THE INCIDENTS / OF / TEN MONTHS TRAVEL THROUGH / TEXAS, NEW MEXICO, ARIZONA, SONORA, AND CALIFORNIA. / INCLUDING TOPOGRAPHY, CLIMATE, SOIL, MINERALS, / METALS, AND INHABITANTS; / WITH A NOTICE OF / THE GREAT INTER-OCEANIC RAIL ROAD / [*decorative rule*] / BY JOHN C. REID. / [*decorative rule*] / SELMA, ALABAMA / [*dotted rule*] / PRINTED AT THE BOOK AND JOB OFFICE OF JOHN HARDY & CO. / [*dotted rule*] / 1858.

A copy in fine condition is worth up to $1,000—and probably more. One sold at auction in 1958 for $1,100, but the price was considered by most dealers to be excessive. A few years previously a copy inscribed by Reid had gone for only $575.

THREE YEARS AMONG
THE CAMANCHES,

Nelson Lee

THE NARRATIVE OF
NELSON LEE,
THE TEXAN RANGER.

ALBANY :
BAKER TAYLOR, 58 STATE ST.
1859.

48. *Three Years Among the Camanches*
By Nelson Lee

It is easy to identify the rare first edition of Nelson Lee's famous little book, *Three Years Among the Camanches,* in which the Texas Ranger described his capture by the Comanche Indians while on his way to California in 1855.

It is an unusual book because it bears two title pages. The first was used as a frontispiece and contains a portrait of the bearded Lee, along with his signature.

The second, with a long-winded subtitle, appeared in the usual place at the front of the book.

The text of the first title page reads as follows:

THREE YEARS AMONG / THE CAMANCHES, / [*portrait*] / [*signature*] / THE NARRATIVE OF / NELSON LEE, / THE TEXAN RANGER. / [*decorative rule*] / ALBANY: / BAKER TAYLOR, 58 STATE ST., / 1859.

The book exists both in clothbound and paperbound covers, with the paperbound covers generally preferred by collectors. Fine paperbound copies are worth at retail as much as $150 to $250, possibly more. Clothbound copies are worth $150 or more.

49. *Guide to the New Gold Region of Western Kansas and Nebraska*

Some time ago I began a "Gold in Your Attic" column by writing: "Week after week, as you read here about

GUIDE

TO THE

NEW GOLD REGION

OF

WESTERN KANSAS AND NEBRASKA,

WITH

TABLE OF DISTANCES AND AN ACCURATE MAP.

NEW-YORK:

JOHN W. OLIVER, STEAM JOB PRINTER, 43 ANN-STREET,

FIFTH DOOR EAST OF NASSAU.

1859.

the fabulous rarities in the world of books, you may shake your head and say, 'That could never happen to me.' But don't be too sure."

I then related the story of W. Warren Curtis, a reader in Holyoke, Massachusetts, who had mailed in for my examination a 32-page paperbound Pike's Peak guidebook that had been passed down in his family. A few nights after receiving it I had the pleasure of telephoning Mr. Curtis an offer of $1,800 on behalf of Kenneth Nebenzahl, a Chicago specialist dealer in rare Americana.

It so happened that, until the discovery of Mr. Curtis' copy, there were only two known copies of this Colorado Gold Rush item in complete form. Two other incomplete copies are also known to exist.

Because it is historically important, it is a highly desirable collector's item. The cover title reads as follows:

GUIDE / TO THE / NEW GOLD REGION / OF / WESTERN KANSAS AND NEBRASKA, / WITH / TABLE OF DISTANCES AND AN ACCURATE MAP. / [*flag and eagle shield*] / NEW-YORK: / JOHN W. OLIVER, STEAM JOB PRINTER, 43 ANN-STREET, / FIFTH DOOR EAST OF NASSAU. / 1859.

The dealer's price was in effect a "wholesale" offer, which I advised Mr. Curtis to accept. When Mr. Nebenzahl listed the booklet in his next catalogue, it bore a price tag of $2,800.

I regarded the $1,800 check he sent to Mr. Curtis as especially generous. Most dealers are inclined to pay only 50% of estimated retail value, and this is universally considered a fair position in the rare book world.

PRICE FIFTY CENTS.

A
HAND BOOK
TO THE
GOLD FIELDS
OF
NEBRASKA AND KANSAS.
Being a complete
GUIDE TO THE GOLD REGIONS
OF THE
SOUTH PLATTE & CHERRY CREEK.

D.B. COOKE & CO.
CHICAGO.

1859.

50. *A Hand Book to the Gold Fields of Nebraska and Kansas*
By William N. Byers and John H. Kellom

When William N. Byers and John H. Kellom published their guide to the Colorado gold fields in 1859, it sold for 50¢ a copy. If you found one today, it would be worth $300 to $600, or possibly more, depending on condition.

The ornate pictorial cover of this extremely rare book reads as follows:

PRICE FIFTY CENTS / A / HAND BOOK / TO THE / GOLD FIELDS / OF / NEBRASKA AND KANSAS, / Being a complete / GUIDE TO THE GOLD REGIONS / OF THE / SOUTH PLATTE & CHERRY CREEK. / D. B. COOKE & CO. / CHICAGO. / 1859.

Bound in paper covers and consisting of 113 pages and a map, it is typical of the pioneer guidebooks of the period. Most of them have disappeared because of their fragile nature, and any that you may find are potentially of value. Libraries, historical societies, and private collectors make up the market.

OVERLAND JOURNEY

TO

CARSON VALLEY, UTAH,

THROUGH

KANSAS, NEBRASKA AND UTAH; ALSO, RETURN TRIP FROM SAN FRANCISCO TO SENECA FALLS VIA. THE ISTHMUS

BY HOZIAL H. BAKER.

SENECA FALLS, N. Y.:
PUBLISHED BY F. M. BAKER.
1861.

51. *Overland Journey to Carson Valley, Utah*
By Hozial H. Baker

It was the late Charles P. Everitt, a Boston dealer of renown, who remarked that it was generally the "little thin" books that brought him the most profit in the rare book business.

One of the really rare items among the thin little overland narratives of the last century is Hozial H. Baker's account of the journey he made, when seventy, from New York State to Utah.

The title page reads as follows:

OVERLAND JOURNEY / TO / CARSON VALLEY, UTAH, / THROUGH / KANSAS, NEBRASKA AND UTAH; ALSO, RETURN / TRIP, FROM SAN FRANCISCO TO SENECA / FALLS, VIA. THE ISTHMUS. / [*rule*] / BY HOZIAL H. BAKER. / [*rule*] / SENECA FALLS, N. Y.: / PUBLISHED BY F. M. BAKER. / 1861.

Baker began his diary east of Chicago on March 29, 1859, and reached the settlement of Chinatown, near Genoa, Nevada, on July 20.

No copy of this 28-page paperbound title has appeared for sale in recent years. A fine copy would be worth a minimum of $1,000, and probably much more, on the current market.

NOTES BY THE WAY.

MEMORANDA

OF A

JOURNEY ACROSS THE PLAINS,

FROM

DUNDEE, ILL., TO OLYMPIA, W. T.

May 7, to November 3, 1862.

By R. H. HEWITT.

OLYMPIA:
PRINTED AT THE OFFICE OF THE WASHINGTON STANDARD.
1863.

52. *Notes by the Way*
By R. H. Hewitt

A recurring problem that has confronted me since the beginning of my column is that of trying to explain to a reader why her handsomely bound set of Dickens is worth very little commercially while a ragged old Western pamphlet I have mentioned in the column is worth a four-figure price.

It is a problem that the dealer in rare books also faces every day. The answer is simply the matter of supply and demand. There are thousands of sets of Charles Dickens' writings available in many different editions. But there may be no more than half a dozen copies of an important historical book or pamphlet.

Randall H. Hewitt's account of his mule team trip to the West in 1862 is a typical example of the latter case.

The title page of this rare narrative reads as follows:

NOTES BY THE WAY. / [rule] / MEMORANDA / OF A / JOURNEY ACROSS THE PLAINS, / FROM / DUNDEE, ILL., TO OLYMPIA, W. T. / May 7, to November 3, 1862. / By R. H. HEWITT. / [*rule*] / OLYMPIA: / PRINTED AT THE OFFICE OF THE WASHINGTON STANDARD. / 1863.

This is a 58-page paperbound book, and the text is set in double columns. A fine copy is worth a minimum of $1,000, and probably much more in the present collector's market.

THE

NORTHERN ROUTE

TO

IDAHO:

AND THE

PACIFIC OCEAN.

PUBLISHED BY
D. D. MERRILL,
BOOK SELLER AND STATIONER,
SAINT PAUL, MINN.

53. *The Northern Route to Idaho and the Pacific Ocean*

From the records, it appears that only two copies of D. D. Merrill's guidebook to the Idaho gold mines have ever appeared at public sale. At the famous Holliday sale of Western Americana in 1954, a copy brought $400. The same copy had sold in 1941 for $225. There is one other sale recorded in the 1920's.

The title page of this clothbound eight-pager, which is accompanied by a folding map, reads as follows:

THE / NORTHERN ROUTE / TO / IDAHO· / AND THE / PACIFIC OCEAN. / [*decorative rule*] / PUBLISHED BY / D. D. MERRILL, / BOOK SELLER AND STATIONER, / SAINT PAUL, MINN.

Printed in gold across the cover of this small volume is the cover title, *Minnesota Route to the Gold Mines of Idaho.*

A peculiarity about this rarity is the map, which was altered because of state boundary changes after printing. It is known as the "Rubber Stamp Map."

LIFE AND MARVELOUS ADVENTURES

OF

WILD BILL,

THE SCOUT.

**BEING A TRUE AND EXACT HISTORY OF ALL THE
SANGUINARY COMBATS AND HAIR-BREADTH
ESCAPES OF THE MOST FAMOUS SCOUT
AND SPY AMERICA EVER PRODUCED.**

BY

J. W. BUEL,

OF THE ST. LOUIS PRESS.

ILLUSTRATED.

CHICAGO:

BELFORD, CLARKE & CO.

1880

54. *Life and Marvelous Adventures of Wild Bill,*
   the Scout
By J. W. Buel

Generally speaking, a book ought to be of some importance to command a high price—even in the fantastically
popular field of Western Americana. Such is not the case,
however, with the rare and expensive first edition of J. W.
Buel's *Life and Marvelous Adventures of Wild Bill, the
Scout.*

Wild Bill Hickock, like Buffalo Bill and certain other
heroes of the old West, is such a favorite that collectors
want every scrap about him, true or false.

Buel's book has been largely discredited, but it still
commands $100 and up in fine condition. The title page
of this paperbound rarity reads as follows:

LIFE AND MARVELOUS ADVENTURES / OF
/ WILD BILL, / THE SCOUT. / BEING A
TRUE AND EXACT HISTORY OF ALL THE
/ SANGUINARY COMBATS AND HAIR-
BREADTH / ESCAPES OF THE MOST FA-
MOUS SCOUT / AND SPY AMERICA EVER
PRODUCED. / BY / J. W. BUEL, / OF THE
ST. LOUIS PRESS. / [*rule*] / ILLUSTRATED.
/ [*rule*] / CHICAGO: / BELFORD, CLARKE &
CO. / 1880.

The reprint of 1888 and 1891 are less valuable.

HISTORY

OF

DEL NORTE COUNTY,

CALIFORNIA

WITH

BUSINESS DIRECTORY

AND

TRAVELER'S GUIDE

BY A. J. BLEDSOE.

EUREKA:
HUMBOLDT TIMES PRINT—WYMAN & CO., PUBLISHERS
1881

55. *History of Del Norte County, California*
By A. J. Bledsoe

The scarcer local histories are always valuable in the rare book market, but few ever reach the extraordinary heights recently attained by one of A. J. Bledsoe's California items. In October, 1959, when the Western Americana holdings of Dr. Henry W. Plath went on the auction block in New York, a copy of Bledsoe's *History of Del Norte County* brought $1,800.

It benefited from the current boom in Western books, for it had previously been classified as an item worth around $250 at retail.

The title page of this paperbound rarity reads as follows:

HISTORY / OF / DEL NORTE COUNTY, / CALIFORNIA / WITH / BUSINESS DIREC-TORY / AND / TRAVELER'S GUIDE. / [*rule*] / BY A. J. BLEDSOE. / [*rule*] / EUREKA: / HUMBOLDT TIMES PRINT—WYMAN & CO., PUBLISHERS / [*rule*] / 1881.

Most of the innumerable county histories around the country have some value beyond the publication price. The range is usually from $5 to $25, depending on the subject and the condition of the book.

A CONCISE HISTORY

OF THE

MORMON BATTALION

IN THE

MEXICAN WAR.

1846-1847.

BY SERGEANT DANIEL TYLER,

1881.

56. *A Concise History of the Mormon Battalion*
By Sgt. Daniel Tyler

As indicated in an earlier article in this series, Mormon historical books from around the middle of the last century are quite often scarce and sought by collectors. The reason, of course, is that the Mormon movement Westward was intimately connected with the whole drama of the expanding frontier, which is a favored field for collectors.

One of the very interesting items is Sgt. Daniel Tyler's eyewitness account of the breaking of the first wagon road from Santa Fe, New Mexico, to San Diego, California. It was published in Salt Lake City in 1882, although the title page says 1881.

The title in full reads as follows:

A CONCISE HISTORY / OF THE / MORMON BATTALION / IN THE / MEXICAN WAR / [*decorative rule*] / 1846-1847. / [*decorative rule*] / BY SERGEANT DANIEL TYLER. / [*rule*] / 1881.

Copies in fine condition are worth $50 to $100 at retail.

——THE——

LIFE AND ADVENTURES

OF

ROBERT McKIMIE,

ALIAS "LITTLE REDDY," FROM TEXAS.

The Dare-Devil Desperado of the Black Hills Region,
Chief of the Murderous Gang of Treasure
Coach Robbers.   Also, a full

ACCOUNT OF THE ROBBERIES COMMITTED

By him and his Gang in Highland, Pike and Ross
Counties; with full particulars of Detective
Norris' Adventures while effecting the
Capture of Members of the Gang.

Compiled from Authentic Sources by **J. W. BRIDWELL.**

HILLSBORO, O., DECEMBER, 1878.

PRINTED AND PUBLISHED AT THE

HILLSBORO GAZETTE OFFICE.

57. *The Life and Adventures of Robert McKimie*
Compiled by J. W. Bridwell

One of the scarcest of Ohio imprints is a 56-page paperbound book, *The Life and Adventures of Robert McKimie,* the story of a Black Hills bandit who used to rob the treasure coaches on the Deadwood-Cheyenne run.

The title page reads, in part, as follows:

THE / LIFE AND ADVENTURES / OF / ROBERT McKIMIE, / ALIAS "LITTLE REDDY," FROM TEXAS. / [*etc., 8 lines*] / [*printer's device*] / Compiled from Authentic Sources by J. W. BRIDWELL. / [*printer's device*] / HILLSBORO, O., DECEMBER, 1878. / PRINTED AND PUBLISHED AT THE / HILLSBORO GAZETTE OFFICE.

McKimie began his daredevil criminal career as a member of the Sam Bass gang. Bridwell's account describes the robberies he committed, including the one in which the stage driver Johnny Slaughter was murdered.

Only a few copies of this rarity are believed to exist. A copy in good condition is worth $150 to $200 on the collector's market.

58. *The Authentic Life of Billy, the Kid*
By Pat. F. Garrett

Among the many stories about Western bad men, one of the prizes sought by collectors is Patrick Floyd Garrett's

THE

AUTHENTIC LIFE

—OF—

BILLY, THE KID,

THE NOTED DESPERADO OF THE SOUTHWEST, WHOSE DEEDS OF DARING AND
BLOOD MADE HIS NAME A TERROR IN NEW MEXICO,
ARIZONA AND NORTHERN MEXICO.

By PAT. F. GARRETT,

SHERIFF OF LINCOLN CO., N. M.,

BY WHOM HE WAS FINALLY HUNTED DOWN AND CAPTURED BY
KILLING HIM.

A FAITHFUL AND INTERESTING NARRATIVE.

SANTA FE, NEW MEXICO:
NEW MEXICAN PRINTING AND PUBLISHING CO
1882.

extremely rare paperbound book, *The Authentic Life of Billy, the Kid.*

It was published by Garrett to counteract widespread criticism of the manner in which he hunted down and killed the desperado, according to Ramon F. Adams, author of *Six-Guns & Saddle Leather,* an excellent bibliography devoted to Western outlaws and gunmen.

I have no record of a recent sale of Garrett's book, but a basic price of $100 is suggested by Paul Schopflin of Evanston, Illinois, a specialist in outlaw books. A fine copy would probably bring even more.

The long-winded title page reads as follows:

THE / AUTHENTIC LIFE / OF / BILLY, THE KID, / THE NOTED DESPERADO OF THE SOUTHWEST, WHOSE DEEDS OF DARING AND / BLOOD MADE HIS NAME A TERROR IN NEW MEXICO, / ARIZONA AND NORTHERN MEXICO. / BY PAT. F. GARRETT, / SHERIFF OF LINCOLN CO., N. M. / BY WHOM HE WAS FINALLY HUNTED DOWN AND CAPTURED BY / KILLING HIM. / A FAITHFUL AND INTERESTING NARRATIVE. / [*decorative rule*] / SANTE FE, NEW MEXICO: / NEW MEXICAN PRINTING AND PUBLISHING CO., / 1882.

When it was first published, Garrett's account sold for $1, and the price was later reduced to 25¢ a copy.

LAST RAID

OF THE

DALTONS

A RELIABLE RECITAL OF THE BATTLE
WITH THE BANDITS

...AT...

COFFEYVILLE, KANSAS·
OCTOBER 5, 1892

By DAVID STEWART ELLIOTT
Editor Coffeyville Journal

FIRST EDITION
ILLUSTRATED BY E. A. FILLEAU

1892.
COFFEYVILLE JOURNAL PRINT,
COFFEYVILLE, KANSAS.

59. *Last Raid of the Daltons*
By David Stewart Elliott

The Dalton gang of Oklahoma outlaws rates extended treatment in any dictionary of Western gunmen. And books about their exploits are eagerly sought by collectors.

One of the more interesting of these is David Stewart Elliott's *Last Raid of the Daltons,* an exceedingly scarce paperback published shortly after the Coffeyville (Kansas) raid in 1892. It was in that raid that four of the gang members were slain. Emmett Dalton, shot twenty-three times, was the single survivor.

A first edition of Elliott's account is worth $100 and up in fine condition. The title page reads as follows:

LAST RAID / OF THE / DALTONS / [rule] / A RELIABLE RECITAL OF THE BATTLE / WITH THE BANDITS / AT / COFFEYVILLE, KANSAS / OCTOBER 5, 1892 / [rule] / BY DAVID STEWART ELLIOTT / Editor Coffeyville Journal / [rule] / FIRST EDITION / ILLUS- TRATED BY E. A. FILLEAU / [rule] / 1892. / COFFEYVILLE JOURNAL PRINT, / COFFEY- VILLE, KANSAS.

A copy of the 71-page first edition, with the pictorial covers intact, was found not long ago by a "Gold in Your Attic" newspaper reader and sold to a rare book dealer. There was also a 60-page edition in 1892. It is worth some- what less than the first—between $25 and $50.

HISTORIC SKETCHES

OF THE

CATTLE TRADE

OF THE

WEST AND SOUTHWEST.

By JOSEPH G. McCOY,

THE PIONEER WESTERN CATTLE SHIPPER.

ILLUSTRATED BY PROF. HENRY WORRALL, TOPEKA, KAS.
ENGRAVED BY BAKER & CO., CHICAGO, ILL.
ELECTROTYPED BY J. T. RETON & CO., KANSAS CITY, MO.

PUBLISHED BY
RAMSEY, MILLETT & HUDSON, KANSAS CITY, MO.,
PRINTERS, BINDERS, ENGRAVERS, LITHOGRAPHERS & STATIONERS.
1874.

60. *Historic Sketches of the Cattle Trade*
By Joseph G. McCoy

A newspaper publisher asked me not long ago about an old cattle trade book in his library. He was astonished to find it quoted at prices up to $175 a copy, depending on condition.

The item happened to be Joseph G. McCoy's scarce history of the Western cattle trade. According to Ramon F. Adams' cattle-trade bibliography, *The Rampaging Herd,* McCoy's clothbound account is "one of the 'big four' cattle books . . . one of the first and most important books on the cattle trade."

Its title page reads as follows:

HISTORIC SKETCHES / OF THE / CATTLE TRADE / OF THE / WEST AND SOUTH-WEST. / BY JOSEPH G. McCOY, / THE PIONEER WESTERN CATTLE SHIPPER. / [*rule*] / ILLUSTRATED BY PROF. HENRY WORRALL, TOPEKA, KAS. / ENGRAVED BY BAKER & CO., CHICAGO, ILL. / ELECTRO TYPED BY J. T. RETON & CO., KANSAS CITY, MO. / [*rule*] / PUBLISHED BY / RAMSEY, MILLETT & HUDSON, KANSAS CITY, MO., / PRINTERS, BINDERS, ENGRAVERS, LITHOGRAPHERS & STATIONERS. / 1874.

There are at least three reprints of McCoy's book, including a facsimile issued in 1932. These are less valuable than the first edition. [See listing in *Gold in Your Attic,* 1958.]

Twenty-four Years a Cowboy and Ranchman

In Southern Texas and Old Mexico

*Desperate Fights with the
Indians and Mexicans*

By
WILL HALE

I LLUSTRATED

Published by
W. H. STONE, · HEDRICK, O. T.

61. *Twenty-four Years a Cowboy and Ranchman*
By Will Hale

In the booming Western Americana market it has become commonplace in recent years to find books of which there are only a handful of known copies bringing $1,000 and more.

What about a title such as William Hale Stone's pseudonymous *Twenty-four Years a Cowboy and Ranchman,* of which there is only one first edition copy known? I asked Wright Howes, the Chicago bibliographer, what another might be worth today—if some lucky reader turned it up. The finder, he guessed, could name his own price.

It seems safe to say that, depending on condition, any price up to $5,000—maybe more—might be reasonable for this paperbound rarity, which oddly enough, is a fairly recent book.

The undated title page reads as follows:

Twenty-four Years a / Cowboy and Ranchman / [*rule*] / In Southern Texas and Old Mexico / [*double rule*] / Desperate Fights with the / Indians and Mexicans / By / WILL HALE / [*rule*] / ILLUSTRATED / [*rule*] / [*double rule*] / Published by / W. H. STONE, -HEDRICK, O. T.

It was printed and bound in Chicago in 1905 and was published in Oklahoma Territory.

PROSE AND POETRY

OF THE

Live Stock Industry

of the United States.

WITH OUTLINES OF THE ORIGIN AND ANCIENT HISTORY OF OUR LIVE STOCK ANIMALS.

Volume I.

ISSUED IN THREE VOLUMES.

Illustrated.

PREPARED BY AUTHORITY OF THE
NATIONAL LIVE STOCK ASSOCIATION.

PUBLISHED BY THE
NATIONAL LIVE STOCK HISTORICAL ASSOCIATION,
DENVER AND KANSAS CITY.

62. *Prose and Poetry of the Live Stock Industry*

We are indebted to Paul Schopflin, Evanston (Illinois) dealer in rare Americana, for a detailed description of a scarce cattle-trade book which came into his possession not so long ago.

It is James W. Freeman's *Prose and Poetry of the Live Stock Industry*, described by J. Frank Dobie, the Western specialist, as "the richest in matter of all the $100-and-up rare books in the field."

The undated, unsigned title page reads as follows:

PROSE AND POETRY / OF THE / LIVE STOCK INDUSTRY / of the United States. / WITH OUT-LINES OF THE ORIGIN AND ANCIENT / HISTORY OF OUR LIVE STOCK / ANIMALS / [rule] / Volume I. / ISSUED IN THREE VOL-UMES. / Illustrated. / [rule] / PREPARED BY AU-THORITY OF THE / NATIONAL LIVE STOCK ASSOCIATION. / [rule] / PUBLISHED BY THE / NATIONAL LIVE STOCK HISTOR-ICAL ASSOCIATION. / DENVER AND KAN-SAS CITY.

This single leatherbound volume, all that was published, was issued in a limited quantity in 1905 for members of the National Live Stock Association. Freeman was the editor. Schopflin Books catalogued its copy (Freeman's own) at $375.

My Life On the Range

BY

JOHN CLAY

Privately Printed

CHICAGO

63. *My Life on the Range*
By John Clay

Another scarce modern book about the cattle trade is the late John Clay's *My Life on the Range,* published in Chicago in 1924. Two readers of my column recently have turned their copies into cash.

Clay was a Scots-born Chicago livestock commission merchant. The book is a vivid, authentic picture of his ranch experiences when he operated in the Northwest. According to Ramon F. Adams, the cattle country bibliographer, Clay is said to have kept copies on his desk, where friends helped themselves until the supply disappeared.

A fine copy will cost as much as $87.50 today. *Gold in Your Attic* (1958), records one recent price of $55.

The title page reads as follows:

My Life / On the Range / BY / JOHN CLAY / [rule] / [printer's ornament] / [rule] / Privately Printed / CHICAGO.

Clay also published other cattle trade books that are scarce and in demand.

THE DAY OF THE
CATTLEMAN

BY
ERNEST STAPLES OSGOOD

MINNEAPOLIS
THE UNIVERSITY OF MINNESOTA PRESS
1929

64. *The Day of the Cattleman*
By Ernest Staples Osgood

Ernest Staples Osgood's *The Day of the Cattleman,* written as a Ph.D. thesis at the University of Wisconsin in 1927, has already become a collector's item.

Copies of the first edition still command as much as $35 today, despite the reprint that appeared in 1954.

The title page of Osgood's historically important book reads as follows:

THE DAY OF THE / CATTLEMAN / BY / ERNEST STAPLES OSGOOD / [*steer head design*] / MINNEAPOLIS / THE UNIVERSITY OF MINNESOTA PRESS / 1929.

In the scarce first edition, the pages are untrimmed. [See *Gold in Your Attic,* 1958.]

65. *Tamerlane*

For a number of years the generally accepted retail price for a first-edition copy of Edgar Allan Poe's *Tamerlane* has been $25,000. The chances are, however, that if you found one today, you could name your own price.

The last public sale of which I have immediate record was in 1945, when a book dealer paid $15,500 for a copy. There are only seven or so copies known, some of them imperfect.

TAMERLANE

AND

OTHER POEMS.

BY A BOSTONIAN.

Young heads are giddy, and young hearts are warm,
And make mistakes for manhood to reform.—COWPER.

—◦◦◦—

BOSTON:
CALVIN F. S. THOMAS......PRINTER.

....

1827.

On the title page of this anonymous volume is the following:

TAMERLANE / AND / OTHER POEMS. / [*rule*] / BY A BOSTONIAN. / [*rule*] / [*quotation from Cowper*] / [*type decoration*] / BOSTON: / CALVIN F. S. THOMAS . . . PRINTER. / [*dotted rule*] / 1827.

Tamerlane was issued in printed paper covers—yellow, or "tea-colored," as Poe's biographer Hervey Allen describes them. There is a decorative border on the cover title.

Poe later wrote that the book was "suppressed for private reasons," which accounts for its scarcity. [See listing in *Gold in Your Attic,* 1958.]

66. *Evangeline*
By Henry Wadsworth Longfellow

No less a critic than Poe, in his essay on "Longfellow and Other Plagiarists," dismissed his sweet-singing contemporary as hardly important. Yet Henry Wadsworth Longfellow's first editions still bring a premium on the collector's market. And he remains the only American poet with a bust in the Poet's Corner of Westminster Abbey.

One of his best-loved works, known to every school child, is the narrative poem, *Evangeline,* which tells the story of the Acadian lovers who are separated in youth and, after years of wandering, are united in death.

The title page of the rare first edition reads as follows:

EVANGELINE,

A

TALE OF ACADIE.

BY

HENRY WADSWORTH LONGFELLOW.

———

BOSTON
WILLIAM D TICKNOR & COMPANY
1847

EVANGELINE, / A / TALE OF ACADIE. / BY / HENRY WADSWORTH LONGFELLOW. / [*rule*] / BOSTON / WILLIAM D. TICKNOR & COMPANY / 1847.

Caution: The first issue of this edition is the valuable one. It is identified by the reading "long" for "lo" in the first line on page 61. A fine copy in original board binding is worth up to $250, possibly more, at retail. Copies with defects or rebound copies are worth less, of course. "Lo" issue copies are worth up to $100, sometimes more, depending on condition.

67. *Macaria*

A book worth looking for is Augusta Jane Evans Wilson's rare *Macaria*, the anonymous Southern Civil War novel that became the *Gone with the Wind* of its day.

One of my readers, a South Dakota minister, turned up with an imperfect copy of this paperbound rarity a few years ago. It is now properly preserved in the collection of Chicago's Newberry Library, having been purchased by a Midwestern collector for presentation to that famed repository.

I recently saw another somewhat defective copy in the home of Richard Barksdale Harwell, a collector of Confederate rarities. Mr. Harwell estimates the probable re-

MACARIA;

OR,

ALTARS OF SACRIFICE.

BY THE AUTHOR OF "BEULAH."

"W. have all to be laid upon an altar; we have all, as it were, to be subjected to the action of fire."—MENTAL.

RICHMOND:
WEST & JOHNSTON, 145 MAIN STREET.
1864.

tail price of a very fine copy, if one should be found, at $300 to $350, but he adds, "That is probably low."

The title page reads as follows:

MACARIA; / OR, / ALTARS OF SACRIFICE. / BY THE AUTHOR OF "BEULAH." / [*quotation from Melville.*] / RICHMOND: / WEST & JOHNSTON, 145 MAIN STREET. / 1864.

A second edition, dated 1865, is less valuable.

Despite the onetime popularity of this novel and Mrs. Wilson's later novel, *St. Elmo*, the author is rarely mentioned as a literary figure today.

68. *The Celebrated Jumping Frog of Calaveras County, and Other Sketches*
By Mark Twain

Depending upon the position of the gold frog on the cover, the price of a fine first edition copy of Samuel Langhorne Clemens' *The Celebrated Jumping Frog of Calaveras County, and Other Sketches* may range from $125 to $200 and more. At a recent auction sale the especially fine Arthur Swann copy brought $275.

Some copies have the frog decoration in the center of the clothbound front cover, but others have it in the lower left hand corner. The latter is favored by collectors.

The title page of this scarce short story collection reads as follows:

THE

CELEBRATED JUMPING FROG

OF

CALAVERAS COUNTY,

And other Sketches.

BY MARK TWAIN.

EDITED BY JOHN PAUL.

New-York:

C. H. WEBB, Publisher, 119 & 121 NASSAU ST.

AMERICAN NEWS CO., AGENTS.

1867.

THE / CELEBRATED JUMPING FROG / OF / CALAVERAS COUNTY, / And other Sketches. / BY MARK TWAIN. / EDITED BY JOHN PAUL. / New-York: / C. H. WEBB, Publisher, 119 & 121 NASSAU ST. / AMERICAN NEWS CO., AGENTS. / 1867.

To qualify as a first edition, first issue, the book must have a leaf of yellowish publisher's advertisements before the title page. The "i" in "this" in the last line of page 198 must be in perfect type. There are several binding colors, with red said to be the scarcest.

. . .

60. *Ragged Dick*
By Horatio Alger, Jr.

For the hundreds of readers of *Gold in Your Attic* who have asked about Horatio Alger titles, here is one that is worth looking for: the first edition of *Ragged Dick*, published in 1868, and worth $100 and more in fine condition.

There are two title pages. The first is a decorative title page, inserted apparently as an afterthought, since it is not numbered. It shows Dick, alone at his usual post in front of New York's City Hall Park. It reads as follows:

RAGGED DICK SERIES / BY / HORATIO ALGER JR, / [*sketch of shoeshine boy*] / RAGGED DICK.

The second title page follows immediately after the first and reads as follows:

RAGGED DICK; / or, / Street Life in New York / With the Boot-Blacks. / by / Horatio Alger, Jr., / Author of "Frank's Campaign," "Paul Prescott's Charge," "Charlie / Codman's Cruise," "Helen Ford." / [*decorative rule*] / Loring, Publisher, / 319 Washington Street, / Boston.

In the first edition, the copyright date is 1868, and *Fame and Fortune* is announced for publication "In December" in the book list on page 2.

Ralph Gardner, a New York advertising agency owner, who is preparing an Alger bibliography, tells me he has turned down an offer of more than $100 for his excellent copy, which is pictured here.

Two other Alger books that are hard to find are the anonymous *Timothy Crump's Ward* and *Seeking His Fortune*. Alger wrote the latter book in 1875 in collaboration with his sister, Olive A. Cheney. Both are Loring publications.

70. *The Story of a Bad Boy*
By Thomas Bailey Aldrich

Book prices in every collecting field are fluid. They move up and down in response to the ever-present influences of scarcity and demand. Sometimes interest in an author or a subject goes into a decline and prices fall. At other times the opposite influence is at work. But the long-term trend for important books is always upward.

In earlier articles in this section, I have mentioned the Bauer and Plath sales which stimulated prices in the field of Western books. There was an equally significant sale in the field of literary first editions in 1960. It gave enor-

THE

STORY OF A BAD BOY

BY

THOMAS BAILEY ALDRICH.

WITH ILLUSTRATIONS.

BOSTON:
FIELDS, OSGOOD, & CO.
1870.

mous impetus to the interest in many of the great books of American literature, and prices throughout the collecting world have been affected.

I refer to the sale in 1960, at the Parke-Bernet Galleries in New York City, of the exceptionally fine book collection built up by the late Arthur Swann. Mr. Swann was extremely finicky about condition, and his books were among the finest ever to be offered at auction in this country. As a result, many new price records were established.

One example from the Swann sale is the $475 auction price achieved by an extraordinarily fine copy of Thomas Bailey Aldrich's *The Story of a Bad Boy*. Few readers of these lines are ever likely to find as nice a copy in their book hunting, for *The Story of a Bad Boy* is hard to find in fine condition. It is, nevertheless, interesting to know the price possibilities.

The title page of this difficult book reads as follows:

THE / STORY OF A BAD BOY / BY / THOMAS BAILEY ALDRICH. / WITH ILLUSTRATIONS. / [*publisher's monogram*] / BOSTON: / FIELDS, OSGOOD, & CO. / 1870.

A point of identification: The reading in line 10 of page 197 must be "abroad" instead of "aboard." The binding is green cloth, and gilt lettering and designs appear on the backstrip. Prices for fine copies before the Swann sale ranged up to $200. Ordinary copies are worth $85 to $100, and worn or defective copies are naturally worth less.

The Story of a Bad Boy is one of the minor classics of American letters. It is the autobiographical story of a boyhood in a New Hampshire town.

DAISY MILLER

A Study

By HENRY JAMES, Jr.

———•———

NEW YORK
HARPER & BROTHERS, PUBLISHERS
FRANKLIN SQUARE
1879

71. *Daisy Miller*
By Henry James, Jr.

Much of Henry James' fiction was too highly stylized to be popular, but an exception was his short novel, *Daisy Miller,* which enjoyed a considerable success when it was published in 1879.

The first issue of the first edition of this work, which dealt with an American girl in Europe, is a scarce item.

The title page reads as follows:

DAISY MILLER / A Study / By HENRY JAMES, Jr. / [*rule*] / NEW YORK / HARPER & BROTH-ERS, PUBLISHERS / FRANKLIN SQUARE / 1879.

Daisy Miller is a very small book and appears in gray paper covers or in cloth. The first issue "point" (of identification) is the last number in the list of books on page 4, which must be 79.

Fine paperbound copies have brought up to $135 at retail, cloth copies up to $100. Brown cloth is specified by the bibliographer Whitman Bennett, in his *American Rare Book Guide,* but one of my readers in Canada has lately shown me a green clothbound copy of the first issue.

UNCLE REMUS

HIS SONGS AND HIS SAYINGS

THE FOLK-LORE OF THE OLD PLANTATION

By JOEL CHANDLER HARRIS

WITH ILLUSTRATIONS BY FREDERICK S. CHURCH AND
JAMES H. MOSER

NEW YORK
D. APPLETON AND COMPANY
1, 3, AND 5 BOND STREET
1881

72. *Uncle Remus: His Songs and His Sayings*
By Joel Chandler Harris

Joel Chandler Harris' famous book, *Uncle Remus: His Songs and His Sayings,* a longtime favorite of adults and children, is an example of a literary work that grows in importance—and in monetary value—with the passing of the years.

Harris' Uncle Remus stories brought the folk tales of the Negro into American literature and thus have been credited with laying the scientific foundation for the study of Negro folklore. They began as a column in the Atlanta Constitution and first appeared in book form in 1881.

The title page of the first edition reads as follows:

UNCLE REMUS / HIS SONGS AND HIS SAY-INGS / THE FOLK-LORE OF THE OLD PLAN-TATION / [*picture of Uncle Remus*] / By JOEL CHANDLER HARRIS / WITH ILLUSTRA-TIONS BY FREDERICK S. CHURCH AND / JAMES H. MOSER / NEW YORK / D. APPLE-TON AND COMPANY / 1, 3, and 5 BOND STREET / 1881.

The identifying point of the first issue is the absence of any mention of the book in the advertisements at the back. A fine copy is worth roughly $75 at retail; the usual worn copies around $25. [See listing in *Gold in Your Attic,* 1958.]

THE

PRINCE AND THE PAUPER

A TALE

FOR YOUNG PEOPLE OF ALL AGES

BY

MARK TWAIN

WITH ONE HUNDRED AND NINETY-TWO ILLUSTRATIONS

BOSTON

JAMES R. OSGOOD AND COMPANY

1882

73. *The Prince and the Pauper*
   By Mark Twain

Nobody seems to know exactly how many copies of Samuel Langhorne Clemens' *The Prince and the Pauper* were printed on China (or India) paper. Some bibliographers say only a few, some say fourteen, others fifteen, and still others as many as twenty.

Regardless of how many there were, this is a rare item and a copy in good condition is worth $500 to $600 if you are lucky enough to find one. The regular first edition copies, bound in green cloth or in leather, are fairly common items and are worth from $10 to $100, depending on issue and condition.

The title page reads as follows:

THE / PRINCE AND THE PAUPER / A TALE / FOR YOUNG PEOPLE OF ALL AGES / BY / MARK TWAIN / WITH ONE HUNDRED AND NINETY-TWO ILLUSTRATIONS / BOS-TON / JAMES R. OSGOOD AND COMPANY / 1882

To qualify as a first edition, first issue, worth $50 to $100 in fine condition, the book must bear the credit line of the Franklin Press near the bottom of the copyright page. The rare and valuable China paper edition, issued for presentation purposes, is bound in white cloth and stamped in gold.

ADVENTURES

OF

HUCKLEBERRY FINN

(TOM SAWYER'S COMRADE)

SCENE: THE MISSISSIPPI VALLEY.
TIME: FORTY TO FIFTY YEARS AGO.

BY

MARK TWAIN.

WITH ONE HUNDRED AND SEVENTY-FOUR ILLUSTRATIONS.

NEW YORK:
CHARLES L. WEBSTER AND COMPANY.
1885.

74. *Adventures of Huckleberry Finn*
By Mark Twain

The sequel to *Tom Sawyer,* Samuel Langhorne Clemens' *Adventures of Huckleberry Finn* was described by Andrew Lang as "a nearly flawless gem of romance and humor." It is a universal favorite of fiction lovers.

The commonly accepted first edition, in green binding, brings $150 and up on the collector's market.

In the desirable first issue, the word "was" appears for "saw" on line 23 of page 57, and "Him and Another Man" is incorrectly recorded in the list of illustrations as being on page 88.

The title page reads as follows:

ADVENTURES / OF / HUCKLEBERRY FINN / (TOM SAWYER'S COMRADE). / SCENE: THE MISSISSIPPI VALLEY. / TIME: FORTY TO FIFTY YEARS AGO. / BY / MARK TWAIN. / WITH ONE HUNDRED AND SEVENTY-FOUR ILLUSTRATIONS. / NEW YORK: / CHARLES L. WEBSTER AND COMPANY. / 1885.

Some copies of the first edition were bound in blue cloth and some in leather, and these are also valuable if they contain the early issue points.

THE TORRENT
AND THE NIGHT BEFORE
BY EDWIN ARLINGTON
ROBINSON, GARDINER
MAINE, 1889-1896

PRINTED FOR THE AUTHOR
MDCCCXCVI

75. *The Torrent and the Night Before*
   By Edwin Arlington Robinson

While "vanity" publication (paid for by the author) is generally indicative of a lack of merit in an author's work, there are notable exceptions, as in the case of the late Edwin Arlington Robinson's first book.

Privately printed at the Riverside Press in 1896, this landmark of American poetry, bound in blue paper covers, is a collector's item that brings $150 and up today in good condition.

The title page reads as follows:

THE TORRENT / AND THE NIGHT BEFORE / BY EDWIN ARLINGTON / ROBINSON, GARDINER / MAINE, 1889-1896 / PRINTED FOR THE AUTHOR / MDCCCXCVI.

Robinson followed this publication in 1897 with a second book, *The Children of the Night,* which is also a much sought after item. In time, he became known as one of the great poetic voices of his time.

Price, 50 Cents

MAGGIE

A Girl of the Streets

(A STORY OF NEW YORK)

By

JOHNSTON SMITH

Copyrighted

76. *Maggie: A Girl of the Streets*
   By Johnston Smith [Stephen Crane]

Since Hollywood made a motion picture of *The Red Badge of Courage,* almost everybody has heard of its author, Stephen Crane. But few people know that Crane also wrote under the name of Johnston Smith.

That is the pseudonym which appears on his classic novel, *Maggie: A Girl of the Streets,* which was first published as a 50-cent paperback in 1893.

It is much esteemed by collectors and eagerly sought. Fine copies are worth as much as $300, and possibly more, at retail.

The cover of this rare little book bears the legend, "Price, 50 cents," in the top right-hand corner. There are three horizontal bars across the top of the cover and three across the bottom, with the cover title sandwiched between. It reads as follows:

MAGGIE / A Girl of the Streets / (A STORY OF NEW YORK) / By / JOHNSTON SMITH / Copyrighted.

No publication date appears on the yellow paper covers. [See listing in *Gold in Your Attic,* 1958.]

St. NICHOLAS BOOKS

THE CRUISE OF THE DAZZLER

BY JACK LONDON

NEW YORK · THE CENTURY CO · MCMII

77. *The Cruise of the Dazzler*
By Jack London

Jack London is best known for his adventure classic, *The Call of the Wild,* but the item most sought after by collectors of his books is his rare juvenile story, *The Cruise of the Dazzler.* The first book edition of this California tale of a banker's son in the world of the Oakland Bay oyster pirates is worth around $100 to $150 in fine condition.

The Cruise of the Dazzler appeared in a briefer version in the July, 1902 issue of St. Nicholas magazine prior to book publication. The title page of the book reads as follows:

ST. NICHOLAS BOOKS / THE CRUISE / OF THE / DAZZLER / By JACK LONDON / NEW YORK. THE CENTURY CO. MCMII.

The type on the title page is enclosed in a decorative border, the design of which includes the twelve signs of the zodiac.

Several of my readers have turned up first edition copies in conditions varying from fair to good, but a fine copy is exceptionally hard to find because of the tendency of the white cloth binding to soil easily. Some years ago I acquired a really fine group of inscribed London firsts, but I finally abandoned it because of my inability to find a nice copy of this keystone item.

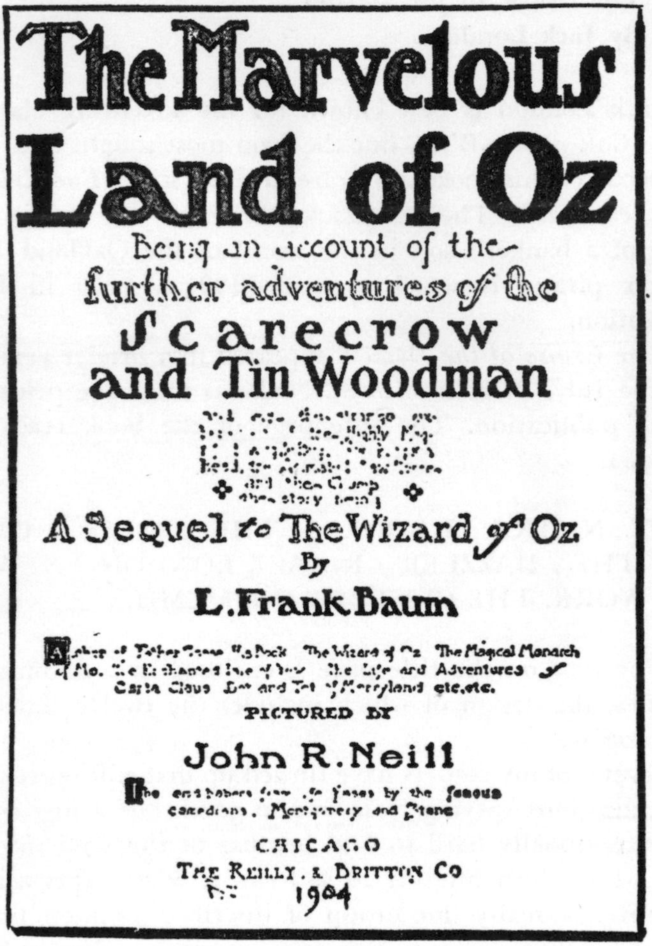

The Marvelous
Land of Oz
Being an account of the
further adventures of the
Scarecrow
and Tin Woodman

[illegible]

A Sequel to The Wizard of Oz
By
L. Frank Baum

Author of Father Goose His Book, The Wizard of Oz, The Magical Monarch of Mo, The Enchanted Isle of Yew, The Life and Adventures of Santa Claus, Dot and Tot of Merryland, etc., etc.

PICTURED BY
John R. Neill

The end papers from life poses by the famous comedians, Montgomery and Stone

CHICAGO
THE REILLY & BRITTON CO
1904

78. *The Marvelous Land of Oz*
By L. Frank Baum

Perhaps no column in the "Gold in Your Attic" series has brought a wider response from readers than the one several years ago about L. Frank Baum's famous children's story, *The Wonderful Wizard of Oz*. Several readers turned up first editions of that rarity, and at least one substantial sale was made as a result of the column. Perhaps there were more.

While somewhat less valuable in the collector's market than *The Wonderful Wizard of Oz*, the first edition, first issue, of the second "Oz" book is also scarce and valuable. A fine copy in original dust jacket is worth up to $150. Others without jacket have sold for as much as $100 and as little as $25 (at auction) in recent years.

The title page reads, in part, as follows:

The Marvelous / Land of Oz / Being an account of the / further adventures of the / Scarecrow / and Tin Woodman / [*etc., 6 lines*] / A Sequel to The Wizard of Oz / By / L. Frank Baum / [*etc., 3 lines*] / PICTURED BY / John R. Neill / [*etc., 2 lines*] / CHICAGO / THE REILLY & BRITTON CO. / 1904.

Caution: In the valuable first issue, the words "Published July, 1904" do not appear on the copyright page.

SOME
REMINISCENCES

By JOSEPH CONRAD

PAUL R. REYNOLDS
NEW YORK
1908

79. *Some Reminiscences*
By Joseph Conrad

What makes a rare book rare? No two cases are ever quite alike.

Take the rare pamphlet first edition of Joseph Conrad's *Some Reminiscences.* About six copies were published for copyright protection in America. The action was necessary because of the literary piracy that flourished in America in the last century and even into recent times.

Some Reminiscences began appearing serially in England in 1908. When a scheme to publish the work in America in 1909 was discovered, Conrad's representatives forestalled it by rushing into print in 1908 with a yellow paperbound edition. The regular book form did not appear until 1912.

The title page of the rare first edition reads as follows:

SOME / REMINISCENCES / By JOSEPH CON-RAD / [*plant design*] / PAUL R. REYNOLDS / NEW YORK / 1908.

When a lone surviving copy was offered for sale some years ago by Scribner's rare-book store in New York, the price tag affixed was $275.

HIKE AND THE AEROPLANE

TOM GRAHAM

80. *Hike and the Aeroplane*
By Tom Graham [Sinclair Lewis]

If you should run across a gray book in pictorial cloth covers bearing the title *Hike and the Aeroplane,* you may be in luck. For this obscure book, one of the most sought after of modern American first editions, is a story for young people written under a pseudonym by the Nobel Prize winning novelist, Sinclair Lewis.

It was Lewis' first book and was published under the pen name Tom Graham in 1912. The publisher was the Frederick A. Stokes Co. of New York City. There is no date on the title page.

On the cover is a sea scene showing an aerial rescue. The cover title is worded as follows:

HIKE AND THE / AEROPLANE / [*the rescue scene*] / TOM GRAHAM.

A couple of decades ago, one could pick up a copy of *Hike* for about $100. A few years ago one came up for auction and was sold to a dealer for $150. I have seen three defective copies listed recently in dealer catalogues at $77, $125, and $150. The last fine copy I saw for sale carried the fancy price tag of $250. [See listing in *Gold in Your Attic,* 1958.]

American Dramatists Series

THIRST

And Other One Act Plays by

EUGENE G. O'NEILL

ARTI et VERITATI

BOSTON: THE GORHAM PRESS
TORONTO: THE COPP CLARK CO., LIMITED

81. *Thirst and Other One Act Plays*
By Eugene G. O'Neill

A giant among our dramatists, the late Eugene O'Neill long ago became a prime favorite among collectors of modern authors. The first published plays of O'Neill appeared in August, 1914, as a part of the American Dramatists Series. The 1,000 copies of the first (and only) edition have long since disappeared from the market.

On the title page is the following:

American Dramatists Series / THIRST / And Other One Act Plays by / EUGENE G. O'NEILL / [*publisher's emblem*] / BOSTON: THE GOR-HAM PRESS / TORONTO: THE COPP CLARK CO., LIMITED.

The title page is undated, but positive identification of this rarity is established through several typographical errors, among them the missing hyphen at the end of line 9 on page 115.

Fine copies of *Thirst,* in the original dark gray boards and with the cream-colored dust jacket intact, are worth up to $100 at retail, sometimes more. Copies lacking a dust jacket have been listed in recent years at prices from $35 to $75. Signed copies bring even higher prices.

SPOON RIVER ANTHOLOGY

BY

EDGAR LEE MASTERS

New York
THE MACMILLAN COMPANY
1915

82. *Spoon River Anthology*
By Edgar Lee Masters

Among modern American first editions, one of the more desirable poetry items is Edgar Lee Masters' *Spoon River Anthology*. A fine copy in original dust jacket was catalogued recently by a leading rare-book dealer at $90. Other copies have been listed at $42.50, $50, and $65.

The unpunctuated title page of this landmark work reads as follows:

SPOON RIVER / ANTHOLOGY / BY / EDGAR LEE MASTERS / New York / THE MACMILLAN COMPANY / 1915 / All rights reserved.

Spoon River Anthology had appeared earlier under the pen name Webster Ford, in William Marion Reedy's Mirror.

A positive clue for identifying the valuable first edition, first issue: It measures exactly 7/8 inches across the top.

❧ THE CENTAUR. A TRANSLATION BY
GEORGE B. IVES FROM THE FRENCH OF
MAURICE DE GUERIN

MDCCCCXV

83. *The Centaur*
By Maurice De Guerin

The ways and whims of book collectors are of endless variety, but for more than half a century there has been a steady demand for books designed by the Indiana-born typographer, Bruce Rogers.

Probably the rarest of Bruce Rogers' items is George B. Ives' translation of Maurice De Guerin's *The Centaur,* published by the Montague Press of Montague, Massachusetts, in 1915.

There were only 135 copies of this edition issued. Bound in boards and bearing a paper label, the book was enclosed in a dust jacket.

The title page reads as follows:

[*type decoration*] / THE CENTAUR. A TRANSLATION BY / GEORGE B. IVES FROM THE FRENCH OF / MAURICE DE GUERIN / [*Bruce Rogers emblem*] / MDCCCCXV.

Copies come up for auction only rarely. The last one I saw listed was inscribed by Rogers and brought $130. Almost all the early Bruce Rogers items bring a premium in the market.

PARNASSUS
ON WHEELS
CHRISTOPHER
MORLEY

84. *Parnassus on Wheels*
By Christopher Morley

Christopher Morley's *Parnassus on Wheels* provides a good example of the ebb and flow of trends in book collecting. In the 1920's, a short time after its publication, the first edition of this novel about an itinerant bookseller began to rise steadily in price. A. Edward Newton, the famed collector, had to pay $40 for a copy. In the 1930's the price soared to $100 and more.

In recent years, *Parnassus* has ranged from $30 to $70. A good copy can be had today for roughly $50, although a mint copy still will bring close to the old top figures. There will come a time, I think, when this book will be even more expensive.

Its title page reads as follows:

Parnassus on Wheels / By / Christopher Morley / [*decoration*] / Garden City New York / Doubleday, Page & Company / 1917.

The identifying point of the valuable first issue is the break that separates the first two letters in the word "years" on line 8 of page 4. The book is bound in boards with a tan cloth spine. (The illustration here is of the front cover of *Parnassus on Wheels*.) [See price listing in *Gold in Your Attic*, 1958.]

RENASCENCE

AND

OTHER POEMS

BY

EDNA ST. VINCENT MILLAY

NEW YORK
MITCHELL KENNERLEY
MCMXVII

85. *Renascence and Other Poems*
By Edna St. Vincent Millay

One of the scarcest of modern books is the 15-copy first issue of the first edition of Edna St. Vincent Millay's *Renascence and Other Poems.*

Signed copies of this issue, printed on Japan paper and bound in boards, have brought up to $950 at auction. The regular issue of the first edition was printed on "Glaslan" watermarked paper and bound in black cloth. Fine copies are worth up to $150 at retail; a signed copy, in dust jacket, recently brought $200 at auction. Unsigned copies lacking the dust jacket bring $50 to $100 in fine condition.

The title page reads as follows:

RENASCENCE / AND / OTHER POEMS / BY / EDNA ST. VINCENT MILLAY / [*publisher's monogram*] / NEW YORK / MITCHELL KEN-NERLEY / MCMXVII.

Most of the early Millay first editions are worth premium prices if in fine condition.

MY ANTONIA

BY

WILLA SIBERT CATHER

Optima dies . . . prima fugit
VIRGIL

WITH ILLUSTRATIONS BY
W. T. BENDA

BOSTON AND NEW YORK
HOUGHTON MIFFLIN COMPANY
The Riverside Press Cambridge
1918

86. *My Antonia*
By Willa Sibert Cather

One of the common misconceptions about book collecting is that a book must be a couple of hundred years old to have attained any great value. Actually, many of the older books have very little commercial worth, simply because they are of no importance or are in plentiful supply. On the other hand, many modern books of importance have become scarce and expensive because of the demand for them.

An example is the first edition, first issue, of Willa Cather's *My Antonia*, the novel usually considered to be that Nebraska writer's masterpiece.

Its title page reads as follows:

MY ANTONIA / BY / WILLA SIBERT CATHER / [*quotation from Virgil*] / WITH ILLUSTRATIONS BY / W. T. BENDA / [*publisher's emblem*] / BOSTON AND NEW YORK / HOUGHTON MIFFLIN COMPANY / The Riverside Press Cambridge / 1918.

To qualify as a first edition, first issue, this book must have illustrations on glazed paper inserted. A fine copy is worth $60 or more at retail. (The extraordinarily nice Arthur Swann copy brought that figure at auction in 1960.)

Jurgen

A Comedy of Justice

By

JAMES BRANCH CABELL

"Of JURGEN eke they maken mencioun,
That of an old wyf gat his youthe agoon,
And gat himselfe a shirte as bright as fyre
Wherein to jape, yet gat not his desire
In any countrie ne condicioun."

NEW YORK
ROBERT M. McBRIDE & CO.
1919

87. *Jurgen*
By James Branch Cabell

Time was when a copy of the rather scarce first edition of James Branch Cabell's romantic novel, *Jurgen,* commanded as much as $150 on the rare-book market. But no more.

A very good copy can be had today for about $25, although mint copies, in dust jacket, fetch up to $60. Inscribed copies, in dust jacket, may bring as much as $70 at retail. My own unjacketed copy, signed "With best wishes, James Branch Cabell," cost me $9, reduced from $17.50, in a Chicago bookstore some years back.

The title page reads as follows:

Jurgen / [*rule*] / A Comedy of Justice / [*rule*] / By / JAMES BRANCH CABELL / [*quotation, 5 lines*] / NEW YORK / ROBERT M. Mc-BRIDE & CO. / 1919.

The tendency of most books of importance is steadily to appreciate in value, so the case of *Jurgen* is somewhat unusual. The chief trouble with Cabell's minor masterpiece is that it was oversold as a "risqué" item by certain reviewers, among them Burton Rascoe, who was a Chicago literary critic (for the Tribune) at the time of its publication. It just does not live up to that unjustified tribute.

GONE
WITH THE
WIND

by
MARGARET MITCHELL

NEW YORK
THE MACMILLAN COMPANY
1936

88. *Gone With the Wind*
By Margaret Mitchell

Fine first-issue copies of Margaret Mitchell's best seller, *Gone With the Wind,* are getting scarcer and more valuable every year. A few years ago I saw a fine first issue, in dust jacket, priced at $7.50 retail. But $35 to $50 is more like it today. Even a slightly defective copy brought $20 at a recent auction, and a signed presentation copy went for $50.

Gone With the Wind is bound in gray cloth and bears blue lettering and scrolls on the cover. In the valuable first issue the words "Published May 1936" appear on the copyright page.

The title page reads as follows:

GONE / WITH THE / WIND / by / MARGARET MITCHELL / NEW YORK / THE MACMIL-LAN COMPANY / 1936.

Worn copies or copies lacking the dust jacket are not worth much. Copies with "June, 1936" on the copyright page are not valuable.

PART THREE

A REPRESENTATIVE PRICE INDEX AND GUIDE TO VALUABLE BOOKS AND PAMPHLETS OF THE NEW WORLD— PREFATORY NOTES

SINCE THIS BOOK is identical in general form with the structural pattern of its predecessor, *Gold in Your Attic,* the arrangement of the book price information that follows will be familiar to many readers. For others, who may not have seen that book or the syndicated newspaper columns of the same title, a careful consideration of these preliminary notes is recommended. They have an important bearing on the interpretation and proper use of the price index on the subsequent pages.

The index includes more than 2,000 individual entries chosen from among the most valuable books and pamphlets published in the New World, primarily on the North American continent. In a very few cases I have also included certain leaflets, periodicals, and broadsides of unusual interest. Many of the entries are of a multiple nature, including under one title various editions of the same book. Thus the actual number of separate books and pamphlets indexed approaches 2,500. Like the 2,500 entries in the first book of this series, these listings were compiled from my own private card index system, from auction sale records, and from various bookseller catalogues. Every effort has been exerted to reflect in this index the state of the market in rare American imprints as of the summer of 1961. My research assistants and I have assembled thousands of price listings from many sources, compared them, and weighed them one against the other in order to reflect this market as accurately as possible. In each case where we were able to do so, we took note of the important influences that may have affected prices, such as condition, the auction (or wholesale) markets, the physical differences in the various editions or issues of books, *et cetera*.

Many readers have indicated that the first *Gold in Your Attic* price index has become for them the nucleus of a continuously revised and expanding handbook of prices in the field of American imprints, and this indeed was one of its original purposes. Some readers, as I have already indicated, have actually gone into the rare book business —and made a success of it—with that price index as a basic guide. Thus the additional entries in the present book will serve as a supplement to and an expansion of this as a basic tool of the trade.

One feature of this new price index that should be given special attention is the inclusion of *revised entries* for certain of the listings that appeared in its predecessor. The nature of the rare book market is such that prices are always in a state of flux, with the tendency being ever upward over the long pull. This is especially true with the more important books. It so happens that the prices on certain very desirable books in the collecting field have been radically affected by major auction sales since the publication of *Gold in Your Attic* in 1958. Some of these price changes were noted and corrected in the second edition of that book; others were not. In the more important of these cases, revisions have been included in the present volume. A few other entries from the first volume appear here again, but in revised form, in order to correct typographical and other errors.

Throughout the present price index, as well as among the articles in the illustrated section (Part Two), there will be found numerous cross references to the preceding volume. As a means of saving space, the abbreviation *"GIYA"* has been used for *Gold in Your Attic;* e. g., "See entry in *GIYA."*

Method of Listing: As in the earlier book, no special effort has been made to conform to orthodox bibliographical procedures in setting down the information in the index. Scholars and bibliographers who are inclined to be purists may question the method of cataloguing I have followed, but this index was not prepared especially for them. Its primary objective has been to be useful to the layman. Many professional bookmen have commended the method used as one most generally helpful to laymen and bookmen alike. For example, I have in many cases entered anonymous or pseudonymous books by title or pseudonym just as these appear on the title pages, rather than under the real name of the author. For example, Mark Twain titles are listed under his pseudonymous title, "TWAIN, Mark", rather than under his real name of Samuel Langhorne Clemens. And T. S. Eliot's anonymous *Ezra Pound: His Metric Poetry* has been entered just as the title appears. Again, as in the earlier index, such procedures have not been uniformly followed in every case, simply because of the extraordinarily exhaustive researches such a precise listing would require.

The Inevitability of Error: In my library there are innumerable bibliographies upon which the most distinguished scholars of the world have worked for many years, and yet I can pick up almost any volume from among them and find them sprinkled with error. I write this merely to emphasize the extremely difficult task of bibliography and to record again, as I did in the preceding volume, the inevitability that in such a non-academic listing as this there are errors of several kinds that may appear— confusion as to exact bibliographical data in respect to names, titles, places of publication, dates of publication, editions, prices, book condition, *et cetera*. This is true because the information comes from a wide variety of sources. In some instances it was impossible to cross-check and verify. In others I had no access to primary sources. Wherever possible my assistants and I have detected and corrected obvious errors of bibliographers and booksellers. In others we have possibly compounded errors and perhaps committed new and more grievous mistakes. In such cases, we beg the understanding of all, and we shall always welcome the help of booksellers, bibliographers, librarians, collectors, and other interested readers in correcting these errors in future printings.

The Price Range—$25 and Up: In *Gold in Your Attic* I explained the reason behind the decision to limit the price index to books valued at $25 or more. It is simply that that is about the point, in my own experience, at which the owner of a scarce or valuable book will begin to consider selling it for cash. There are literally tens of thousands of books that are valued in the range below $25.

Any effort to include all these in a single compilation would mean the publication of a price index that, even in the most abbreviated form, would run into many, many volumes. For those readers who are interested in the figures on the lower-priced volumes, there are several sources available. J. Norman Heard's *The Bookman's Guide to Americana,* Parts 1 and 2 (two separate volumes, Scarecrow Press, 1953 and 1956), is a specialized series listing many of the lower-priced items. (The first volume lists history and biography, and the second is devoted to literature.) Philip M. Roskie's *The Bookman's Bible, 1850-1899* and its supplement, Vol. 2, *The Bookman's Bible, 1900-1924* (Roskie & Wallace, 1957 and 1960), is a coded guide, primarily for booksellers, to the pricing of books in English and covers a great many titles worth $3 and up. Finally, for those willing to pursue the complexities of the auction market and to learn how to interpret auction prices, there is the annual publication, *American Book-Prices Current,* which lists all American auction sales of $5 and up. In many of the larger libraries these books are standard reference room items (as is *Gold in Your Attic*) and may be inspected there. They are expensive books and generally beyond the interest of the general reader. By far the best guide to book prices in the lower ranges may be found on second-hand bookstore shelves themselves and in the catalogues of second-hand and rare-book dealers. The latter are usually obtainable for the asking.

One point about auction prices that should be emphasized is the fact that in general the prices of books sold at auction both in America and abroad tend to be nearer the wholesale level than the retail. The reason for this is that most of those attending auction sales are dealers. The dealer's markup is usually 50% to 100%. Thus, if a book brings $10 at auction, it is reasonable to assume that the bookseller who buys it will catalogue it eventually at $15 to $20, and sometimes higher. An exception to this rule of thumb is, of course, the occasional rare book which brings a very high figure at auction. While a $5,000 auction price may still have been made by a bookseller, the likelihood is that the purchase was being made for a special customer on a commission arrangement. In such cases, the bookseller's margin may have been only 10% to 15% above the price paid rather than the usually accepted markup of 50% to 100%, or sometimes more.

What the Price Index Includes: No attempt has been made, in compiling the price index, to break the material down into various classifications such as "Americana," "Fiction," "First Editions." Books are simply listed by author or title, regardless of category. Almost no "collected works" are included. The other exclusions include most McGuffey readers, most old Bibles, most "fine bindings," and most periodicals. (Readers interested in the reasons behind these various exclusions are referred to *Gold in Your Attic.*)

The present index differs in one major respect from the first *Gold in Your Attic* index in that in a great number of cases more detailed information is supplied concerning the contents of books. This information is usually in the form of specifications for the number of pages included in the edition, the number of maps or plates included, and the style of binding. The decision to supply this additional information was made on the basis of experience with the first price index. A hypothetical example of how such information can be useful may be drawn from the third

entry: *"ABSARAKA, Home of the Crows."* The entry
states that there is a folding map in this first edition. If a
reader finds a copy of this book with the map missing, he
must expect that defect to affect the price of the book
accordingly. The importance of maps is well demonstrated
in the case of one of my readers who discovered a $1,200
book, *A Journal of Captain Cook's Last Voyage,* with a
part of the map torn away. In that defective condition the
book was worth less than a tenth of its normal price.

The abbreviations and terminology in the index have
again been kept as simple as possible. (Detailed explana-
tions can be found in the "Brief Dictionary for Book
Hunters" in the preceding volume.) Here is a brief key to
the more difficult terms: "1st issue" and "1st state" are
bibliographical jargon indicating the very first appearance
of a first edition. The abbreviation "pp." stands for
"pages." "Foxed" is a bookman's word for spotting or
browning of pages. In some listings the statements "No
place" and "No date" appear, sometimes separately, sometimes together. They mean that the book concerned does
not contain on its title page a statement as to the place of
publication or the date of publication, as the case may be.
In the event the information is known, it follows in brack-
ets after the statement in the listing. Thus: "No place
[Milwaukee], no date [1919]" or "No place, no date
[1916]," *et cetera.* In the case of pseudonymous or anonymous works, the author's name, if known, is carried in
parentheses after the date of publication.

Interpreting the Prices: The most important single
thing a user of this price list must keep in mind is this:
These prices in general are *average retail prices* for books
in *fine condition.* This does NOT mean that these are

prices that dealers will pay. A dealer usually can be expected to pay UP TO ONE-HALF the expected retail price but rarely more. Further, the price may be adjusted accordingly if the book is not in fine condition. "Fine" condition, as interpreted by bookmen, means, for new books, in NEW condition; for older books, in as FINE condition as can reasonably be expected considering the age of the book.

For the reader who wants to sell his own books at retail —for example, to a local collector—the use of the full price figures listed here should not be unreasonable provided the books are in FINE condition. If they are less than fine, he should adjust the prices accordingly. (This matter is covered in detail in Part One.)

In a number of cases, the entries show several prices to indicate the range within which a book has been offered or sold. In other cases an average price has been listed. In still others, auction (wholesale level) prices have been recorded. The prices shown—and I repeat it for emphasis— are for books in *fine* condition unless otherwise stated; where defective copies are listed, the reader may make his own adjustments.

The aim throughout has been to provide for the layman, the bookseller, the collector, and the librarian alike an up-to-date and reliable index on which he can safely base his own estimate of book values.

PRICE INDEX AND GUIDE

A

ABBEY, James. *California. A Trip Across the Plains* 64 pp., paperbound. New Albany, Ind., 1850. $600 and up. (In 1954, a copy with back cover missing brought $550 at auction.)

ABEL, Thomas. *Subtensial Plain Trigonometry.* 7 folding plates. Boards. Philadelphia, 1761. 1st ed. Lacking most of calf spine, lacking flyleaf, $62.50.

ADSARAKA, Home of the Crows. Folding map. Philadelphia, 1868. (By Margaret C. Carrington.) 1st ed. $35.

ABSTRACT of Land Titles of Texas. 4 vols. in 3. Galveston and Austin, 1878-81. $175.

ACCURATE Version of Historical Truth (An). Details of the Conspiracy That Led to the Overthrow of the Monarchy, etc. 80 pp., paperbound. Honolulu, 1897. $50.

ACKLEY, Mary E. *Crossing the Plains and Early Days in California.* San Francisco, 1928. $65.

ACT Incorporating the Town of Berkeley (The). 44 pp., paperbound. Berkeley, 1878. $50.

ACT to Incorporate the Mamouth Mining Co. of Washington, Jefferson and Franklin Counties (An). 4 pp. St. Louis, 1849. $25.

ACTS of Assembly Now in Force in the Colony of Virginia. Williamsburgh, 1752. Hinge repaired, $100.

ACTS and Laws, of His Majestie's Colony of Connecticut in New-England, etc. Unbound sheets in facsimile. Hartford, 1919. One of 30 sets. $385.

ACTS and Laws of His Majesty's Colony of Rhode-Island and Providence-Plantations, in New-England, in America. Paperbound. Newport, R. I., 1752, 1st ed. $50.

ACTS Passed at the 3d Congress of the United States of America. Sheepskin. Philadelphia, 1794. Binding worn, $45.

ACTS, Resolutions and Memorials, Adopted by the 2d Legislative Assembly of the Territory of Arizona. Boards. Prescott, 1865. $47.50. Same, for 3d Assembly, Prescott, 1867. Boards, front cover loose, $37.50.

ADAMS, Hannah. *An Alphabetical Compendium of the Various Sects Which Have Appeared in the World from the Beginning of the Christian Aera to the Present Day.* Boston, 1784. 1st ed. $25, $35, $45.

ADAMS, John. *A Defence of the Constitutions of Government of the United States.* Sheepskin. Philadelphia, 1787. 1st Am. ed. Rebacked, foxed, small defects, $26.50.

ADAMS, John. *Message of the President . . . April 3, 1798. Instructions to and Dispatches from the U. S. Envoys Extraordinary to the French Republic.* (Caption title.) Pamphlet. No place, no date [Philadelphia, 1798]. Foxed, $28.50.

ADAMS, John. *Poems on Several Occasions.* Boston, 1745. $100.

ADAMS, John. *Twenty-Six Letters . . . Respecting the Revolution of America.* No place, no date [New York, 1789]. 1st

Am. ed. Uncut, contemporary paper covers, $37.50. New York, 1789. 2d Am. ed. Unbound, $25.

ADAMS, John Quincy. *Oration on the Life and Character of Gilbert Motier de Lafayette*. Morocco. Washington, 1835. 1st ed. One of a few copies on thick paper, specially bound, $65. Other bindings $5 to $10.

ADAMS, The Rev. John. *The Flowers of Ancient History*. Philadelphia, 1795. 1st ed. $35.

ADDRESS to the Freemen of Pennsylvania (An). Stitched, uncut. Germantown, 1799. One leaf torn, $25.

ADE, George. *Stories of the Streets and of the Town*. Edited by Franklin J. Meine. Chicago, 1941. $25.

ADE, George. *The Sultan of Sulu*. Paperbound. New York, 1903. $25.

ADMIRARI, Nil. *The Trollopiad; or, Travelling Gentlemen in America*. New York, 1837. (By Frederick William Shelton.) $25.

ADMITTED and Re-Admitted: List of Persons Admitted and Re-Admitted to Cherokee Citizenship by the National Council and Commissions on Citizenship in the Year 1880, etc. 56 pp., paperbound. No place, no date. $50.

ADVENTURES of a Yankee (The), or The Singular Life of John Ledyard. By a Yankee. Boards. Boston, 1831. 1st ed. Small hole in two leaves, $67.50.

AFFECTING History of the Dreadful Distresses of Frederic Manheim's Family. Paperbound. Philadelphia, 1800. In folding case, $25.

AGED Wanderer (An); A Life Sketch of J. M. Parker, a Cowboy on the Western Plains in the Early Days. (Cover title.) 32 pp., paperbound. San Angelo, Tex., no date. $40.

AGEE, G. W. *Rube Burrows, King of Outlaws*. 194 pp., paperbound. Chicago, no date [1890]. $35. [For Cincinnati ed., see *GIYA*.]

AITKEN, R. *Aitken's General American Register . . . for 1773.* Philadelphia, no date [1772]. $45.

AKEN, David. *Pioneers of the Black Hills.* Paperbound and clothbound. Milwaukee, no date [1900?]. Paperbound, $45. Clothbound, $35. [Supersedes listing in *GIYA*.]

ALCOTT, Amos Bronson. *Sonnets and Canzonets.* 24 portraits. Boston, 1882. 1st ed. One of 50, signed. Cover soiled, $85.

ALCOTT, Louisa May. *Kitty's Class Day. A Stitch in Time Saves Nine.* 12 pp., paperbound. Boston, 1868. 1st ed., state B, with "Rockwell & Rollins" at foot of page 2 and front cover reading "LORING'S Tales of the Day. Kitty's Class-Day." $50.

ALCOTT, Louisa May. *Morning-Glories.* Boston, 1868. 1st ed. $75.

ALCOTT, Louisa May. *An Old-Fashioned Girl.* Boston, 1870. 1st ed., 1st issue, with no ads on copyright page. Rubbed, inner binding cracked, $27.50.

ALCOTT, Louisa May. *The Rose Family.* 47 pp., paperbound. Boston, 1864. 1st ed. Back cover and spine missing, frayed, $37.50.

ALDRICH, Thomas Bailey. *The Story of a Bad Boy.* Boston, 1870. 1st ed., 1st issue, green cloth, with line 20, page 14, reading "scattered" for "scatter" and line 10, page 197, reading "abroad" for "aboard." Up to $250 for fine copies. (Arthur Swann's extraordinarily nice copy brought $475 at auction in 1960.) Ordinary copies, $85 to $125. Badly worn, defective copies, $25 up. [Supersedes entry in *GIYA*.]

ALDRIDGE, Reginald. *Life on a Ranch.* Paperbound. New York, 1885. Rebound in cloth, paper covers bound in, $27.50.

ALEXANDER, E. P. *Military Memoirs of a Confederate.* New York, 1907. Slightly worn, $35.

ALEXANDER, Francesca. *Tuscan Songs.* Cambridge, 1897. One of 50. In dust jacket, $25.

ALEXANDER, John H. *Mosby's Men.* New York, 1907. $40.

ALGER, Horatio, Jr. *Ragged Dick, or Street Life in New York With the Boot-Blacks.* Boston, no date [1868]. 1st ed., 1st issue, 1868 copyright, with decorative title page inserted and with *Fame and Fortune* listed in ads for publication "In December." $100 and up.

ALGER, Horatio, Jr. *The Western Boy; or, The Road to Success.* No place, no date [New York, 1878]. 1st ed. of *Tom, the Boot-black.* Carleton, publisher. $32.50.

ALLAN, J. T. (comp.). *Central and Western Nebraska, and the Experiences of Its Stock Growers.* (Cover title.) 16 pp., paperbound. (Published by U.P.R.R.) Omaha, 1883. $75.

ALLAN, J. T. (comp.). *Western Nebraska and the Experiences of Its Actual Settlers.* 16 pp., paperbound. Omaha, 1882. $75.

ALLEN, Miss A. J. (comp.). *Ten Years in Oregon.* Ithaca, 1848. 1st ed. $30.

ALLEN, Lt. G. N. *Mexican Treacheries and Cruelties.* 32 pp., paperbound. Boston, 1847. $50. Boston, 1848, 32 pp., paperbound, $25 and $45. Another, rebound in morocco, paper covers bound in, $27.50.

ALLEN, Ira. *A Concise Summary of the Second Volume of the Olive Branch.* Paperbound. Philadelphia, 1807. $115.

ALLEN, J. A. *Notes on the Natural History of Portions of Montana and Dakota.* 61 pp., paperbound. Boston, 1874. $27.50.

ALLEN, W. A. *Adventures with Indian and Game.* Chicago, 1903. 1st ed. Spine worn, $25.

ALLEN, W. A. *The Sheep Eaters.* New York, 1913. $25.

ALMONTE, Juan Nepomuceno. *Noticia Estadistica sobre Tejas.* Boards. Mexico, 1835. 1st ed. Slight tear on title page repaired, $425.

ALTER, J. Cecil. *James Bridger, Trapper, Frontiersman, Scout and Guide.* Columbus, 1951. One of 1,000. $25. [For 1st ed., 1925, see *GIYA*.]

ALTISONANT, Lorenzo. *Letters to Esq. Pedant, in the East.* Boards. Cambridge City, Ind., 1844. (By Samuel Klinefelter Hoshour.) 1st ed. Lacking blank end leaf, $87.50.

AMERICAN Annual Register (The), or Historical Memoirs . . . 1790. Boards. Philadelphia, 1797. (By James Thomson Callender.) Uncut, spine worn, $35.

AMERICAN Church Silver of the 17th and 18th Centuries. Boards. Boston, 1911. $27.50.

AMERICAN Cruiser (The). Boston, 1846. (By Capt. George Little.) 1st ed. $65.

AMERICAN Ethnological Society. Transactions of. No. 1. New York, 1845. $25. New York, 1848. Same, *No. 2.* $25.

AMERICAN Review (The). Vol. 1. (Contains Poe's "The Raven"—first printing.) New York, 1845. Hinges weak, calf binding defective, $30.

AMERICAN Shooter's Manual (The) . . . By a Gentleman of Philadelphia County. Frontispiece, two plates, errata. Philadelphia, 1827. (By Dr. Jesse Y. Kester?) 1st ed. Contemporary calf binding, $100. Another, foxed, $82.50.

AMERICANA—Beginnings: A Selection from the Library of Thomas W. Streeter. 97 pp., paperbound. Morristown, N.J., 1952. One of 325. $25 and $30.

AMERICA'S First Big Parade. ("Story of Cherokees by an Indian with his photo but no name.") Little Rock, 1932. Covers stained, $25.

AMSDEN, Charles. *Navaho Weaving.* 122 plates, many in color. Santa Ana, 1934. 1st ed. $50. Albuquerque, 1948 [1949]. Reprint. $20.

ANCIENT and Modern Michilimackinac. 48 pp., paperbound. No place [St. James, Mich.], MDCCCLIV (1854). (By James Jesse Strang.) 1st ed., 1st issue. $1,000 and up. Another, dated 1854, but "obviously" on later paper, up to $300.

ANDERSON, John. *Vindiciae Cantus Dominici: or, a Vindication of the Doctrine Taught in a Discourse on the Divine Ordinance of Singing Psalms.* Boards, calf spine. Philadelphia, 1793. $27.50.

ANDREAS, A. T. *History of the State of Kansas.* Folding map. Chicago, 1883. Rebacked, $40.

ANDREAS, A. T. *Illustrated Historical Atlas of the State of Iowa.* Chicago, 1875. New spine, three pages missing, including world map, $30.

ANDREWS, Eliza Frances. *The War-Time Journal of a Georgia Girl, 1864-65.* New York, 1907. New buckram, $25.

ANDREWS, William Loring. *An Essay on the Portraiture of the American Revolutionary War.* Green morocco. New York, 1896. One of 185. Spine faded, $25.

ANGEL, Myron. *History of San Luis Obispo County, California.* Oakland, 1883. Spine worn, title page torn, small section missing, $100. Another, $45. [Supersedes entry under *History* in *GIYA*.]

ANNUAL Review. History of St. Louis, etc. Folding map. 47 pp., paperbound. St. Louis, 1854. Covers frayed, $25. Another, ex-library, $29.50.

ANTI-TEXASS Legion (The). Protest of Some Free Men, States, and Presses Against the Texass Rebellion. 72 pp., paperbound. New York, 1844. Worn, back cover missing, $27.50.

APPEAL by the Convention of Michigan . . . in Relation to the Boundary Question Between Michigan and Ohio. 176 pp., sewed, uncut. Detroit, 1835. $75.

APPEAL to the American People (An): Being an Account of the Persecutions of the Church of Latter Day Saints. 60 pp., paperbound. Cincinnati, 1840. 2d ed., revised. $250.

APPLEGATE, Jesse. A Day with the Cow Column in 1843. Boards. No place [Portland], 1952. One of 225. $45. [For another ed., see GIYA.]

APPLEGATE, Jesse. Recollections of My Boyhood. 99 pp., paperbound. Roseburg, Ore., 1914. 1st ed. $200. Another, paper covers bound in, $75.

APPONYI, F. H. The Libraries of California. San Francisco, 1897. $25.

APTHORP, East. The Constitution of a Christian Church. Stitched. Boston, 1761. $32.50.

ARIKARA Campaign. Documents Accompanying the Message of the President . . . Relative to Hostilities of the Arickaree Indians. Folding tables. Washington, 1823. 1st ed. Unbound, $27.50.

ARLEGUI, Fray Joseph. Crónica de la Provincia de N.S.P.S. Francisco de Zacatecas. Plate. Boards. Mexico City, 1851. $75. Another, $67.50.

ARMOR, Samuel. History of Orange County, California. Los Angeles, 1921. $37.50.

ARMSMEAR: The House, The Arm and the Armory of Col. Samuel Colt. A Memorial. Engraved plates, map. Morocco. New York, 1866. Presentation copy from Mrs. Samuel Colt, $100.

ARNOLD, Henry V. The History of Old Pembina, 1780-1872. Paperbound. Larimore, N. D., 1917. $85.

ARRANGEMENT of Places. Will Each Gentleman Kindly Take in to Dinner the Lady Seated on His Right. 12 pp., paperbound. (Program booklet for seventieth birthday dinner for Mark Twain at Delmonico's.) No place [New York], 1905. $32.50.

ARRICIVITA, Juan Domingo. *Crónica Seráfica y Apostólica del Colegio de Propaganda Fide de la Santa Crus de Queretaro en la Neuva España.* Vellum. Mexico, 1792. Pages 55-58 "not bound with this copy," supplied in photostat, $35.

ARRILLAGA, Jose. *Recopilación de Leyes, Decretos, Bandos, Reglamentos, Circulares y Providencias de los Supremos Poderes Formada de Orden del Supremo Gobierno.* Half calf. Mexico, 1838. 2d printing. $325.

ART of Domestick Happiness and Other Poems (The). By the Recluse. Mottled calf. Pittsburgh, 1817. (By Aquilla M. Bolton.) 1st ed., with errata leaf. $25.

ARTHUR, T. S. *Anna Milnor.* New York and Philadelphia, 1845. 1st ed. Rebound, $75.

ARTICLES of Religion, as Established by the Bishops, the Clergy, and Laity of the Protestant Episcopal Church in the United States of America, etc. 22 pp., half morocco. New York, 1802. $60.

ARTISTS and Tradesman's Guide (The). Boards. Utica, 1827. (By John Shephard.) 1st ed. Foxed, label lacking, $25.

ASHLEY, Clifford W. *The Yankee Whaler.* Boards. Boston, 1926. $25. [Limited, signed, $47.50; see *GIYA.*]

ATHERTON, William. *Narrative of the Suffering and Defeat of the North-Western Army Under Gen. Winchester.* Boards. Frankfort, Ky., 1842. $32.50, $50, and $60. Covers loose, $25.

ATLAS of Jefferson County, Ohio. Colored folding maps. 36 pp. Published by Beers. New York, 1871. $35.

ATLAS of New York and Vicinity. 43 sheets of colored maps and plans. Published by Beers. New York, 1868. $25.

ATWATER, Caleb. *Remarks Made on a Tour to Prairie du Chien; Thence to Washington City.* Boards. Columbus, 1831. 1st ed. Embossed stamp, $30.

AUDUBON, John James. *The Birds of America.* Introduction by William Vogt. 500 full-page color plates. Buckram. New York, 1937. Boxed, limited ed., all-rag paper. $25. [For 1st and other eds., see *GIYA*.]

AUDUBON, John W. *Audubon's Western Journal, 1849-50.* Folding map, 6 plates. Cleveland, 1906. $25.

AUSTIN, Edward S. *The Housekeepers' Manual.* Paperbound. Chicago, 1869. 1st ed. $50.

AUSTIN, Stephen F. *An Address Delivered by . . . on the 7th of March, 1836.* 30 pp., paperbound. Lexington, 1836. Pink paper covers lacking, $250.

AUSTIN, Stephen F. *Esposicion al Publico sobre los Asuntos de Tejas.* 32 pp. Mexico, 1835. 1st ed., with page 29 misnumbered 31. Rebound in full red morocco, $1,250.

AUTHENTIC Narrative of the Seminole War (An); and of the Miraculous Escape of Mrs. Mary Godfrey and Her Four Female Children. Plain paper covers, uncut. Providence, 1836. Stained, half of frontispiece missing, $100. [For New York, 1836, ed., see author entry in *GIYA*.]

AVERY, David. *The Lord is to be Praised for the Triumphs of His Power.* Stitched. Norwich, 1778. 1st ed. $45.

AVIRETT, James B. *The Memoirs of Gen. Turner Ashby and His Compeers.* Baltimore, 1867. Worn, $50.

B

BABBITT, E. L. *The Allegheny Pilot.* 64 pp., paperbound. Freeport, Pa., 1855. In ¾ morocco, original covers bound in, $65.

BACA, Manuel C. de. *Vincente Silva and His 40 Bandits.* Translated by Lane Kauffmann. Washington, 1947. One of 175 on all-rag large paper. $27.50. Also, 300 copies case-bound and signed, $35.

BACON, Francis. *Essays Moral, Economical and Political.* Boards, paper label. Boston, 1807. 1st Am. ed. In slip case, uncut, foxed, stained, spine repaired, hinges reinforced, $30.

BAKER, D. W. C. (comp.). *A Texas Scrap-Book.* New York, no date [1875]. 1st ed. $25. Another copy, newly bound, $35.

BAKER, Hozial H. *Overland Journey to Carson Valley, Utah.* 28 pp., paperbound. Seneca Falls, N.Y., 1861. 1st ed. $1,000 and up.

BALDWIN, Sara and Robert M. *Illustriana Kansas.* Hebron, Neb., 1933. $30.

BALDWIN, Simeon. *An Oration Pronounced Before the Citizens of New-Haven, July 4, 1788.* New Haven, 1788. Unbound, $25.

BANDELIER, Adolph F. A. *The Gilded Man.* New York, 1893. 1st ed. $25.

BANGS, John K. *The Battle of College Point.* 12 pp., paperbound, stitched. No place, 1897. 1st ed. One of 100, signed. $25.

BARAGA, The Rev. Frederick. *A Theoretical and Practical Grammar of the Otchipwe Language.* Detroit, 1850. $150. Montreal, 1878. $75.

BARBIERE, Joe. *Scraps from the Prison Table.* Doylestown, 1868. Rebound in buckram, $30.

BARCLAY, Robert. *An Apology for the True Christian Divinity.* Newport, R.I., 1729. 6th ed. in English. Two blank leaves missing, $28.50.

BARKER, Eugene C. *The Life of Stephen F. Austin.* Folding maps, 6 portraits. Nashville [Dallas?], 1925. Unopened, $25.

BARLOW, Joel. *The Columbiad. A Poem.* Morocco. Portrait and 11 plates. Philadelphia, 1807. Rubbed, some foxing, $45.

BARLOW, Joel. *Joel Barlow to His Fellow Citizens of the United States.* Paperbound. No place, no date [Philadelphia, 1801]. 1st Am. ed. $32.50.

BARLOW, Joel. *The Vision of Columbus.* Hartford, 1787. $25.

BARNES, Charles Merritt. *Combats and Conquest of Immortal Heroes.* Full morocco and cloth. San Antonio, 1910. 1st ed. Morocco, $28. Another, signed by author, $41.50. Clothbound, $10 to $15.

BARNES, David M. *The Draft Riots in New York, July, 1863.* 117 pp., paperbound. New York, 1863. 1st ed. Back cover lacking, in slip case, $60.

BARNES, Henry. *The Guerrilla-Bride: A Poem.* Bellefontaine, O., 1858. $30.

BARNES, Joseph. *Remarks on Mr. John Fitch's Reply to Mr. James Rumsey's Pamphlet.* 16 pp. Philadelphia, MDCCLXXXVIII (1788). Half morocco, $75.

BARNUM, H. L. *The Spy Unmasked; or, Memoirs of Enoch Crosby.* Map, 5 plates. Boards. New York, 1828. 1st ed. Foxed, stained, rubbed, $25.

BARRETT, Ellen C. *Baja California, 1535-1956: A Bibliography.* Los Angeles, 1957. $25.

BARRIE, James M. *A Tillyloss Scandal.* New York, no date

[1893]. 1st ed., 1st issue, published by Lovell Coryell & Co. $27.50.

BARRY, T. A. and B. A. Patten. *Men and Memories of San Francisco, in the Spring of '50.* San Francisco, 1873. $25.

BARTLETT, E. R. *The Killing Edwards and the Causes Leading Thereto.* 20 pp., paperbound. Kahoka, Mo., 1901. $25.

BARTLETT, Elisha, M.D. *An Essay on the Philosophy of Medical Science.* Philadelphia, 1844. 1st ed. $25.

BARTLETT, Elisha, M.D. *The History, Diagnosis and Treatment of Typhoid and of Typhus Fever.* Philadelphia, 1842. 1st ed. $32.50.

BARTLETT, J. S., M.D. *The Physician's Pocket Synopsis.* Boston, 1822. 1st ed. Rubbed, $27.50.

BARTLETT, John. *A Discourse, on the Subject of Animation.* Boston, 1792. $55.

BARTON, Benjamin Smith. *Fragments of the Natural History of Pennsylvania. Part First.* (All published.) Paperbound. Philadelphia, 1799. Rebound, covers bound in, $60. Another, marbled boards, $42.50.

BARTON, Benjamin Smith. *New Views on the Origin of the Tribes and Nations of America.* Philadelphia, 1797. Foxed, name on title page, newly bound in buckram, $50. [For 1795 ed., see *GIYA*.]

BARTON, James L. *Commerce of the Lakes.* Folding table. 80 pp., paperbound. Buffalo, 1847. 1st ed. In slip case, $40.

BARTRAM, William. *Travels Through North and South Carolina, Georgia, East and West Florida, the Cherokee Country, etc.* Folding map, 8 plates. Philadelphia, 1791. $250.

BASS, W. W. *Adventures in the Canyons of the Colorado by Two of Its Earliest Explorers, James White and W. W. Hawkins.* 38 pp., paperbound. Grand Canyon, 1920. $25.

BASTIAT, Frederic. *Essays on Political Economy*. Chicago, 1869. $35.

BATES, Ed. F. *History . . . of Denton County*. Denton, Tex., no date [1918]. $50.

BATES, J. H. *Notes of a Tour in Mexico and California*. New York, 1887. 1st ed. $30 and $35.

BATES, S. P. *A Brief History of the One Hundredth* [sic] *Pennsylvania Regiment (Roundheads)*. Portrait. 32 pp. New Castle, 1884. $25.

BAXTER, William. *Pea Ridge and Prairie Grove*. Cincinnati, 1864. 1st ed. New buckram, $25.

BAY, J. C. *The Fortune of Books*. Chicago, no date [1941]. In dust jacket, $30.

BAY, J. C. *Three Handfuls of Western Books*. No place [Cedar Rapids], 1941. One of 35. $35.

BAYLEY, Richard. *An Account of the Epidemic Fever . . . in the City of New York . . . 1795*. Boards. New York, 1796. 1st ed. $32.50.

BEAN, Edwin F. (comp.). *History and Directory of Nevada County, California*. Black leather. Nevada, Calif., 1867. $200.

BEAN, Col. Ellis P. *Memoir*. Edited by W. P. Yoakum. No place [Houston], 1930. One of 200. $35.

BEATTIE, George W. and Helen P. *Heritage of the Valley*. Pasadena, 1939. In dust jacket, $25.

BEAUFORT, James. *Hoyle's Games Improved*. Boston, 1796. 1st Am. ed. $35.

BEAUMONT, William, M.D. *Experiments and Observations on the Gastric Juice*. Boards. Boston, 1834. Rebacked, light staining, rubbed, $100. [For 1st ed., 1833, see *GIYA*.]

BEDFORD, Hilory G. *Texas Indian Troubles*. Dallas, 1905. $100 and up.

BEECHEY, Frederick William. *An Account of a Visit to California.* Colored plates, map. No place, no date [San Francisco, 1941]. One of 350. $25, $35, $45.

BEE-HIVE Songster (The). 32 pp., paperbound (self wrappers). Salt Lake, 1868. (By John Davis.) $35.

BEERBOHM, Max. *The Happy Hypocrite.* Paperbound. New York and London, 1897. Uncut, $27.50. Another, edges worn, in slip case, $25.

BELCOURT, The Rev. George Antoine. *Anamihe-Masinahigan Jesus ot Ijittwawin gave Anamihe-Nakamunan Takobihiharewan.* Kebekong (Quebec), 1859. $57.50.

BELKNAP, Jeremy. *A Sermon on Military Duty, Preached at Dover, Nov. 10, 1772.* Paperbound, stitched. Salem, 1773. 1st ed. Half title, two other leaves torn, $45. Another, $27.50.

BELL, John. *Discourses on the Nature and Cure of Wounds.* 2 vols. in 1. Walpole, N.H., 1807. 1st ed. $37.50.

BELL, Solomon. *Tales of Travel West of the Mississippi.* Map, plates. Boards. Boston, 1830. (By William J. Snelling.) Library blind stamp, $55.

BELLAMY, Edward. *Looking Backward, 2000-1887.* Green cloth. Boston, 1888. 1st ed., 1st issue, with printer's imprint "JJA" on copyright page. $80 to $100. Other copies, $60, $35. [See *GIYA* for paperbound issue of 1888.]

BELLE Valley Boarding School Exposure (The). Paperbound. Philadelphia, 1872. 1st ed. (By Charles Wesley Alexander?) Covers soiled, $75.

BENDIRE, Charles. *Life Histories of North American Birds.* 7 colored plates of birds' eggs. Washington, 1895. $25.

BENEDICT, Almon H. *A "Wide Awake" Poem.* (Lincoln campaign item.) 16 pp. Cortland Village, 1860. Uncut, $60.

BENÉT, Stephen Vincent. *The Devil and Daniel Webster.* Weston, Vt., no date [1937]. 1st ed. One of 700, signed. $25.

BENÉT, Stephen Vincent. *Tuesday, Nov. 5, 1940.* 8 pp., paperbound. 1st ed. One of 50. $25.

BENÉT, Stephen Vincent and Rosemary. *A Book of Americans.* New York, 1933. 1st ed. One of 125, signed. $25.

BENEZET, Anthony. *The Plainness and Innocent Simplicity of the Christian Religion.* Stitched. Philadelphia, 1782. 1st ed. Unbound, library stamp on title page, $35.

BENICIA: Its Resources and Advantages for Manufacture. Map. 16 pp., paperbound. Oakland, no date [1881]. $45.

BENJAMIN, Asher. *The American Builder's Companion.* 63 plates. Boston, 1826. 5th ed. Rubbed, back cover weak, lacking front flyleaves, $25. Boston, 1827. 6th ed. Foxed, front cover loose, $25. [For 1st ed., see *GIYA*.]

BENJAMIN, Asher. *Elements of Architecture.* 28 plates. Boston, 1843. 1st ed. Ex-library, crudely rebacked with tape, $25.

BENJAMIN, Asher. *Practice of Architecture.* 60 full-page plates. Boston, 1833. 1st ed. Ex-library, $27.50. Philadelphia, 1836. $25.

BENJAMIN, Asher. *The Rudiments of Architecture.* 34 plates. Boston, 1820. 2d ed. Stains on several pages, $27.50.

BENNETT, Emerson. *The Prairie Flower.* 128 pp., paperbound. Cincinnati and St. Louis, 1849. 1st ed. Up to $200. Recent auction record: $130.

BENSON, Frank W. *Etchings and Drypoints.* 285 reproductions. 4 vols., boards. Boston, 1917. One of 275. All except Vol. 1 in dust jacket, $150. [Supersedes entry in *GIYA*.]

BENTON, Frank. *Cowboy Life on the Sidetrack.* No place, no date [Denver, 1903]. $25.

BEOWULF. Verse translation by William Ellery Leonard. Rockwell Kent lithographs. New York, 1932. 1st ed. One of 950. $25.

BEVIER, Robert S. *History of the 1st and 2d Missouri Confederate Brigades, 1861-1865.* St. Louis, 1879. Lacking portrait, rebound, $35.

BICKERSTAFF, Isaac. *The Rhode-Island Almanac for 1842.* Stitched, unbound, uncut. Providence, no date [1841]. (Contains "Indian Barbarity," concerning Miss Fleming's captivity.) In slip case, $27.50.

BICKERSTAFF'S Boston Almanack, for the Year of our Lord 1768, etc. 8 woodcuts. Stitched. Boston, no date [1767]. $32.50. [For 1778, see *GIYA.*]

BIDDLE, Owen. *The Young Carpenter's Assistant.* 46 full-page and folding plates. Philadelphia, 1805. 1st ed. Calf-bound, label missing, $150.

BIGGERS, Don H. *From Cattle Range to Cotton Patch.* 156 pp., paperbound. Abilene, no date [1904 or 1908?]. 1st ed. $200. Another, cover repairs, $175.

BILL to Authorize the People of the Territory of Kansas to Form a Constitution and State Government, etc. (A). 14 pp., thick paper, sewed. Washington, 1856. 1st issue, Senate document "S. 356," with handwritten ms. correction. Uncut, unopened, $75.

BILLINGS, John S. *A Report on Barracks and Hospitals.* 12 plates. Washington, 1870. $40.

BILLINGS, John S. *A Report on the Hygiene of the United States Army.* Folding map, 12 plates. Washington, 1875. Spine worn, $50.

BIOGRAPHICAL and Historical Memoirs of Adams, Clay, Hall and Hamilton Counties, Nebraska. Chicago, 1890. $25.

BIOGRAPHICAL and Historical Record of Greene and Carroll Counties, Iowa. Chicago, 1887. $30.

BIOGRAPHICAL History of Crawford, Ida and Sac Counties, Iowa. Chicago, 1893. $32.50.

BIOGRAPHICAL History of Page County, Iowa. Chicago, 1890. $32.50.

BIOGRAPHICAL Notice of Com. Jesse D. Elliott (A). Boards. Philadelphia, 1835. (By Russell Jarvis.) Corners worn, $25.

BIOGRAPHICAL Sketch, Words of the Songs, Ballads, etc. of the Composer and Vocalist, Stephen Massett, "Jeems Pipes, of Pipesville." Portrait. 52 pp., paperbound. New York, 1858. 1st ed. $40.

BIOGRAPHY of James Lawrence. Boards. New Brunswick, 1813. $90.

BIRDSONG, James C. *Brief Sketches of the North Carolina State Troops in the War Between the States.* Raleigh, 1894. Rebound in buckram, $30.

BISHOP, Abraham. *Oration in Honor of the Election of President Jefferson, etc.* 24 pp., sewed. No place [Hartford], 1804. $25.

BLACK, William L. (of Texas). *A New Industry or, Raising the Angora Goat and Mohair for Profit.* No place, no date [Fort Worth, 1900]. $27.50.

BLACKBIRD, A. J. *History of the Ottawa and Chippewa Indians of Michigan.* Ypsilanti, 1887. 1st ed. $50.

BLANCHARD, Rufus. *Discovery and Conquests of the North West.* 6 parts, paperbound, bound together in morocco. Wheaton, Ill., 1879. 1st ed. $250.

BLEDSOE, A. J. *History of Del Norte County, California.* 176 pp., paperbound. Eureka, 1881. $1,800 (auction price, 1959).

BLOOMER, J. G. *Pacific Cryptograph*. San Francisco, 1874. Worn, writing throughout. $37.50.

BÖERSCHMANN, Ernst. *Chinesiche Architektur*. 340 plates. 2 vols. New York, no date [1925]. $75.

BOGGS, Mae Helene Bacon. *My Playhouse Was a Concord Coach*. No place, no date [Oakland, 1942]. $125.

BOLTON, Herbert E. (trans.). *Font's Complete Diary of the 2d Anza Expedition*. Berkeley, 1931. $25. Berkeley, 1933, $25.

BOLTON, Herbert E. *Guide to Materials for the History of the United States in the Principal Archives of Mexico*. Washington, 1913. $25.

BONNEY, Edward. *The Banditti of the Prairies*. Woodcut engravings. 224 pp., paperbound. Philadelphia, no date [1855]. Uncut, $75. [For 1st ed., 1850, see *GIYA*.]

BOOK of Common Prayer (The). Vellum binding, metal clasps. New York, 1893. Soiled, front hinge weak, $25.

BORDEN, Gail, Jr. *Letters of . . . to Dr. Ashbel Smith, etc.* 9 pp., paperbound. Galveston, 1850. 1st ed. $125.

BORDEN, Spencer. *The Arab Horse*. New York, 1906. $30.

BORDLEY, John Beale. *Essays and Notes on Husbandry and Rural Affairs*. Plates. Philadelphia, 1799. 1st ed. Newly rebound, $75.

BORNEMAN, Henry S. *Pennsylvania German Illuminated Manuscripts*. 38 reproductions in full color. Norristown, 1937. $45.

BOSCANA, Father Geronimo. *Chinigchinich*. Translated by Alfred Robinson. Colored plates, maps. Boards. Santa Ana, 1933. $45.

BOSQUI, Edward. *Memoirs*. No place [Oakland], 1952. Reprinted. One of 350. $25.

BOSWELL, H. James & Son. *American Blue Book, Texas Attorneys, 1926*. No place, 1926. One of 150. $25.

BOSWORTH, Newton. *Hochelaga Depicta, the Early History and Present State of the City and Island of Montreal*. 2 folding maps. Montreal, 1839. $25.

BOURKE, John G. *Scatologic Rites of All Nations*. Washington, 1891. 1st ed. Uncut, $35. Another, $30.

BOWDOIN, James. *A Philosophical Discourse, Addressed to the American Academy, of Arts and Sciences*. Boston, 1780. Unbound, $25.

BOWEN, Abel. *The Naval Monument*. 25 woodcuts. Boston, 1816. 1st ed., with errata slip. Calfbound, text pages browned, $29.50.

BOX, Capt. Michael J. *Adventures and Explorations in New and Old Mexico*. New York, 1861. 1st ed. $60. New York, 1869. Reprinted. Rebound, $30.

BOYD, Belle. *Belle Boyd in Camp and Prison, Written by Herself*. New York, 1865. Rebound in buckram, $30. New York, 1866. White ink spots on cover, $30.

BRACE, Jack. *Marie; or the Gambler of the Mississippi*. Boards. No place, no date [New York, 1861]. (By Justin Jones.) $25.

BRACKENRIDGE, Hugh H. *Gazette Publications*. Carlisle, 1806. $35.

BRACKENRIDGE, Hugh H. *Incidents of the Insurrection in the Western Parts of Pennsylvania, in the Year 1794*. Philadelphia, 1795. 1st ed. Contemporary calf, one hinge cracked, $65.

BRACKENRIDGE, H. M. *A Eulogy on the Lives and Characters of John Adams and Thomas Jefferson*. 18 pp., paperbound. Pensacola, 1826. In morocco case, $350.

BRACKENRIDGE, H. M. *Journal of a Voyage up the River Missouri*. Boards. Baltimore, 1816. 2d ed., with cover date 1815. In slip case, $75.

BRACKENRIDGE, H. M. *Views of Louisiana*. Baltimore, 1817. Rebacked, $45. [For 1st ed., 1814, see *GIYA*.]

BRADLEY, James. *The Confederate Mail Carrier*. 15 plates. Mexico, Mo., 1894. $25.

BRADY, William. *Glimpses of Texas*. Colored folding map. Houston, 1871. $45. Another, lacking map, $32.50.

BRAMAH, Ernest. *The Wallet of Kai Lung*. Boston, 1900. 1st ed., Am. issue, pale green cloth, 1½ inches across top, Am. ads at end, gilt top, $25.

BRATT, John. *Trails of Yesterday*. 22 plates. Lincoln, Neb., 1921. $27.50 and $30.

BRAZER, Esther Stevens. *Early American Decoration*. 34 colored plates. Springfield, no date [1950]. In dust jacket, $27.50.

BRECK, Robert. *Past Dispensations of Providence Called to Mind*. Hartford, 1784. 1st ed., with half title. In ¾ morocco, $35.

BRICE, Wallace A. *History of Fort Wayne*. Fort Wayne, 1868. $27.50.

BRIDWELL, J. W. *The Life and Adventures of Robert Mc-Kimie*. 56 pp., paperbound. Hillsboro, O., 1878. $150 to $200.

BRIGAND Chief of California (The). (About Joaquin Murieta.) Colored plates, folding reward poster in facsimile. San Francisco, 1932. $50.

BRIGGS, L. Vernon. *Arizona and New Mexico 1882, California 1886, Mexico 1891*. Boston, 1932. $25.

BRIGGS, L. Vernon. *History of Shipbuilding on North River*. 57 illustrations. Boston, 1889. 1st ed. Spine chipped, $65.

BRIGHT, *Beautiful, Bounteous Barnes, the Banner County of North Dakota.* Paperbound view book. Valley City, 1882. $75.

BRILLAT-SAVARIN, J. A. *The Physiology of Taste.* New York, 1949. One of 1,500, boxed. $35.

BRINGAS Y ENCINAS, Diego Miguel. *Sermon Politico-Moral que para dar Principio a la Mision Extraordinaria, etc.* 44 pp., vellum. Mexico, 1813. $250.

BRISBIN, James S. *The Beef Bonanza.* 8 plates. Philadelphia, 1881. 1st ed. $27.50 and $30.

BRITTON, Wiley. *Memoirs of the Rebellion on the Border, 1863.* Chicago, 1882. $25.

BROOKE, H. K. *Annals of the Revolution.* Boards. Philadelphia and New York, no date [1848]. Scotch taped at top and bottom of spine, $60.

BROOKS, Bryant B. *Memoirs of.* Glendale, 1939. Limited to 250. $40.

BROTHERHEAD, William (ed.). *The Book of the Signers.* Philadelphia, 1861. One of 99 on large paper. $35. Philadelphia, no date [1872]. *Centennial Book, etc.* 100 engravings. Morocco. $25.

BROTHERS (The), *or Consequences. A Story of What Happens Every Day, with an Account of Savings Banks.* 63 pp., paperbound. Boston, 1823. $50.

BROWER, Jacob V. *Memoirs of Explorations in the Basin of the Mississippi. Vol. 1.* Maps. St. Paul, 1898. One of 300. $32.50. *Vol. 8,* St. Paul, 1904. $32.50.

BROWN, Mrs. D. C. *Memoir of the Late Rev. Lemuel Covell.* 2 vols. in 1. Brandon, 1839. $35.

BROWN, J. Willard. *The Signal Corps, U.S.A., in the War of the Rebellion.* Boston, 1896. Worn, ex-library, $25.

BROWN, James Cabell. *Calabazas, or Amusing Recollections of an Arizona City*. Paperbound. San Francisco, 1892. In slip case, $75. Another, less fine, $35.

BROWN, James S. *Life of a Pioneer*. Portrait, 2 plates. Salt Lake City, 1900. $50.

BROWN, Jesse and A. W. Willard. *The Black Hills Trails*. Rapid City, 1924. $35.

BROWN, John Henry. *History of Dallas County from 1837 to 1887*. 114 pp., paperbound. Dallas, 1887. $75. Another, $35. (Both quotations from Texas dealers.)

BROWN, John Henry. *History of Texas*. 25 plates. 2 vols. St. Louis, no date [1892-3]. $57.50. Another, rebound in calf, $45.

BROWN, John Henry. *Indian Wars and Pioneers of Texas*. 124 plates. Austin and St. Louis, no date [1896]. $37.50. Another, rebound, $50.

BROWN, John Henry. *Reminiscences and Incidents of "The Early Days" of San Francisco . . . 1845-1850*. Folding plan. 53 pp. San Francisco, no date [1886]. 1st ed. $325. Another, rebound, some defects, $175. [Supersedes entry in *GIYA*.] Reprint ed.: San Francisco, 1933, edited by Douglas Sloane Watson, one of 550 copies. $30 and $42.50.

BROWN, John P. *Old Frontiers: The Story of the Cherokee Indians, etc.* Kingsport, Tenn., 1938. $25.

BROWN, Riney. *Riney Brown's Diary*. Boerne, Tex., 1949. $50.

BROWN, Samuel R. *The Western Gazetteer, or Emigrant's Directory*. Auburn, N.Y., 1817. 1st ed. Lacking errata slip, $37.50.

BROWN, Col. William C. *The Sheepeater Campaign in Idaho*. Folding map. 32 pp., paperbound. Boise, 1926. One of 50. $30.

BROWNE, J. Ross. *Report of the Debates in the Convention of California on the Formation of the State Constitution, etc.* Washington, 1850. Hinges broken, $25.

BRUFF, J. Goldsborough. *Gold Rush: The Journals of.* 2 vols. New York, 1944. 1st ed. $50.

BRUFFEY, George A. *Eighty-one Years in the West.* 152 pp., paperbound. Butte, 1925. $25.

BRUNSON, Edward. *Profits in Sheep and Cattle in Central and Western Kansas.* 16 pp., paperbound. Kansas City, 1883. $40.

BRYANT, John Howard. *Poems.* New York, 1855. 1st ed. $25.

BRYANT, Wilbur F. *The Blood of Abel.* Paperbound. Hastings, Neb., 1887. 1st ed. $25.

BRYANT, William Cullen. *Poems.* Boards. New York, 1832. $45. [For 1821 title, see *GIYA*.]

BUCK, Irving A. *Cleburne and His Command.* New York, 1908. Rebound, $50.

BUCKLEY, S. B. *Second Annual Report of the Geological and Agricultural Survey of Texas.* 96 pp., paperbound. Houston, 1876. $45.

BUECHLER, A. F., R. J. Barr and Dale P. Stough. *History of Hall County, Nebraska.* Lincoln, 1920. Worn, new spine, $25.

BUEL, J. W. *The Border Outlaws* [and] *The Border Bandits.* 2 vols. in 1. St. Louis, 1881. $30.

BUEL, J. W. *Life and Marvelous Adventures of Wild Bill, the Scout.* 92 pp., paperbound. Chicago, 1880. 1st ed. $100 and up.

BUFFUM, E. Gould. *Six Months in the Gold Mines.* Philadelphia, 1850. 1st ed. $47.50.

BUNNELL, Lafayette Houghton. *Discovery of the Yosemite.* Chicago, no date [1880]. 1st ed., Revell. $25.

BUNTLINE, Ned. *The Mysteries and Miseries of New York: A Story of Real Life.* 5 parts in 1 vol. New York, 1848. (By E. Z. C. Judson.) 1st ed. $35.

BUNYAN, John. *Pilgrim's Progress.* Edited by G. B. Harrison. 29 Blake illustrations. New York, 1941. One of 1,500. $50.

BURKE, Aedanus. *Considerations on the Society or Order of Cincinnati.* Philadelphia, 1783. Unbound, $45. Newport, no date [1783]. Half morocco, $70.

BURKE, Edmund. *The Speech of . . . on Moving His Resolutions for Conciliation with the Colonies, March 22, 1775.* New York, 1775. 1st Am. ed. Half morocco, title page strengthened, $85.

BURKE, W. S. *Directory of the City of Council Bluffs and Emigrants' Guide to the Gold Regions of the West.* Folding map. Council Bluffs, 1866. In morocco case, $850.

BURLAGE, John and J. B. Hollingsworth. *Abstract of Valid Land Claims . . . Texas.* Austin, 1859. $150.

BURNEY, G. E., et al. *Report of the Joint Select Committee to Investigate the Facts in Regard to the Burning of Brenham.* 54 pp. Austin, 1866. $50.

BURNS, Robert. *Poems, Chiefly in the Scottish Dialect.* Philadelphia, 1788. 1st Am. ed. Calfbound, $150. New York, 1788. $50.

BURPEE, Lawrence J. *The Search for the Western Sea.* Toronto, no date [1908]. 1st ed. $45.

BURROUGHS, Edgar Rice. *Tarzan of the Apes.* Chicago, 1914. 1st ed. $40 to $50.

BURROUGHS, Stephen. *Memoirs.* Calfbound. Hanover, N. H., 1798. 1st ed. Date trimmed off bottom of title page by binder, $32.50.

BURSON, William. *A Race for Liberty; or, My Capture, Imprisonment and Escape.* Wellsville, 1867. Spine chipped, $25.

BURTON, Harley True. *A History of the JA Ranch.* Austin, 1928. $50.

BUTCHER, S. D. *Pioneer History of Custer County.* Broken Bow, 1901. 1st ed. $65.

BUTTERFIELD, C. W. *An Historical Account of the Expedition Against Sandusky.* Cincinnati, 1873. $25.

BUTTERWORTH, Benjamin J. *The Growth of Industrial Art.* 200 full-page plates. Washington, 1892. 1st ed. $50. Another, binding stained, $42.50.

BYRENHEIDT, A. *Hydropathy, or the Treatment of Diseases by Water.* No place, no date [Lafayette, La., 1844]. $45.

BYRNE, B. M. *Letters on the Climate, Soils, and Productions of Florida.* 28 pp., paperbound. Jacksonville, 1851. 2d ed. $200. [For 3d ed., 1866, see *Florida and Texas* entry in *GIYA.*]

C

CABELL, James Branch. *Jurgen.* New York, 1919. 1st ed., 1st issue, measuring only ¾ inches across top. Up to $60. Signed, in dust jacket, $70. Another, signed, lacking dust jacket, $25. [Supersedes entry in *GIYA.*]

CABEZA DE VACA, Alvar Nunez. *The Narrative of.* Translated by Buckingham Smith. Washington, 1851. Some of the maps missing, $150. New York, 1871. One of 100, in ¾ morocco. $50.

CABEZA DE VACA, Alvar Nunez. *Relation . . . of What Befel the Armament in the Indias Whither Pamphilo de Narvaez Went for Governor, etc.* Boards. San Francisco, 1929. One of 300. In cloth case, $85 and $75.

CALDWELL, J. A. *History of Belmont and Jefferson Counties, Ohio.* Wheeling, 1880. Rubbed, $35.

CALDWELL, J. F. J. *History of a Brigade of South Carolinians.* Philadelphia, 1866. 1st ed. $45. Another, ex-library, rebound, $50.

CALIFORNIA Historical Society. Papers of the. Vol. 1, Parts I and II. 94 and 440 pp., paperbound. San Francisco, 1887. (Contain John T. Doyle's "History of the Pious Fund of California.") $50.

CALKIN, A. *General Report of the Auditor of Public Accounts for the Territory of Utah.* 8 pp. Salt Lake, 1854. Unopened, $45.

CALLENDER, John. *An Historical Discourse on the Civil and Religious Affairs of the Colony of Rhode-Island and Providence Plantations in New-England in America.* Stitched. Boston, 1739. $90.

CANFIELD, Chauncey L. (ed.). *The Diary of a Forty-Niner.* Colored map. San Francisco, 1906. (Diary of Alfred T. Jackson.) 1st ed. $25.

CANNON, J. P. *Inside of Rebeldom; The Daily Life of a Private in the Confederate Army.* Washington, 1900. Rebound in buckram, paper brittle, $50.

CAPRON, Elisha Smith. *History of California.* Colored map. Boston, 1854. $27.50.

CAPT. SMITH and Princess Pocahontas. An Indian Tale. Boards. Philadelphia, 1805. (By John Davis.) 1st ed., 1st issue, with undated copyright notice. Uncut, most of spine gone, $1,200.

CARES About the Nurseries. Two Brief Discourses. Boston, 1702. (By Cotton Mather.) 1st ed. Calf, somewhat pitted, 3 leaves worm-eaten, $650.

CAREY, C. H. *History of Oregon.* Chicago, 1922. $25.

CAREY, Mathew. *Carey's Pocket Atlas.* 19 state and territorial maps. Philadelphia, 1796. Original ed. $75.

CARLETON, Robert. *The New Purchase: or, Seven and a Half Years in the Far West.* 2 vols., boards. New York, 1843. (By Baynard R. Hall.) 1st ed. In slip case, $50.

CAROLINA Folk-Plays. 2d Series. New York, 1924. 1st ed. (Contains Thomas Wolfe's first appearance in a book.) $45.

CAROLINE Tracy; the Spring Street Milliner's Apprentice. 78 pp. New York and Cincinnati, 1849. Half morocco, $45.

CARR, John. *Early Times in Middle Tennessee.* Nashville, 1857. $25.

CARROLL, H. Bailey and J. V. Haggard (trans.). *Three New Mexico Chronicles.* Albuquerque, 1942. $25.

CARROLL, Lewis. *Alice's Adventures in Wonderland.* Boston, 1869. (By Charles L. Dodgson.) 1st ed. printed in America. Rubbed, inner hinges cracked, $35. [For rarer actual 1st Am. ed., see *GIYA*.]

CARSON, James H. *Life in California.* Map. Tarrytown, 1931. $35.

CARSTARPHEN, J. E. *My Trip to California in '49.* Paperbound. No place, no date [Louisiana, Mo., 1914]. In cloth case, $32.50.

CARTER, Robert G. *The Old Sergeant's Story.* New York, 1926. 1st ed. $30 and $28.50. Another, rebound, $25.

CARTER, Robert G. *Pursuit of Kicking Bird: A Campaign in the Texas "Bad Lands."* 44 pp., paperbound. Washington, 1920. One of 100. $35.

CARTER, Lieut.-Col. W. H. *From Yorktown to Santiago with the 6th U. S. Cavalry.* Baltimore, 1900. $25.

CARTWRIGHT, George. *A Journal of Transactions and Events During a Residence of Nearly 16 Years on the Coast of Labrador.* Folding maps. 3 vols. Newark, 1792. Half morocco, uncut, $100.

CARVER, Jonathan. *Three Years Travels Through the Interior Parts of North America.* Philadelphia, 1796. Spine repaired, new end papers, $25.

CASE and Claim of the American Loyalists Impartially Stated and Considered (The). No place, no date [1783]. $45.

CASE Decided in the Supreme Court of the United States in February, 1793. 120 pp., paperbound. Philadelphia, 1793. $25.

CASE of Judge John C. Watrous. (House of Rep. Report No. 540.) 464 pp., sewed. Washington, 1858. Part of first page torn away, $40.

CASS, Lewis. *Address Delivered Before the New England Society of Michigan, Dec. 22, 1848.* 47 pp., sewed. Detroit, 1849. $37.50.

CASS, Lewis. *Substance of a Speech Delivered by Hon. Lewis Cass, of Michigan . . . on the Ratification of the Oregon Treaty.* 16 pp., sewed. Detroit, 1846. $60.

CASTORENA Y URSUA, Juan Ignacio. *El Minero mas Feliz que Halló el Tesoro Escondido de la Virtud en el Campo Florido de la Religión, etc.* 28 pp., paperbound. Mexico, 1728. $325.

CATALOGUE of Books, Maps, and Charts Belonging to the Library of the Two Houses of Congress. 10 pp., half morocco. Washington, 1802. 1st ed. $100.

CATALOGUS Personarum, et Officiorum Provinciae Mexicanae Societatis Jesus in Indiys 1764. 55 pp., vellum. Mexico, 1764. $750.

CATECHISM: The Man of God Furnished . . . a Threefold. I. Milk for Babes. II. An Abridgement of the Assemblies Catechism. III. Supplies from the Tower of David. Boston, 1708. (By Cotton Mather.) Pages 25-44 missing, $28.50.

CATES, Cliff D. *Pioneer History of Wise County.* Decatur, Tex., 1907. Rebound, $45.

CATHER, Willa. *Alexander's Bridge*. Lavender cloth. Boston, 1912. 1st ed. 1st issue, with initials "WSC" on spine. $40.

CATHER, Willa. *Death Comes for the Archbishop*. 2 vols., full vellum. New York, 1937. 1st ed. One of 50, signed, on Japan vellum, boxed. $75 to $100. Trade ed., same date, in dust jacket, $25.

CATHER, Willa. *O Pioneers!* Boston, 1913. 1st ed., 1st issue, ribbed cloth. In dust jacket, $100. Others, fine, lacking jacket, $35 and $50. [Supersedes entry in *GIYA*.]

CATHER, Willa. *The Professor's House*. Boards. New York, 1925. 1st ed. One of 185, signed. Unopened, $25.

CATHERINE Brown, the Converted Cherokee: a Missionary Drama, Founded on Fact. Written by a Lady. 27 pp., paperbound. New Haven, 1819. 1st ed., gray covers. Uncut, $75.

CATLIN, George. *North American Indians, Being Letters and Notes on Their Manners, Customs, and Conditions*. 320 color plates. 2 vols. Philadelphia, 1913. One of 75 on handmade paper, $110. Another, $75.

CATTLE Raising in South Dakota. 32 pp., paperbound. No place, no date [Forest City, 1904]. $40.

CELEBRATION of the 73d Anniversary of the Declaration of Independence . . . on Board the Barque "Hannah Sprague," etc. 16 pp., paperbound. New York, 1849. 1st ed. $55.

CELIZ, Fray Francisco. *Diary of the Alarcon Expedition into Texas, 1718-1719*. Translated by Fritz L. Hoffman. 10 plates. Los Angeles, 1935. One of 600. $27.50. Another, $32.50.

CELLARIUS, Frederick J. *Atlas of the City of Dayton and Adjoining Territory*. City map, 33 plates, linen-mounted. No place [Dayton], 1807. $25.

CERVANTES, Miguel de. *El Ingenioso Hidalgo Don Quixote de la Mancha*. Facsimiles of the 1st eds. of 1605-16. 2 vols.

No place [New York], no date. One of 100 on Arnold hand-made paper, boxed. $100.

CHADWICK, Henry. *The Game of Base Ball. How to Learn It, How to Play It, and How to Teach It.* New York, no date [1868]. 1st ed., with rules for 1868. Rubbed, $67.50.

CHAMBERS, Andrew Jackson. *Recollections by.* 40 pp., half morocco. No place, no date [1947]. $75 and $150. Other copies, stapled wire covers, $60, $75, and $77.50. [Supersedes entry in *GIYA*.]

CHANDLER, Thomas Bradbury. *An Appeal to the Public, in Behalf of the Church of England in America.* New York, 1767. 1st ed. Writing on title page, $27.50.

CHANNING, William Ellery. *The Duties of Children.* Paperbound. Boston, 1807. 1st ed. $60.

CHANNING, William Ellery. *John Brown, and The Heroes of Harper's Ferry.* Boston, 1886. 1st ed. $30.

CHANNING, William Ellery. *A Sermon Delivered at the Ordination of the Rev. Jared Sparks, etc.* Stitched, uncut. Boston, 1819. 1st ed. $45.

CHAPMAN, George. *Captivity in Australia.* 38 pp., paperbound. Providence, 1871. 1st ed. $30.

CHARLES Linn; or How to Observe the Golden Rule. New York, 1847. (By Mrs. Emily C. Judson.) 2d ed. Foxed, $30.

CHARTER of Dartmouth College (The). Stitched, uncut. Hanover, 1815. $35.

CHARTER, Laws, and Catalogue of Books (The), of the Library Company of Philadelphia. (Printed by Benjamin Franklin.) Philadelphia, 1764. Half morocco, $100.

CHARTER and Organization of the Texas State Horticultural and Pomological Association. 18 pp., paperbound. Houston, 1876. $25.

CHAUNCY, Charles. *The Horrid Nature and Enormous Guilt of Murder*. Boston, 1754. 1st ed. Unbound, $25.

CHAUNCY, Charles. *A Letter to a Friend*. Stitched, uncut. Boston, 1767. 1st ed. $27.50.

CHAUNCY, Charles. *An Oration*. New Haven, 1797. Unbound, $25.

CHAUNCY, Charles. *Seasonable Thoughts on the State of Religion in New England*. Boston, 1743. 1st ed. Rubbed, $25.

CHAUNCY, Charles. *A Sermon Preached at Boston, at the Ordination of the Rev. Mr. Joseph Bowman*. Paperbound. Boston, 1762. $55.

CHEAT Unmask'd (The); Being a Refutation of That Illegitimate Letter, Said to be Wrote by a Clergyman in Town, etc. Philadelphia, 1764. Rebound in half morocco, closely cut, affecting imprint, $50.

CHICAGO Illustrated. 52 tinted views. Text by James W. Sheahan. Oblong, half leather and cloth. No place, no date [Chicago, 1866-67]. (Jevne and Almini, publishers.) 2d issue (original issue was in 13 parts). $750 and $650. [For a modern reprint, see *GIYA*.]

CHILDREN'S Hour (The). By E. W. S. and S. W. M. Philadelphia, 1864. (By Elizabeth W. Sherman and S. Weir Mitchell.) 1st ed. One illustration loose, $100.

CHILD'S Botany (The). Boards, calf back. Boston, 1828. (By Samuel Griswold Goodrich.) 1st ed. $45.

CHILDS, C. G. *Views of Philadelphia*. 26 engraved views. Boards. Philadelphia, 1827. Front cover loose, $37.50.

CHIPMAN, Nathaniel. *Sketches of the Principles of Government*. Rutland, 1793. 1st ed. $32.50.

CHITTENDEN, Hiram M. *The American Fur Trade of the Far West*. Map, plan, 3 facsimiles, 6 plates. 3 vols. New York, 1902. 1st ed. $90.

CHITTENDEN, Hiram M. *History of Early Steamboat Navigation on the Missouri River.* 16 plates. 2 vols. New York, 1903. One of 950. $60.

CHRISTLICHE Betrachtungen über die Evangelischen Texte, so man pfleget zu lesen an den Sonntagen und hohen Festen . . . durch Erasmum Weichenan. Germantaun (Germantown, Pa.), 1791. $25.

CHRYSTAL, Peter. *A Voice from the Oppressed Spirits in Prison.* 11 pp., paperbound. No place, no date [New Orleans, 1848]. $25.

CHURCH, John A. *The Comstock Lode.* 6 plates. New York, 1879. $25.

CINDERELLA; or, The Little Glass Slipper. Colored pictorial boards. 10 pp. text, plus illustrations. (McLoughlin Bros. Pantomime Toy Book.) New York, no date [about 1880]. Rubbed, $27.50.

CLAIBORNE, John Herbert. *Seventy-Five Years in Old Virginia.* New York and Washington, 1905. $25.

CLAIRAC, Louis André Chevalier De. *L. Ingénieur de Campagne; or, Field Engineer, etc.* 39 folding engravings. Philadelphia, 1776. 1st ed. Writing on end paper and title page, bookplate, $150.

CLAP, Thomas. *An Essay on The Nature and Foundation of Moral Virtue and Obligation.* New Haven, 1765. Half morocco, $35.

CLARK, Daniel M. *The Southern Calculator, or Compendious Arithmetic.* Boards. Lagrange, Ga., 1844. $35.

CLARK, John A. *Gleanings by the Way.* Philadelphia, 1842. $25.

CLAVIJERO, Francisco Javier. *Historia de la Antigua o Baja California.* Translated from the Italian. Boards. Mexico, 1852. $45.

CLAYTON, A. M. *Centennial Address on the History of Marshall County.* (Mississippi). 32 pp., paperbound. Washington, 1880. $45.

CLEVELAND, Richard J. *A Narrative of Voyages and Commercial Enterprises.* 2 vols. Cambridge, 1842. Library stamp on title page, $60.

COBB, Irvin S. *Piano Jim and the Impotent Pumpkin Vine, or "Charley Russell's Best Story—To My Way of Thinking."* 24 pp., paperbound. No place, 1947. One of 100. $25.

COBURN, Wallace D. *Rhymes from a Round Up Camp.* Illustrated by Charles M. Russell. Great Falls, 1899. 2d ed., with 14 line engravings not in 1st ed. $62.50. [For 1st ed., same date, see *GIYA.*]

COFFIN, Joshua. *A Sketch of the History of Newbury, Newburyport, and West Newbury.* Map, tables. Boston, 1845. Uncut, unopened, $25.

COHN, David L. *New Orleans and Its Living Past.* Boston, 1941. Limited, signed ed. $25.

COKE, Richard. *Inaugural Address.* 14 pp., paperbound. Austin, 1874. $35.

COKE, Richard. *Message to the 14th Legislature.* 14 pp., sewed. Austin, 1874. $30. Same, to 15th Legislature, 1st session: Houston, 1876, 68 pp., sewed, $35.

COLE, Emma. *Life and Sufferings.* Plates. 36 pp., paperbound. Boston, 1844. $65.

COLECCION de Casos, en Ilustracion de las Propiedades Restaurativas i Santivas de la Panacea de Swain, etc. Boards. Filadelfia, 1831. Back cover loose, front hinge cracked, $25.

COLLATED Statutes of the Territory of Minnesota, etc. Boards. St. Paul, 1853. $27.50.

COLLECTION of Original Papers Relative to the History of the Colony of Massachusetts Bay (A). Boston, 1769. (By Thomas Hutchinson.) 1st ed. $50.

COLLECTION (A), of Such Acts of the General Assembly of Virginia of a Public and Permanent Nature as Are Now in Force, etc. 2 vols. Richmond, 1803-8. $50.

COLLINS, Charles (comp.). *Omaha Directory.* Printed boards. No place, no date [Omaha, 1866]. 1st ed. $450.

COLLINS, James L. *Contestación a Ciertas Representaciónes Infamatorias de R. H. Weightman, etc.* 22 pp., sewed. Santa Fe, 1852. Last leaf in facsimile, $150.

COLLINS, Lieut. R. M. *Chapters from the Unwritten History of the War Between the States.* St. Louis, 1893. Rebound in buckram, $65. Another, worn, $27.50.

COLMAN, Benjamin. *Ossa Josephi; or, The Bones of Joseph.* Boston, 1720. Half morocco, $35.

COLTON, J. H. *Particulars of Routes, Distances, Fares, etc. . . . With Map of the United States, etc.* 11 pp. of text. New York, 1849. 1st ed., 1st issue, with "longitude West from Greenwich" at top of map. $125.

COLTON, Walter. *Three Years in California.* Map, 12 plates, folding facsimile. New York, 1850. 1st ed. $50. Another, $25. [Supersedes entry in *GIYA.*]

COMBS, Gen. Leslie. *Narrative of the Life of, etc.* 23 pp., plus errata leaf. No place, no date [New York, 1852]. 1st ed. $75. Washington, 1855, 24 pp., paperbound, $25.

COMISION Mixta de Reclamaciónes de Mexico y los Estados-Unidos. Mexico, 1876. $57.50.

COMMERCIAL Conduct of the United States of America Considered (The), etc. New York, MDCCLXXXVI (1786). 1st ed. Uncut, half calf, $100. Another, ex-library, unbound, $55.

*COMMON Sense; Addressed to the Inhabitants of America,
etc.* 64 pp., paperbound. Norwich, no date [1776]. (By
Thomas Paine.) $40.

*CONCLINS' New River Guide or a Gazeteer of All the Towns
on the Western Waters.* 44 full-page route maps. 128 pp.,
paperbound. Cincinnati, 1850. $50. Another, morocco, cov-
ers bound in, $25.

CONDON, Thomas. *The Two Islands and What Became of
Them.* Portland, 1902. 1st ed. $25. Autographed, $30.

CONDUCT of the Paxton-Men (The). Lancaster, 1764. (By
Thomas Barton.) Uncut, half morocco, half title repaired,
title page creased, affecting imprint, $75.

CONFEDERATE Receipt Book. Paperbound. Richmond,
1863. 1st ed. $35 or more.

CONFESSIONS of an English Opium-Eater. Boards, paper label. Philadelphia, 1823. (By Thomas DeQuincey.) 1st ed. $40.

CONNECTICUT Gore Title (The). Paperbound. Hartford,
1799. 1st ed. $85.

CONNELLEY, William E. *Wild Bill and His Era.* New York,
1933. 1st ed. One of 200. In dust jacket, $25.

CONNELLY, Marc. *The Green Pastures.* Green morocco. Also
green paper boards. New York, 1930. 1st ed. One of 550,
signed. Morocco, in slip case, $50. Boards, in slip case, $30.

CONNICK, Charles J. *Adventures in Light and Color.* New
York, 1937. 1st regular ed. $30 to $40.

CONRAD, Joseph. *Some Reminiscences.* Paperbound. New
York, 1908. 1st ed. $275.

CONRAD, Capt. Thomas Nelson. *The Rebel Scout.* Washington City, 1904. Binding waterstained, $45.

CONSIDERANT, Victor. *European Colonization in Texas.*
38 pp., paperbound. New York, 1855. $50.

CONSIDERATIONS on the Mode and Terms of a Treaty of Peace with America. Stitched, uncut. Hartford, 1799. $45.

CONSTITUTION and Laws of the Muskogee Nation. St. Louis, 1880. Spine broken, $100.

CONSTITUTION and Playing Rules of the International Baseball Association . . . and Championship Record for 1877. 77 pp., paperbound. Jamaica Plain, Mass., 1878. $25.

CONSTITUTION (The) of the Presbyterian Church in the United States of America. Philadelphia, 1789. 1st ed. $125. Another, with defects on several leaves, $80.

CONSTITUTION of the Republic of Mexico and the State of Coahuila and Texas (The), etc. 108 pp. New York, 1832. Half calf, $150.

CONSTITUTION and Rules of Business of the Essex Western Emigration Co. 8 pp., paperbound. Lawrence, 1856. $125.

CONSTITUTIONS of the Free-Masons (The). (Printed by Benjamin Franklin.) Philadelphia, 1734. Imperfect copy, $600 (auction price).

CONSTITUTIONS of the Several Independent States of America; the Declaration of Independence, etc. Boston, 1785. In ¾ morocco, $27.50.

CONTESTACIONES Habidas entre el Supremo Gobierno Mexicano, etc. 36 pp., paperbound. Mexico, 1847. 1st ed., 1st issue, with horn of plenty at foot of last page. $75. 2d issue, with Herrera's letter on last page. $75.

CONWAY, Moncure D. *Barons of the Potomack and Rappahannock.* New York, 1892. One of 360. $25.

COOK, David J. *Hands Up, or 20 Years of Detective Life in the Mountains and on the Plains.* 32 plates. Paperbound. Denver, 1882. 1st ed. $150 and up. Also, clothbound, same date, later issue, $100 and up. Denver, 1897. 2d ed., en-

larged, with *20 Years* changed to *35 Years* in title. $35.
[Supersedes entry in *GIYA*.]

COOK, Joel. *The Siege of Richmond.* Philadelphia, 1862. $25.

COOKE, Giles B. *Just Before and After Lee Surrendered to Grant.* 8 pp., paperbound. No place, no date [Houston, 1922] 1st ed. Printing errors corrected in ink, $35.

COOKE, Philip St. George. *The Conquest of New Mexico and California.* Folding map. New York, 1878. $45.

COOPER, Samuel. *A Sermon Preached Before His Excellency Thomas Pownall, etc.* Boston, no date [1759]. 1st ed. Morocco, $65.

COOPER, Samuel. *A Sermon Preached in Boston, New-England, Before the Society for Encouraging Industry.* Boards. Boston, 1753. In pamphlet binder, $25.

CORAM, Robert. *Political Inquiries; To Which is Added, a Plan for the General Establishment of Schools Throughout the United States.* 108 pp., unbound. Wilmington, 1791. 1st ed. $25.

CORNER, William. *San Antonio de Bexar.* Map, 16 plates. San Antonio, 1890. $27.50.

CORNWALL, Bruce. *Life Sketch of Pierre Barlow Cornwall.* 6 portraits. Boards. San Francisco, 1906. $30 to $35.

COSTANSO, Miguel. *The Spanish Occupation of California.* San Francisco, 1934. One of 550. $45.

COTTON, John. *God's Awful Determination Against a People, That Will Not Obey His Voice, by His Word, and Judgments.* Boston, 1728. $35.

COTTON, John. *Spiritual Milk for Boston Babes in Either England.* 13 pp. Cambridg, 1656. 1st Am. ed., without the "e" on "Cambridge." Price: Up to the finder (only one copy known).

COUES, Elliott (ed.). *New Light on the Early History of the Greater Northwest.* 3 vols. New York, 1897. One of 1,000. $75. Another set, same date, one of 100 on large paper, half vellum and boards, $100.

COULTER, E. Merton. *Travels in the Confederate States: A Bibliography.* Norman, 1948. $25.

COURSEY, O. W. *"Wild Bill."* Mitchell, no date [1924]. 1st ed. $28.50.

COUTS, Cave J. *From San Diego to the Colorado in 1849.* 3 maps on 2 sheets. Los Angeles, 1932. $35.

COX, Isaac. *The Annals of Trinity County.* San Francisco, 1940. One of 350. In slip case, $25.

COX, James. *Historical and Biographical Record of the Cattle Industry.* 2 vols., boxed. New York, 1959. $85. [For 1st ed., 1895, see *GIYA.*]

COX, Palmer. *The Brownies: Their Book.* Green glazed pictorial boards. New York, no date [1887]. 1st ed., 1st issue, with DeVinne Press seal immediately below copyright notice. In dust jacket, slightly torn, "very fine," $250. Another, "nice," lacking dust jacket, binding slightly rubbed, $22.50.

COX, Palmer. *Queer People Such as Goblins, Giants, Merry-Men and Monarchs, and Their Kweer Kapers.* Colored pictorial glazed boards. Philadelphia, no date [1888]. 1st ed. Binding worn, $25.

COX, Sandford C. *Recollections of the Early Settlement of the Wabash Valley.* Lafayette, Ind., 1860. $25.

COXE, Tench. *An Address to an Assembly of the Friends of American Manufactures.* Paperbound, stitched. Philadelphia, 1787. 1st ed. Uncut, $32.50.

COY, E. & Co. *Twin Cities Directory and Business Mirror for the Year 1860. Vol. 1.* Davenport, 1859. $65.

COY, Owen C. *California County Boundaries.* Berkeley, 1923. $42.50.

COZZENS, James Gould. *Confusion.* Boston, 1924. 1st ed. $25.

CRAIG, John. *Ranching with Lords and Commons.* 16 plates. Toronto, 1903. $45.

CRAMER, Zadok. *Cramer's Pittsburgh Magazine Almanack for the Year of our Lord 1816. No. XIII.* 72 pp., sewed. Pittsburgh, no date [1815]. In slip case, $50. Another, $27.50. [For other years, see *GIYA.*]

CRANE, Stephen. *Legends.* 4 pp., paperbound. Ysleta, 1942. 1st ed. One of 45. $37.50.

CRAWFORD, Lucy. *The History of the White Mountains.* Portland, 1846. $27.50.

CREATIONS in Ecclesiastical Art. New York, no date [1925]. Limited ed. $25.

CREEK Treaty Correspondence Preliminary to the Treaty of Aug. 7, 1856. Boards. Washington, 1856. Spine broken, $50.

CREEK Treaty, Passed in Congress, Feb. 1901. 11 pp., paperbound. Muskogee, 1901. $45.

CREUZBAUR, Robert (comp.). *Route from the Gulf of Mexico and the Lower Mississippi Valley to California and the Pacific Ocean.* 5 maps. 40 pp., clothbound. New York, 1849. Up to $1,000. Copy with maps missing, worn on covers, $150.

CREVECOEUR, F. F. *Old Settlers' Tales.* Onaga, Kan., 1901-02. $35.

CRIES of London (The), As They Are Daily Exhibited in the Streets. 40 pp., paperbound. Philadelphia, 1805. Rubbed, spine missing, $50.

CROCKET, G. L. *Two Centuries in East Texas.* Dallas, no date [about 1932]. 1st ed. $45. Another, $50.

CROCKETT, Col. David. *An Account of Col. Crockett's Tour to the North and Down East.* Philadelphia, 1835. (By Augustin S. Clayton?) 1st ed. $25 and $27.50.

CROCKETT, Col. David. *"Go Ahead." Davy Crockett's Almanack, of Wild Sports of the West, and Life in the Backwoods. 1835.* Stitched. Nashville, no date [1834]. $100 or more. Copy with stitching torn, $37.50. For 1839: Nashville, 1839, $32.50. [For other Crockett almanacs, see *GIYA*, page 152.]

CROIX, Teodoro de. *Instrucción para Formar una Linea o Cordón de Quince Presidios sobre las Fronteras de las Provincias Internas de este Reino de Nueva-España, etc.* 80 pp., folio. Mexico, 1771. Full calf binding, $2,500.

CROSBY, Sylvester S. *The Early Coins of America.* 10 plates. Half morocco. Boston, 1878. Ex-library, rubbed, $35.

CULLEN, William. *Synopsis and Nosology.* Hartford, 1793. 1st ed. In English. $37.50.

CULMANN, Leonhart. *Sententiae Pueriles Anglo-Latinae . . . Sentences for Children, English and Latin.* Translated into English by Charles Hoole. Boston, 1723. 2d Am. ed. Scribbling on a few leaves, $97.50.

CUMINGS, Samuel. *The Western Navigator. Vol. 2.* (Text; Vol. 1 consisted of atlas alone.) Printed boards. Philadelphia, 1822, $75.

CUMINGS, Samuel. *The Western Pilot.* Printed boards. Cincinnati, 1825. Early issue with errata inside rear cover, errors in original state. Later cloth back, $60. [For later editions, see *GIYA*.]

CUMMINGS, E. E. *&.* (Yes, the symbol for "and" is the title of the book.) Boards. New York, 1925. 1st ed. One of 111 on Vidalon paper, signed. $25.

CUMMINGS, E. E. *50 Poems.* New York, no date [1940]. 1st ed. One of 150, signed. In slip case, $30.

CUMMINGS, E. E. *A Miscellany*. New York, 1958. 1st ed. One of 75, signed. $25.

CUMMINGS, E. E. *Tulips and Chimneys*. Boards. New York, 1923. 1st ed. In dust jacket, $25.

CUMMINS, Ella Sterling. *The Story of the Files*. Errata leaf. Boards. San Francisco, 1893. $25 and $40.

CUMMINS, Sarah J. *Autobiography and Reminiscences*. Paperbound. LaGrande, Ore., 1914. 1st ed. $32.50.

CUNNINGHAM, Eugene. *Triggernometry: A Gallery of Gunfighters*. New York, 1934. 1st ed., 1st issue. In dust jacket, $25.

CUNYNGHAME, H. H. *European Enamels*. 63 plates. New York and London, 1906. $29.50.

CURRIE, William. *An Historical Account of the Climates and Diseases of the United States of America*. Philadelphia, 1792. 1st ed. Ex-library copy, dampstained, $75.

CURTIS, Edward S. *The Apsaroke*. Edited by Frederick W. Hodge. (Vol. 4 of *The North American Indian*.) Text volume, morocco-bound, plus portfolio of 36 plates. New York, 1909. $60. [For the 40-vol. set, see *GIYA*.]

CURTISS, Daniel S. *Western Portraiture, and Emigrants' Guide*. New York, 1852. 1st ed. $25.

CUSHMAN, H. B. *A History of the Choctaw, Chickasaw and Natchez Indians*. Greenville, Tex., 1899. 1st ed. $50. Another, leaves browned, $25. Another, with marginal notes and underlining, $27.50.

CUTBUSH, James. *The American Artist's Manual*. 39 plates. 2 vols. Philadelphia, 1814. $175.

CUTTS, James M. *The Conquest of California and New Mexico*. Map, 3 plans. Philadelphia, 1847. 1st ed. $75. [Supersedes listing in *GIYA*.]

CYCLOPEDIA of Michigan: Historical and Biographical.
New York, no date [1900]. $25.

D

D., H. (Hilda Doolittle). *The Tribute and Circe.* Boards.
Cleveland, 1917. 1st ed. One of 50. Soiled, $25.

DAGGETT, David. *An Oration, Pronounced in . . . the City
of New Haven, on the 4th of July, A.D. 1787.* Paperbound.
New Haven, no date [1787]. 1st ed. Uncut, signed by author,
$27.50.

DAMON, Samuel C. *A Journey to Lower Oregon and Upper
California, 1848-49.* San Francisco, 1927. One of 250. $35.

DANA, Charles A. *The United States Illustrated.* Paperbound.
[Prospectus.] New York, no date [1853]. Uncut, $30.

DANA, James. *The African Slave Trade.* Paperbound. New
Haven, 1791. 1st ed. $27.50.

DANIELS, L. E. (ed.). *Personnel of the Texas State Government.* San Antonio, 1892. Rebound, $25.

DANIELS, L. E. (ed.). *Types of Successful Men in Texas.*
Austin, 1890. Rebound, $25.

DARBY, William. *The Emigrant's Guide to the Western and
Southwestern States and Territories.* Folding map. New
York, 1818. $32.50.

DARBY, William. *A Tour from the City of New-York, to
Detroit, in the Michigan Territory.* 3 folding maps. Boards.
New York, 1819. In slip case, $50.

DARNELL, Elias. *A Journal Containing an Accurate and
Interesting Account of the Hardships, Sufferings, Battles,
Defeat, and Captivity of Those Heroic Kentucky Volunteers
and Regulars Commanded by Gen. Winchester.* 36 pp.,
boards. Philadelphia, 1854. Rebacked, $37.50.

DAVIDSON, Alexander and Bernard Stuve. *A Complete History of Illinois from 1673 to 1873.* Springfield, 1874. Rebound, $35.

DAVIS, Duke. *Flashlights from Mountain and Plain.* Bound Brook, N. J., 1911. 1st ed. $30.

DAVIS, Ellis A. *Commercial Encyclopedia of the Pacific Southwest.* Oakland, 1915. Front hinge torn, $40.

DAVIS, H. S. *Reminiscences of Gen. William Larimer.* Lancaster, Pa., 1918. $125.

DAVIS, Paris M. *An Authentic History of the Late War Between the United States and Great Britain.* Ithaca, 1829. $35.

DAVIS, Rebecca Harding. *Kent Hampden.* New York, 1892. 1st ed. $25.

DAVIS, Richard Harding. *Dr. Jameson's Raiders vs. the Johannesburg Reformers.* Paperbound. New York, 1897. 1st ed. $35.

DAVIS, William Heath. *Seventy-five Years in California.* San Francisco, 1929. 2d ed., limited. $40. [For 1st ed., 1889, see *GIYA*.]

DAVIS, William J. (ed.). *The Partisan Rangers of the Confederate States Army.* Louisville, 1904. (By Adam R. Johnson.) Covers spotted, $32.50. Another, rebound, $40.

DAVIS, William W. H. *El Gringo; or New Mexico and Her People.* New York, 1857. 1st ed. $30.

DAVIS, William W. H. *The Spanish Conquest of New Mexico: 1527-1703.* Folding map, plate. Doylestown, 1869. Presentation copy, autographed, $75. Another, unsigned, $50. Another, slightly worn, front blank leaf missing, $50. Another, map in photostat, $32.50.

DAWSON, S. J. *Report on the Exploration of the Country Between Lake Superior and the Red River Settlement and the Assiniboine and Saskatchewan.* 3 maps. 45 pp. Toronto, 1859. $40.

DAWSON, William L. and John Bolles. *The Birds of Washington.* 2 vols. Seattle, 1909. 1st ed. One of 200, signed. $50 to $100.

DAY, S. *Report of the Committee on Internal Improvements, on the Use of the Camels on the Plains, May 30, 1855.* 11 pp. No place [Sacramento], 1855. In pamphlet binder, $42.50.

DEADWOOD Gulch Hydraulic Mining Co. of Deadwood Gulch, Lawrence County, Black Hills, of the Territory of Dakota. Folding map. 12 pp., paperbound. [Prospectus.] Deadwood, 1883. $150.

DEAN, James. *An Alphabetical Atlas, or, Gazetteer of Vermont.* Montpelier, 1808. 1st ed. Unbound, $27.50.

DEARBORN, Henry. *Revolutionary War Journals of . . . 1775-1783.* 6 plates. Chicago, 1939. One of 350 for the Caxton Club. In slip case, $25.

DEBATES and Proceedings (The), of the Convention of the State of New York, Assembled at Poughkeepsie, on the 17th June, 1788. Marbled boards. New York, 1788. Rebacked, foxed, name on title page and flyleaf, $87.50.

DEBOUCHEL, Victor. *Histoire de la Louisiane.* Boards. Nouvelle-Orleans, 1841. $75.

DECALVES, Don Alonso. *New Travels to the Westward.* 48 pp., sewed. Greenwich, Mass., 1805. $75. [For 1795 ed., see *GIYA.*]

DECLARATION of the Immediate Cause Which Induce and Justify the Secession of South Carolina from the Federal Union, and the Ordinance of Secession. Paperbound. Charleston, 1860. 1st ed., 1st issue, with misprinted "Cause" for "Causes." $125.

DE CORDOVA, J. *The Texas Immigrant and Traveller's Guide Book.* Austin, 1856. 1st ed. $125.

DEFOE, Daniel. *The Life and Surprising Adventures of Robinson Crusoe.* 54 pp., paperbound. New York, no date [1864]. 1st Beadle Dime Classic ed., 1st issue, with publisher's address 118 William Street. $35.

DE FOREST, John W. *The Wetherel Affair.* New York, 1873. 1st ed. $25.

DE GRESS, J. O. *Regulations to be Observed Under an Act to Establish and Maintain a System of Public Free Schools in Texas.* 7 pp., paperbound. Galveston, 1873. $25.

DE GRIJALVA, Juan. *The Discovery of New Spain in 1815.* Translated by Henry R. Wagner. No place, 1942. One of 200. $50.

DE GUERIN, Maurice. *The Centaur.* Translated by George B. Ives. Designed by Bruce Rogers. Boards. No place [Montague, Mass.], MDCCCCXV (1915). 1st ed. In dust jacket, $55 to $130.

DELANO, Alonzo. *Life on the Plains and Among the Diggings.* Auburn and Buffalo, 1854. 1st ed., 1st issue, with page 219 misnumbered 119. In cloth folding case, slight foxing, $135. Another, $75. [Supersedes entry in *GIYA*.]

DELANO, Alonzo. *Pen-Knife Sketches, or Chips of the Old Block.* Colored illustrations. San Francisco, 1934. One of 550. $27.50 and $25.

DEMOCRATIC Book, 1936 (The). Leather, paper covers bound in. No place, 1936. Limited ed., signed by F. D. R. $40.

DENTON, Sherman F. *Moths and Butterflies of the United States East of the Rocky Mountains.* 2 vols. Boston, 1900. One of 500. Rubbed, $60.

DEPREDATIONS and Massacre by the Snake River Indians.

16 pp., sewed. No place [Washington], 1861. Uncut and unopened, $25.

DER Hundert und neunzhnte Psalm. Ein Examengeschent an die Neunortischen Lutherischen Schulkinder. 8 pp., unbound. Philadelphia, 1791. (By Johann Christoph Kunze.) 1st ed. $75.

DESCRIPTION of the Largest Ship in the World, the New Clipper Great Republic. Boston, 1853. $75.

DESCRIPTION of Tremont House (A), with Architectural Illustrations. Boards. Boston, 1830. (By William G. Eliot.) 1st ed. $30. Signed, $35.

DESCRIPTIVE Catalogue of the Marine Collection to be Found at India House (A). 35 plates, 11 hand-colored. New York, 1935. (By Carl C. Cutler.) One of 1,000. $100.

DESCRIPTIVE and Priced Catalogue of Books (A), etc. (Thomas Wayne Norris catalogue. Grabhorn Press.) Boards. Oakland, 1948. One of 500. $30.

DE SMET, Pierre-Jean. *Letters and Sketches.* 13 plates, 11 views, folding leaf, "The Catholic Ladder." Philadelphia, 1843. 1st ed. $125. [Supersedes listing in *GIYA*.]

DES MOINES Navigation and Railroad Co. (The), Defendants in Error; Adam Calvin Burr, Plaintiff in Error. 30 pp., sewed. No place, no date [about 186-?]. Unopened, $25.

DE VINNE, Theodore L. *Aldus Pius Manutius.* With original leaf from *Hypnerotomachia Poliphili,* printed by Aldus in 1499. San Francisco, 1924. One of 250. $30.

DE VINNE, Theodore L. *Title-pages as Seen by a Printer.* New York, 1901. One of 340. $25.

DE WITT, David Miller. *The Judicial Murder of Mary E. Surratt.* Baltimore, 1895. Rebound, signed, $25.

DE WOLFF, J. H. *Pawnee Bill.* No place, 1902. $25.

DEXTER, A. Hersey. *Early Days in California.* No place [Denver], 1886. $75.

DEXTER, F. Theodore. *Forty-Two Years' Scrapbook of Rare Ancient Firearms.* Los Angeles, 1954. $35.

"DICKENS, Charles." *The Mystery of Edwin Drood.* Brattleboro, Vt., 1873. (By Thomas P. James.) 1st ed. $27.50.

DICKINSON, Emily. *Letters of.* Edited by Mabel Loomis Todd. 2 vols. Boston, 1894. 1st ed., with the reading on p. v: "and committed their preparation to me." In dust jackets, $125.

DICKINSON, Capt. Henry C. *Diary of, etc.* Denver, no date. One of 225. $35.

DICKINSON, John. *Reply to a Piece Called the Speech of Joseph Galloway, Esquire.* Philadelphia, 1764. Half morocco, $40.

DICKINSON, John. *A Speech Delivered in the House of Assembly of the Province of Pennsylvania, May 24, 1764.* Philadelphia, 1764. Half morocco, $40.

DIDIMUS, H. *New Orleans As I Found It.* Double columns, 125 pp., paperbound. New York, 1845. (By Edward Henry Durrell.) $100.

DIENST, Dr. Alex. *The Navy of the Republic of Texas, 1835-1845.* Blue leather. Temple, Tex., no date [1909]. $75. Others, $55 and $35. [Supersedes entry in *GIYA*.]

DINKINS, Capt. James. *1861 to 1865, by an Old Johnnie.* Cincinnati, 1897. Worn, spotted, $50.

DIRECTORY of Newark for 1835-6. Newark, 1835. 1st ed. $50 to $60.

DISCOURSE on the Genuineness and Authenticity of the New-Testament (A). Stitched, uncut. New York, 1794. (By Timothy Dwight.) $37.50.

DISTURNELL, John. *Disturnell's Guide Through the Middle, Northern, and Eastern States.* Map of New York City, folding map. New York, 1847. $30.

DISTURNELL, John. *The Emigrant's Guide to New Mexico, California, and Oregon.* Large folding map. New York, 1849. 1st ed., 1st issue, with map by Colton. $600.

DISTURNELL, John. *Mapa de los Estados Unidos de Mejico, California, etc.* Colored map, folded. New York, 1849. In cloth case, $67.50.

DIX Ans sur la Côte du Pacifique par un Missionaire Canadien. 100 pp., paperbound. Quebec, 1873. (By F. X. Blanchet.) $37.50.

DIXON, Sam H. *The Poets and Poetry of Texas.* Austin, 1885. $25.

DOBIE, J. Frank. *John C. Duval, First Texas Man of Letters.* Dallas, 1939. One of 950. $35.

DOBIE, J. Frank. *The Mustangs.* Horsehide. Boston, 1952. 1st ed. One of 100, boxed. $200.

DOBIE, J. Frank and others (eds.). *Mustangs and Cow Horses.* Austin, 1940. 1st ed. $37.50 and $50.

DOCUMENTOS Relativos al Piadoso Fondo de Misiones para Conversion y Civilizacion de las Numerosas Tribus Barbaras de la Antiua y Nueva California. 60 pp., bound with 8 pp. *Esposicion a la Comision, etc.* Mexico, 1845. New paper covers, $250.

DODGE, William Sumner. *A Waif of the War; or, The History of the 75th Illinois Infantry.* Chicago, 1866. Worn, $30.

DODSON, W. D. (ed.). *Campaigns of Wheeler and His Cavalry.* Atlanta, 1899. Rebound in buckram, $27.50.

DOMESTIC Cookery: The Experienced American Housekeeper. Calfbound. New York, 1823. Worn at hinges, $25.

DONAN, P. *Gold Fields of Baker County, Eastern Oregon.* Folding map. 36 pp., paperbound. Portland, no date [1898]. $32.50.

DONNAVAN, Corydon. *Abenteuer in Mexico.* 144 pp., paperbound. Kutztaun, Pa., 1848. $27.50.

DONOHO, M. H. *Circle-dot, a True Story of Cowboy Life 40 Years Ago.* Topeka, 1907. $25.

DOOMED City (The). . . . *Prepared and Written by a Journalist.* Folding map. 54 pp., paperbound. Detroit, 1871. (By Charles H. Mackintosh.) $25.

DOUGLAS, The Rev. James. *The Gold Fields of Canada.* 18 pp., paperbound. Quebec, 1863. Small part of back cover missing, $50.

DOUGLASS, William. *A Summary, Historical, and Political of the First Planting, Progressive Improvements, and Present State of the British Settlements in North America.* 2 vols. Boston, 1749-51. 1st ed. Bookplates, names on end papers, $165.

DOW, G. F. *Whale Ships and Whaling.* Salem, 1925. $25.

DOYLE, John T. *On Behalf of the Roman Catholic Church of Upper California. Points in Reply Submitted by Messrs. Doyle and Doyle of Counsel for the Prelates.* 8 pp., paperbound (self wrappers). No place, no date [1902]. $25. Another edition, 11 pp., paperbound, no place, no date [Menlo Park, Calif., 1902], $35.

DOYLE, John T. *In the International Arbitral Court of the Hague: The Case of the Pious Fund of California.* 106 pp., unbound. San Francisco, 1906. Original signatures, unbound, unopened, $75.

DOYLE, John T. *The Pious Fund Case.* 67 pp., unbound. San Francisco, 1904 (?). Original signatures unbound, unopened, $40.

DRAGOON Campaigns to the Rocky Mountains, etc. By a Dragoon. New York, 1836. (By James Hildreth.) 1st ed. Lightly foxed, $57.50. [Supersedes listing in *GIYA*.]

DRAKE, Benjamin. *Tales and Sketches of the Queen City.* Cincinnati, 1838. 1st ed. $25 and $30.

DRAKE, Daniel and Guy W. Wright (eds.). *The Western Medical and Physical Journal, Original and Eclectic. Vol. 1.* Cincinnati, 1827-8. Leatherbound, $65.

DRAKE, Joseph Rodman. *The Culprit Fay and Other Poems.* New York, 1835. 1st ed. $50.

DRANNAN, Capt. William F. *Thirty-one Years on the Plains and in the Mountains.* Chicago, 1899. $25. Chicago, 1900. $10. Chicago, 1904. $6.

DRAPER, John William. *A Treatise on the Forces Which Produce the Organization of Plants.* 4 plates. New York, 1844. $60.

DRAYTON, John. *Letters Written During a Tour Through the Northern and Eastern States.* 3 plates. Boards. Charleston, 1794. Uncut, in slip case, $250.

DREISER, Theodore. *The Carnegie Works at Pittsburgh.* Chelsea, N.Y., no date [1927]. One of 27 on antique paper. In dust jacket, uncut and unopened, $25.

DREISER, Theodore. *The "Genius."* New York, 1915. 1st ed., 1st issue, with page 497 numbered. $25. Later issue, not numbered, $5.

DREW, C. S. *Communication from C. S. Drew, Late Adjutant of the 2d Regiment of Oregon Mounted Volunteers.* 48 pp., paperbound. Washington, 1860. 1st ed. $35.

DRIPS, Sgt. J. H. *Three Years Among the Indians in Dakota.* 139 pp., paperbound. Kimball, S.D., 1894. 1st ed. In morocco case, $300. Another, rebound in fabrikoid, original covers bound in, $150.

DRUMHELLER, "Uncle Dan." *"Uncle Dan" Drumheller Tells Thrills of Western Trails in 1854.* Spokane, 1925. $25.

DUFLOT de Mofras, Eugene. *Travels on the Pacific Coast.* Translated by Marguerite E. Wilbur. 2 folding maps, 8 plates. 2 vols. Santa Ana, 1937. $60 and $65.

DUKE, Basil W. *History of Morgan's Cavalry.* Cincinnati, 1867. 1st ed. $35. Another copy, stained, rebound in buckram, $25.

DUNBAR, Paul Laurence. *Majors and Minors.* Green cloth. No place, no date [Toledo, 1895]. 1st ed. $30.

DUNCAN, Andrew. *The Edinburgh New Dispensatory.* 6 plates. Worcester, 1805. $25.

DUNCAN, L. Wallace. *History of Montgomery County, Kansas.* Iola, 1903. Rebound, $30.

DUNDASS, Samuel. *Journal of Samuel Rutherford Dundass.* 60 pp. Steubenville, Ohio, 1857. Rebound, $550 (auction price).

DUNLAP, William and Francis L. Clarke. *The Life of the Most Noble Arthur, Marquis and Earl of Wellington.* Frontispiece and map. Boards. New York, 1814. 1st ed. Rebacked, uncut, $30.

DUNTON, John. *Letters from New-England.* Boston, 1867. One of 150. Half morocco, $25.

Du PONT, Rear Adm. Samuel F. *Official Dispatches and Letters, 1846-48; 1861-63.* Wilmington, 1883. $125.

DUSTIN, Fred. *The Custer Tragedy.* Folding map in pocket. Ann Arbor, 1939. 1st ed. One of 200. $125.

DWIGGINS, W. A. *Towards a Reform of the Paper Currency.* Boards. New York, 1932. One of 452, signed. $25.

DWIGHT, Timothy. *A Discourse on Some Events of the Last Century.* New Haven, 1801. Unbound, $32.50.

DWIGHT, Timothy. *Greenfield Hill: A Poem in Seven Parts.* New York, 1794. Worn, $32.50.

DWIGHT, Timothy. *The Nature and Danger of Infidel Philosophy.* New Haven, 1798. Unbound, $25.

DWIGHT, Timothy. *The Psalms of David, Imitated in the Language of the New Testament.* Hartford, 1801. 1st ed. $37.50.

DWIGHT, Timothy. *A Valedictory Address to the Young Gentlemen, Who Commenced Bachelors of Arts, at Yale-College, July 25th, 1776.* New Haven, no date [1776]. Unbound, $55.

DYER, Frederick H. *A Compendium of the War of the Rebellion.* Des Moines, 1908. 1st ed. Ex-library, rebound in cloth, $60.

DYKES, W. R. *The Genus Iris.* Color plates. Cambridge, 1913. $75.

E

EARLY, Gen. Jubal A. *Autobiographical Sketch and Narrative of the War Between the States.* Philadelphia, 1912. Spine worn, $40.

EARLY, Lieut. Gen. Jubal A. *A Memoir of the Last Year of the War for Independence in the Confederate States of America.* Paperbound. Lynchburg, 1867. Rebound in buckram, $35.

ECHO (The). Marbled boards, roan back and corners. No place, no date [New York, 1807]. 1st ed. Slightly rubbed, $27.50.

ECHO from the Temple of Wisdom, etc. . . . . In a Series of Letters, By Socrates, etc. Philadelphia, 1779. Uncut, half morocco, $35.

ECKENRODE, H. J. and Bryan Conrad. *James Longstreet, Lee's War Horse*. Chapel Hill, 1936. $25.

EDMONSTON, Catherine Devereux. *The Journal of . . . 1860-1866*. Edited by Margaret Mackay Jones. No place [Mebane, N.C.?], no date. $25.

EDWARD, David B. *The History of Texas; or The Emigrant's, Farmer's and Politician's Guide*. Folding map. Cincinnati, 1836. 1st ed. $125. Others: $77.50, $30. [Supersedes entry in *GIYA*.]

EDWARD Lear on My Shelves. No place, 1833. One of 155. $27.50.

EDWARDS, Billy. *Gladiators of the Prize Ring*. Chicago, 1895. $30.

EDWARDS Chicago Directory (The). 40 pp., boards. Chicago, 1871. Fire ed. $27.50.

EDWARDS, E. I. *The Valley Whose Name is Death*. Map. Pasadena, 1940. 1st ed. $25.

EDWARDS, Frank S. *A Campaign in New Mexico with Col. Doniphan*. Map. 184 pp., plus 24 pp. ads. Clothbound and paperbound (latter with cover dated 1848). Philadelphia, 1847. 1st ed. Clothbound, $75. Another, spine repaired, $75. Another, rebound in ¾ morocco, $75. Another, lacking map, $45.

EDWARDS, John N. *Noted Guerrillas, or The Warfare of the Border*. St. Louis, 1877. $65. Another, foxed, $25. Another, rebound in buckram, original cloth mounted on front cover, $55. [Supersedes entry in *GIYA*.]

EDWARDS, John N. *Shelby and His Men*. Cincinnati, 1867. Rebound, $25.

EDWARDS, John N. *Shelby's Expedition to Mexico*. Kansas City, 1872. 1st ed. $75. Another, worn, inner hinge cracking, $50.

EDWARDS, Jonathan. *Some Thoughts Concerning the Present Revival of Religion in New-England.* Lexington, 1803. Foxed, $26.50.

EDWARDS, Jonathan. *A Treatise Concerning Religious Affections.* Boston, 1746. 1st ed. $25.

EDWARDS, Philip Leget. *The Diary of . . . The Great Cattle Drive from California to Oregon in 1837.* Boards. San Francisco, 1932. One of 500. $35 and $25.

EDWARDS, Samuel E. *The Ohio Hunter.* Battle Creek, 1893. $25.

1862 Trip to the West (An). Map. No place, no date [Pawtucket, 1926]. (By Lyman Bullock Goff.) $67.50 and $90.

ELIOT, John (trans.). *Mamusse Wunneetupanatamwe Up-Biblum God.* (Holy Bible in Natick, American Indian, translation.) Cambridge, 1663. $20,160 (auction price, 1958). [Supersedes entry in *GIYA*.]

ELIOT, T. S. *Poems.* Boards, uncut. New York, 1920. 1st Am. ed. In dust wrapper, $25.

ELLICOTT, Andrew. *The Journal of . . . During 1796-1800.* 14 folding maps and plans. 299 and 155 pages. Philadelphia, 1814. 2d ed. Rebound in modern blue half morocco, $57.50. [For 1st ed., 1803, see *GIYA*.]

ELLIOT, D. G. *The Birds of North America.* Hand-colored plates. 2 vols. $400.

ELLIOTT, The Rev. Charles. *Indian Missionary Reminiscences.* Boards. New York, 1835. 1st ed. Back repaired with tape, $25.

ELLIOTT, David Stewart. *Last Raid of the Daltons.* 71 pp., paperbound. Coffeyville, Kan., 1892. 1st ed. $100. Coffeyville, 1892, 60 pp., 2d ed., generally less valuable, $25 to $50.

ELLIOTT, W. W. *History of Arizona Territory.* Map. San Francisco, 1884. $275.

ELLIS, W. T. *Memories of My 72 Years in the Romantic County of Yuba, California.* Eugene, Ore., 1939. In dust jacket, $26.50. Another, $25.

ELLIS, William. *The American Mission in the Sandwich Islands.* Boards. Honolulu, 1866. $40.

ELLSWORTH, Henry W. *Valley of the Upper Wabash, Indiana.* Folding map, 3 folding lithographs. New York, 1838. $35.

ELLSWORTH, Lincoln. *The Last Wild Buffalo Hunt.* New York, 1916. 1st ed. $30.

ELMER, Jonathan. *An Eulogium on the Character of Gen. George Washington.* 25 pp. Trenton, 1800. Half morocco, $200.

ELTON, R. H. *Jackson Almanac, 1836.* 36 pp., paperbound. No place, no date [New York, 1835]. $25.

EMILY Parker, or Impulse, Not Principle. Boards. Boston, 1827. (By Lydia Maria Francis Child.) 1st ed. $150.

EMMONS, Samuel Franklin. *Atlas to Accompany a Monograph on the Geology and Mining Industry of Leadville, Colorado.* Large atlas, paper covers, unbound, 35 single and double leaves, charts, etc., some in color. Washington, 1883. $32.50.

EMORY, W. H. *Notes of a Military Reconnaissance.* House version. 64 plates, 2 small folding maps, 3 plans, large folding map in separate pocket. Washington, 1848. 1st ed. $50. Senate version: Washington, 1848. 1st ed., 1st issue, 40 plates, 3 plans, folding map in pocket, Emory named as "Lieut. Col." $250. 2d issue, Emory designated as "Brevet Major." $25. [Supersedes entry in *GIYA*.]

ENGELHARDT, Zephyrin. *The Franciscans in Arizona.* Map, plates. 236 pp., paperbound. Harbor Springs, Mich., 1899. $45. Another, uncut, unopened, $27.50.

ENGELHARDT, Zephyrin. *The Franciscans in California.* Harbor Springs, Mich., 1897. $25.

ENQUIRY Into the Constitutional Authority of the Supreme Federal Court (An), Over the Several States, in Their Political Capacity. By a Citizen of South-Carolina. 49 pp., pamphlet. Charleston, 1792. (By Timothy Ford.) Signature on title page, $27.50.

EPITOME of Electricity and Galvanism (An). Boards. Philadelphia, 1809. (By Jacob Green and E. Hazard.) 1st ed. $75.

EPPES, Susan Bradford. *Through Some Eventful Years.* Macon, Ga., 1926. Spine worn, $30.

ESCALANTE, P. Thomas de. *Sermón Funebre que Predico el P. Thomás de Escalante de la Compañia de Jesus de Mexico Professo de Quatro Votos de Ella.* 118 pp., paperbound. Mexico, 1694. In morocco case, $900.

ESCANDON, Manuel and Jose Rascon. *Observaciónes que los Actuales Terceros Possedores de los Bienes que Pertenecieron al Fondo Piadoso de Californias, etc.* 12 pp., paperbound. Mexico, 1845. $75.

ESPEJO, Antonio de. *New Mexico. Otherwise the Voiage of Anthony Espeio, Who in the Yeare 1583, With His Company, Discovered a Lande of 15 Provinces, etc.* Boards. No place, no date [Lancaster, 1928]. 1st ed. One of 200. $35 and $45.

ESPINOSA, Isidro Felix de. *Crónica Apostólica, y Seráphica de Todos los Colegios de Propaganda Fide de esta Nueva-España.* 24 pp., vellum. Mexico, 1746. $250.

ESPINOSA, Isidro Felix de. *El Peregrino Septentrional Atlante: Delineado en la Vida Fr. Antonio Margil.* Plate of Father Margil preaching to the Indians. Vellum. Mexico, 1737. 1st ed. $300 and $350. [Supersedes title entry in *GIYA.*]

ESPINOSA, Isidro Felix de. *Nuevas Empressas del Peregrino Americano Septentrional Atlante, Descubiertas, etc.* Vellum, with rawhide ties. Mexico, 1747. $400.

ESSAY on Marriage (An); or, The Lawfulness of Divorce, in Certain Cases, Considered. Stitched, uncut. Philadelphia, 1788. $27.50.

ESSAY on the Merchandize of Slaves and Souls of Men (An). *By a Gentleman.* Boston, 1731. (By Paul Dudley.) 1st ed. $45.

ESSAY Towards Propagating the Gospel (An), Among the Neighboring Indians, etc. 18 pp., unbound. New London, 1756. $75.

ESTAVA, José Maria. *La Campaña de la Mision.* Boards. Xalapa-Enriquez, Mexico, 1894. $50.

ETHELL, Henry C. *The Rise and Progress of Civilization in the Hairy Nation and the History of Davis County.* Bloomfield, Iowa, 1883. $50.

ETHNOLOGIC Dictionary of the Navajo Language (An). By the Franciscan Fathers. Japan vellum. 536 pp., paperbound. St. Michaels, Ariz., 1910. One of 200. $100.

EUROPEAN Traveller in America (The). Marbled boards. Hartford, 1795. (By Thomas Brockway.) 1st ed. $125.

EVANS, Elwood. *Washington Territory, etc.* 51 pp. Olympia, 1877. $60.

EVANS, John. *A Narrative of the Proceedings of the Religious Society of the People Called Quakers, in Philadelphia, Against John Evans.* Paperbound (cloth spine). Philadelphia, 1811. 1st ed. $35.

EVANS, Lewis. *Geographical, Historical, Philosophical and Mechanical Essays.* Philadelphia, 1755. 1st ed. Unbound, few leaves waterstained, lacking map, $45.

EVANS, Oliver. *The Young Mill-Wright and Miller's Guide.* 25 plates. Philadelphia, 1795. Name on title page, $50.

EVANS, Capt. S. B. (comp.). *History of Wapello County, Iowa.* Chicago, 1901. Front hinge broken, $32.50.

EVENTFUL Lives of Helen and Charlotte Lenoxa (The), the Twin Sisters of Philadelphia. Paperbound. Memphis, Richmond, Baltimore and Philadelphia, 1853. 1st ed., 1st issue, with date 1852 on cover. Edges worn, $85.

EVERETT, Horace. *Regulating the Indian Department.* Folding map. 133 pp., sewed. No place, no date [Washington, 1934]. $27.50.

EVERLASTING Gospel (The). Germantown, 1753. $27.50.

EVERTS and Kirk. *The Official State Atlas of Nebraska.* Plates, 207 colored maps. Philadelphia, 1885. Worn, $75.

EVIDENCE Concerning Projected Railways Across the Sierra Nevada Mountains, etc. Carson City, 1865. $325.

EWELL, Thomas T. *A History of Hood County, Texas.* Grandbury, Tex., 1895. 1st ed. $60.

EXAMINATION of the Late Rev. President Edwards's "Enquiry on Freedom of Will" (An). Boston, 1770. (By James Dana.) Unbound, $25.

EXAMINATION of the President's Reply to the New Haven Remonstrance (An). Paperbound. New York, 1801. (By William Coleman.) 1st ed. $32.50.

EXPOSICIÓN del Ministro de Hacienda. (Cover title.) 11 pp., paperbound. Mexico, 1836. $57.50.

EXTRACTS from the Autobiography of Calvin Coolidge. Miniature book. Blue calf. Kingsport, Tenn., 1930. $25.

EXTRACTS from the Votes and Proceedings of the American Continental Congress, Held at Philadelphia on the 5th of September, 1774. Boston, 1774. In ¾ morocco, uncut, $37.50.

EYRE, John. *The Christian Spectator.* (Bound with his *The European Stranger in America.*) 84 and 24 pp., original cloth. Albany, 1838. $75.

EZRA Pound: His Metric and Poetry. Boards. New York, 1917. (By T. S. Eliot.) 1st ed. $35.

F

FAIRFIELD, Asa M. *Pioneer History of Lassen County, California.* Map. San Francisco, 1916. $25.

FAITH Gartney's Girlhood. Boston, 1863. (By Mrs. A. D. T. Whitney.) 1st ed. Worn, shaken, flyleaf missing at rear, $25.

FALCONER, Thomas. *Letters and Notes on the Texan Santa Fe Expedition, 1841-42.* New York, 1930, $25.

FARIA, Francisco Xavier de. *Vida. Y Heroycas Virtudes del Vble. Padre Pedro de Velasco.* Boards. Mexico, 1753. $450.

FARNHAM, S. B. *The New York and Idaho Gold Mining Co.* Folding map. 23 pp., paperbound. New York, 1864. $100.

FARNHAM, Thomas J. *Travels in the Californias, and Scenes in the Pacific Ocean.* 96 pp., paperbound (actually Part 1, though not so designated: There were 4 orig. paperbound parts, 2, 3, and 4 being paged continuously). New York, 1844. 1st ed. $72.50. Hardbound: New York, 1844, 416 pp., half roan and boards. 1st ed., 2d issue. $150 (auction price, 1959, for lightly foxed copy). Another copy, rebound in morocco, front cover loose, library stamp on title page, $112.50. [Supersedes entry in *GIYA.*]

FARNHAM, Thomas J. *Travels in the Great Western Prairies.* Boards. Poughkeepsie, 1843. With imprint spelled "Ploughkeepsie." $85. [For paperbound copy, same date, see *GIYA.*]

FARQUHAR, Francis P. (ed.). *Joaquin Murieta, the Brigand Chief of California.* San Francisco, 1932. In glassine wrapper, $50.

FAST, Edward G. *Catalogue of Antiquities and Curiosities Collected in the Territory of Alaska.* 32 pp., paperbound. No place [New York], 1869. $45.

FATHER'S Advice to His Child (A), or the Maiden's Best Adorning. 8 pp., sewed. Exeter, N.H., 1792. 1st Am. ed. $25.

FAULKNER, J. P. *Eighteen Months on a Greenland Whaler.* New York, 1878. $25.

FAULKNER, William. *A Green Bough.* New York, 1933. 1st ed. One of 360, signed. Uncut, $35 and $37.50.

FAULKNER, William. *Idyll in the Desert.* New York, 1931. 1st ed. Limited. $60.

FAULKNER, William. *Sanctuary.* New York, no date [1931]. 1st ed., 1st binding, gray end papers and magenta over-all design. In dust jacket, $35.

FAULKNER, William. *Sartoris.* New York, no date [1929]. 1st ed. In dust jacket, $30.

FAULKNER, William. *The Sound and the Fury.* New York, no date [1929]. 1st ed. In dust jacket, $25.

FEATURES of Mr. Jay's Treaty. Paperbound. Philadelphia, 1795. (By Alexander Dallas.) $55.

FEDERALISM Triumphant in the Steady Habits of Connecticut Alone, etc. No place [New Haven?], 1802. 1st ed. Unbound, $75.

FEDERALIST (The). 2 vols., boards or calf, 227 and 284 pp. New York, MDCCLXXXVIII (1788). (By Alexander Hamilton and others.) Thick-paper copies, uncut, up to $1,200 (auction price) and possibly more. Regular paper copies, up to $600 and more. [Supersedes entry in *GIYA*.]

FEMALE Review (The): or, Memoirs of an American Young Lady . . . By a Citizen of Massachusetts. Dedham, Mass., 1797. (By Herman Mann.) 1st ed., with 6 pages of subscribers' names at end. Hinges weak, foxing, $65.

FENLEY, Florence. *Oldtimers. Their Own Stories.* Uvalde, Tex., 1939. Signed, $32.50. Another copy, not signed, $30.

FERNANDEZ DE SAN SALVADOR, Agustin. *Los Jesuitas Quitados y Restituidos al Mundo. Historia de la Antigua California.* Mexico, 1816. $75.

FEUCHTWANGER, Dr. Lewis. *A Treatise on Gems.* New York, 1838. $50.

FEWKES, Jesse Walter. *Hopi Katcinas.* 53 plates in color. Washington, 1902. $35. Washington, 1903, with 63 color plates, $25.

FIDFADDY, Frederick Augustus. *The Adventures of Uncle Sam in Search After His Lost Honor.* Middletown, 1816. In ¾ morocco, $30.

FIGUEROA, Jose. *The Manifesto, etc.* (Translated from the original as published in Monterey in 1835.) Paperbound. San Francisco, 1855. $500 (auction price, 1959). Another rebound in leather, $350.

FILISOLA, Gen. Vicente. *Representación dirigida al Supremo Gobierno por el General Vicente Filisola, en Defensa de Su Honor y Aclaración de Sus Operaciónes como General en Gefe del Ejército sobre Tejas.* 82 pp., paperbound. Mexico, 1836. $375. Another, bound in calf, $375.

FILSON, John. *The Discovery, Settlement, and Present State of Kentucky.* Folding map. New York, 1793. 2d ed. Rebound in morocco, $50. [For 1st ed., 1784, see *GIYA*.]

FINLEY, Ernest L. (ed.). *History of Sonoma County.* Santa Rosa, 1937. $25.

FINLEY, James B. *History of the Wyandott Mission at Upper Sandusky, Ohio.* Cincinnati, 1840. 1st ed. $40.

FINLAY, John. *Journal Kept by Hugh Finlay, Surveyor of Post Roads.* Brooklyn, 1867. One of 150. $40.

FIRST Annual Report of the Directors of the Central Mining Co., etc. 13 pp., paperbound. Detroit, 1855. $35.

FIRST Annual Review of Pierce County. (Wisconsin). 48 pp., paperbound. Prescott, 1855. $75.

FIRST Published Life of Abraham Lincoln (The). (Reprint of John Locke Scripps biography.) Half vellum. No place, no date [Detroit, 1900]. One of 245 by the Cranbrook Press. Uncut and unopened, $35 to $50.

FIRST Settlers of New England (The), or, Conquest of the Pequods, Narragansets and Pokanokets . . . By a Lady of Massachusetts. Boards. Boston, no date [1829]. (By Lydia Maria Child.) 1st ed., 1st issue. Front cover loose, uncut, $27.50.

FISH, H. C. *The Voice of Our Brother's Blood.* 16 pp., sewed. Newark, 1856. $75.

FISHER, George (ed.). *The American Instructor.* Calfbound. New York, 1760. 12th ed. Worn, $60.

FISHER, O. C. *It Occurred in Kimble.* Houston, 1937. 1st ed. One of 500. $27.50.

FISK, Capt. James L. *Expedition from Fort Abercrombie to Fort Benton.* (Caption title.) House Exec. Doc. No. 80. 36 pp., sewed. No place, no date [Washington, 1863]. 1st ed. $25. Another, ¾ morocco, $25.

FISKE, Nathan. *Remarkable Providences to Be Gratefully Recollected, etc.* Boston, 1776. Half morocco, $75. Another, $25. [See *GIYA*.]

FITE, Emerson D. and Archibald Freeman (eds.). *A Book of Old Maps Delineating American History.* 74 maps in facsimile. Cambridge, 1926. Binding rubbed, $37.50.

FITHIAN, Philip Vickers. *Journal and Letters, 1767-1774.* Princeton, 1900. 1st ed. $35.

FITZGERALD, F. Scott. *All the Sad Young Men.* New York, 1926. 1st ed. In dust jacket, $25.

FITZGERALD, F. Scott. *Tales of the Jazz Age.* New York, 1922. 1st ed. $25.

FITZGERALD, F. Scott. *Tender is the Night.* New York, 1934. 1st ed. In dust jacket, $35.

FIVE Years in a Lottery Office. Paperbound. Boston, 1841. (By John J. More.) 1st ed. Ex-library, spine chipped, $25.

FLEMING, C. B. *Early History of Hopkins County, Texas.* No place, 1902. Covers spotted, pages yellowed, $50.

FLEMING, Sanford. *Memorial of the People of Red River to the British and Canadian Governments.* 7 pp., printed front paper cover. Quebec, 1863. $200.

FLETCHER, Charles H. *Jefferson County, Iowa, Centennial History.* 35 pp., paperbound. Fairfield, 1876. $40.

FLETCHER, W. A. *Rebel Private, Front and Rear.* Beaumont, 1908. $75.

FLICKINGER, Robert E. *Pioneer History of Pocahontas County, Iowa.* Fonda, 1904. $32.50.

FLINT, Micah P. *The Hunter and Other Poems.* Boards. Boston, 1826. 1st ed. Worn, uncut, $50.

FLINT, Timothy. *Indian Wars of the West.* Cincinnati, 1833. $25.

FOGGY Night at Newport (A). 39 pp., paperbound. St. Louis, 1860. (By Henry C. Brokmyer.) 1st ed. $60.

FOOTE, Henry Stuart. *Texas and the Texans.* 2 vols. Philadelphia, 1841. $100.

FORBES, Edwin. *Life Studies of the Great Army.* 40 plates. Half morocco. No place [New York], 1876. $50.

FORD, James Everett. *A History of Grundy County, Missouri.* Trenton, 1908. $27.50.

FOREMAN, Grant. *Advancing the Frontier.* Norman, 1933. 1st ed. In dust jacket, $25.

FOREMAN, Grant. *Indian Removal.* Norman, 1932. 1st ed. In dust jacket, $45.

FORESTER, Frank. *The Warwick Woodlands.* New York, 1851. (By Henry William Herbert.) 2d ed. Binding worn. some pages stained, $25.

FORNEY, Col. John W. *What I Saw in Texas.* Map. 92 pp., paperbound. No place, no date [Philadelphia, 1872]. $75.

FORSYTH, James W. and F. D. Grant. *Report of an Expedition up the Yellowstone River, Made in 1875.* Folding map. 17 pp., paperbound. Washington, 1875. $25.

FOSTER, G. L. *The Past of Ypsilanti.* 48 pp., paperbound. Detroit, 1857. $30.

FOSTER, Isaac. *The Foster Family.* Santa Barbara, no date [1925]. $100.

FOSTER, James S. *Outlines of History of the Territory of Dakota and Emigrant's Guide to the Free Lands of the Northwest.* Folding map. 127 pp., paperbound. Yankton, 1870. $500.

FOUNTAIN, Albert J. *Bureau of Immigration of the Territory of New Mexico: Report of Dona Ana County.* 34 pp., errata, paperbound. Santa Fe, 1882. $40.

FOX, William F. *Regimental Losses in the American Civil War, 1861-1865.* Albany, 1889. Rebound, back pages stained, $25.

FOXCROFT, Thomas. *Observations Historical and Practical on the Rise and Primitive State of New-England.* Paperbound. Boston, 1730. 1st ed. Removed from binding, $45.

FRANCE, Its King, Court, and Government, By an American. New York, 1840. (By Gen. Lewis Cass.) 1st ed. $45.

FRANCHERE, Gabriel. *Relation d'un Voyage à la Côte du Nord-Ouest de l'Amérique Septentrionale, dans les Années 1810-1814.* Montreal, 1820. $325. [For 1st ed. in English, see *GIYA.*]

FRANKS, David. *The New-York Directory.* 82 pp. New York, MDCCLXXXVI (1786). $2,500 (auction price). New York, 1909. (Reprint.) About $15.

FREDERIC, Harold. *The Deserter and Other Stories.* Boston, no date [1898]. 1st ed. $27.50.

FREDERICK, J. V. *Ben Holladay, the Stagecoach King.* Folding map. Glendale, 1940. $25.

FREEMAN, G. D. *Midnight and Noonday.* Caldwell, 1892. 2d ed., with witness certificate on page 406. $40.

FREJES, Francisco. *Historia Breve de la Conquista de los Estados Independientes del Imperio Mejicano.* Mexico, 1839. Stained, $75.

FREMONT, Brevet Col. [J. C.] *Oregon and California. The Exploring Expedition to the Rocky Mountains, Oregon and California.* Buffalo, 1849. $75. [One of several reprints of Fremont's *Report of the Exploring Expedition,* 1845. See *GIYA.*]

FRENCH, Capt. W. J. *Wild Jim, the Texas Cowboy and Saddle King.* Portrait. 76 pp., paperbound. Antioch, Ill., 1890. 1st ed. Edges of last page worn, $150.

FRENCH, William. *Some Recollections of a Western Ranchman.* New York, no date [1928]. 1st Am. ed. In dust jacket, $50. Another copy, lacking jacket, $35.

FREYTAS, Father Nicholas de. *The Expedition of Don Diego Dionisio de Penalosa, from Santa Fe to the River Mischipi and Quivira in 1662.* Edited by John G. Shea. Boards. No place [New York], 1882. $35.

FRIENDLY *Address to All Reasonable Americans (A), on the Subject of our Political Confusions, etc.* New York, 1774. (By Thomas Bradbury Chandler). 1st ed. In ¾ morocco, $100.

FROST, Robert. *The Gold Hesperidee.* 8 pp., paperbound. No place, no date [Cortland, N.Y., 1935]. 1st ed., 1st issue. $30.

FRUGAL *Housewife (The).* Boston, 1837. Boards. (By Lydia Maria Child.) 1st ed. Text loose in binding, $50.

FRY, James B. *Army Sacrifices.* New York, 1879. $57.50.

FULLER, C. L. *Pocket Map and Descriptive Outline History of the Black Hills of Dakota and Wyoming.* Folding map. 56 pp., paperbound. Rapid City, 1887. $450.

FULLER, S. Margaret. *Woman in the 19th Century.* Paperbound. New York, 1845. 1st ed. $35.

G

GAG, Wanda. *Millions of Cats.* Boards. New York, 1928. 1st ed. One of 250. $30.

GALLATIN, Albert. *Considerations on the Currency and Banking System of the United States.* Paperbound. Philadelphia, 1831. 1st ed. $30.

GALLOWAY, Joseph. *The Speech of . . . In Answer to the Speech of John Dickinson.* 45 pp. Philadelphia, 1764. Half morocco, $35.

GANOE, W. A. *History of the United States Army.* New York, 1924. 1st ed. $25.

GARCIA, Father Bartholme. *Manual para Administrar los Santos Sacramentos . . . al los Indios, etc.* 88 pp., vellum, leather ties. Imprenta de los Herederos de Dona Maria de Rivera (Mexico), 1760. $750.

GARLAND, Hamlin. *A Member of the Third House.* Paperbound. Chicago, no date [1892]. 1st ed. $30.

GARLAND, Hamlin. *A Pioneer Mother.* Paperbound. Chicago, 1922. 1st ed. One of 500. $25.

GARLAND, James. *Letter of . . . to His Constituants.* 31 pp., sewed, uncut. No place, no date [Washington, 1840]. $25.

GARNEAU, Joseph. *Nebraska: Her Resources, Advantages and Development.* 24 pp., paperbound. Omaha, 1893. $35.

GARRARD, Lewis H. *Wah-To-Yah and the Taos Trail.* San Francisco, 1936. One of 550. $27.50 and $25. [For 1st ed., 1850, see *GIYA*.]

GARRETT, Pat F. *The Authentic Life of Billy, the Kid.* 137 pp., paperbound. Santa Fe, 1882. 1st ed. $100, possibly more.

GARVIE, James. *Abraham Lincoln toni kin, qa Aesop tawoyake kin. Life of Abraham Lincoln and Aesop's Fables.* 17 pp., paperbound. Santee Agency, Neb., 1893. $150.

GASS, Patrick. *A Journal of the Voyages and Travels of a Corps of Discovery, Under the Command of Capt. Lewis and Capt. Clarke, etc.* Philadelphia, 1810. 2d ed. Spine worn, hinges loose, $25. Philadelphia, 1812. 4th ed. Rebacked, $45. [For 1st ed., 1807, see *GIYA*.]

GAYERRE (Gayarre?), Charles. *A Sketch of Gen. Jackson: by Himself.* 21 pp., paperbound. New Orleans, 1857. $40.

GEM (A). *"The City of the Plains." Abilene. The Centre of the "Golden Belt."* 64 pp., paperbound. Burlington, Iowa, 1887. $45.

GENERAL *Instructions to Deputy Surveyors.* Folding diagram. 25 pp., sewed. Little Rock, 1837. $75.

GENERAL Laws and Memorials and Resolutions of the Territory of Dakota, Passed at the 1st Session of the Legislative Assembly. Yankton, 1862. $25.

GENERAL Orders Affecting the Volunteer Force. Adjutant General's Office. 1863. Washington, 1864. Foxed, $27.50.

GENERAL Orders Affecting the Volunteer Force. Adjutant General's Office. 1864. Washington, 1865. $27.50.

GENET, Edmond Charles. *Memorial on the Upward Forces of Fluids.* Plates. Tan boards. Albany, 1825. 1st ed. Minor foxing, all plates present, $275.

GEOLOGICAL Survey of Texas. 1st Annual Report. Austin, 1890. $35. Austin, 1891, 2d report, $30. Austin, 1892, 3d report, $25.

GESCHICHTE des Amerikanischen Krieges, von 1812, von Anfang bis zum Endichen Schluss vor New-Orleans. Reading, 1817. (By William McCarthy) $30.

GIDDINGS, Marsh. *First Annual Message to the Legislative Assembly of the Territory of New Mexico.* 54 pp., paperbound. Santa Fe, 1871. $45.

GIDE, Andre. *If It Die . . . An Autobiography.* Translated by Dorothy Bussy. Silk binding. New York, no date [1935]. 1st ed. One of 100. Uncut, in slip case, $25.

GILLELEN, F. M. L. *The Oil Regions of Pennsylvania.* Folding map, 16 charts. Paperbound. Pittsburgh, 1865. In ¾ morocco, original covers bound in, $75.

GIRARD, Just (Roy, Just J. E.?). *Adventures of a French Captain at Present a Planter in Texas.* New York, 1878. $40.

GIST, Christopher. *Journals.* Maps. Pittsburgh, 1893. One of 10 "large paper" copies. $47.50.

GLEANINGS of 50 Years: The Sisters of the Holy Names of Jesus and Mary in the Northwest, 1859-1909. No place, no date [Portland, 1909]. $25.

GLEANINGS from the Inside History of the Bonanzas. 40 pp., paperbound. No place, no date [San Francisco, 1878]. $125.

GLENN, Allen. *History of Cass County, Missouri.* Topeka, 1917. New spine, $30.

GOETHE, Johann Wolfgang von. *Faust.* Translated by A. Hayward. Lowell, 1840. 1st Am. ed. $45.

GOLD, Silver, Lead, and Copper Mines of Arizona. 40 pp., paperbound. No place, no date [Philadelphia, 1867]. In morocco case, $250.

GOLDSMITH, Oliver. *The Vicar of Wakefield.* Boards. Philadelphia, 1772. 1st Am. ed. Rubbed, writing on title page, $32.50.

GOOD, P. P. *A Materia Medica Botanica.* 48 colored plates. New York, 1845. $75.

GOODWIN, H. C. *Pioneer History.* 3 portraits. New York, 1859. $32.50.

GORDON, Donald (ed.). *M. L. Gordon's Experiences in the Civil War.* Boston, 1922. Inscribed "by the editor," $25.

GORDON, S. *Recollections of Old Milestown.* Miles City, 1918. $50.

GORRELL, J. R. *A Trip to Alaska.* 40 pp., paperbound. Newton, Iowa, 1905. $45.

GOSNELL, Harper Allen (ed.). *Before the Mast in the Clippers.* New York, 1937. 1st ed. One of 950. $55.

GOUGE, William M. *The Fiscal History of Texas.* Philadelphia, 1852. Spine worn, $25.

GOULD, A. C. *The Modern American Pistol and Revolver.* Boston, 1888. $25.

GOULD, E. W. *Fifty Years on the Mississippi.* St. Louis, 1889. 1st ed. $45 to $65. [Supersedes entry in *GIYA*.]

GRABHORN, Jane Bissell (ed.). *A California Gold Rush Miscellany*. Colored plates, folding map. No place [San Francisco], 1934. $32.50.

GRADUATION Lands: A Review of Sec. McClelland's Circular, by a Citizen of Central Michigan. 9 pp., half cloth. No place, no date [1856]. $25.

GRAHAM, Col. W. A. *The Official Record of a Court of Inquiry Convened . . . Upon the Request of Maj. Marcus A. Reno, etc.* 2 vols. Pacific Palisades, 1951. One of 125. $200.

GRAHAME, Kenneth. *Dream Days*. New York and London, 1899. 1st ed., 1st issue, with 15 pp. of ads at end, dated 1898. $25.

GRANT, Arthur Hastings. *The Grant Family*. Poughkeepsie, 1878. $25.

GRANT, Blanche C. (ed.). *Kit Carson's Own Story of His Life*. 138 pp., paperbound. Taos, N. M., 1926. 1st ed. $30.

GRANT, U. S. *Headquarters of the Army: General Orders No. 74*. 43 pp., sewed. Washington, 1868. $75.

GRANT, U. S. *Message Communicating the Report and Journal of Proceedings of the Commission Appointed to Obtain Concessions from the Sioux Indians*. 90 pp., sewed. Washington, 1876. $25.

GRANT, U. S. *Personal Memoirs*. 2 vols. New York, 1885-86. 1st ed. Large paper issue, $75. Regular issue, up to $10.

GRAVES, The Rev. H. A. (comp.). *Reminiscences and Events of Rev. John Wesley DeVilbiss*. Galveston, 1886. Worn, $35.

GREAT Eastern Gold Mining Co. (The). Map. 7 pp., paperbound. New York, 1880. $25.

GREELEY, Horace. *Overland Journey*. New York, 1860. 1st ed. $25

GREENBURG, Dan W. *Sixty Years. A Brief Review. The Cattle Industry in Wyoming, etc.* 73 pp., paperbound. Cheyenne, 1932. $40.

GREENHOW, Robert. *Memoir, Historical and Political.* Map. Washington, 1840. 1st ed. Unbound, restitched, $27.50.

GREER, J. *Buck Barry, Texas Ranger.* Dallas, 1932. 1st ed. $40.

GREGORY, John. *Industrial Resources of Wisconsin.* Milwaukee, 1855. $45.

GREGORY, Thomas Jefferson and others. *History of Solano and Napa Counties, California.* Maps. Los Angeles, 1912. Back hinge split, $37.50.

GRIERSON, Gen. B. H. *Annual Report on the Department of Arizona, Bowie and Selden and the Point Loma and Navajo Reservations.* 32 pp. No place, 1889. $35.

GRIFFITH, William. *A Treatise on the Jurisdiction and Proceedings of Justices of the Peace in Civil Suits.* Burlington, 1796. $25.

GRINNELL, Joseph, H. J. Bryant and T. D. Storer. *Game Birds of California.* Berkeley, 1918. $30.

GRINNELL, Joseph, Joseph Dixon and Jean M. Linsdale. *Vertebrate Natural History of a Section of Northern California Through the Lassen Peak Region.* Folding colored map. Berkeley, 1930. $27.50.

GRINNELL, Joseph and T. D. Storer. *Animal Life in the Yosemite.* Berkeley, 1924. $30.

GRISWOLD, W. M. *A Descriptive List of Novels and Tales Dealing with American Country Life.* 52 pp., saddle-stitched. Cambridge, 1890. 1st ed. $25.

GROOS, J. J. *Report of the General Land Office.* 21 pp., paperbound. Houston, 1874. $25. Houston, 1876, 27 pp., paperbound. $25.

GUERRA, Father Joseph. *Fecunda Nube del Cielo Guadalupano y Mistica Paloma del Estrecho Palomar de el Colegio Apostólico de Nuestra Señora de Guadalupe.* Vellum. Mexico, no date [1726]. $450.

GUIDE to Emigrants in Minnesota (A). By a Tourist. Map. 16 pp., paperbound. St. Paul, 1857. $45.

GUILD, Josephine C. *Old Times in Tennessee.* 503 pp. Nashville, 1878. $25 to $30.

GUNN, Donald. *History of Manitoba.* Ottawa, 1880. $37.50.

GUTHRIE, William. *A New System of Geography.* 2 vols. Philadelphia, 1795. $50.

GUZMAN, Jose Maria. *Breve Noticia del Actual Estado del Territorio de la Alta California.* Mexico, 1833. One of 100 facsimile reprints. $30. [For original ed., see *GIYA.*]

H

HAINES, Elijah M. *Historical and Statistical Sketches of Lake County, State of Illinois.* Folding frontispiece. 112 pp., paperbound. Waukegan, 1852. $150.

HAIR, James T. *Gazetteer of Madison County.* (Illinois). Alton, 1866. $32.50.

HAKES, Hon. Harlo. *Landmarks of Steuben County, New York.* Syracuse, 1896. 1st ed. $27.50.

HALE, Will. *Twenty-four Years a Cowboy and Ranchman in Southern Texas and Old Mexico.* 268 pp., paperbound. Hedrick, Oklahoma Territory, no date [1905]. (By William Hale Stone.) 1st ed. (Only one copy is known.) Estimated price: $5,000.

HALEY, J. Evetts. *Charles Schreiner, General Merchandise: The Story of a Country Store.* Austin, 1944. $25.

HALL, Bert L. *Roundup Years.* No place, no date [Pierre, S.D., 1954]. 1st ed. $25.

HALL, Carroll. *Heraldry of New Helvetia.* Half calf and boards. San Francisco, 1945. One of 250. $30.

HALL, Frederic. *The History of San Jose and Surroundings.* Map. San Francisco, 1871. $35.

HALL, James. *Notes on the Western States.* Philadelphia, 1838. $27.50.

HALLEY, William. *Centennial Year Book of Description of the Contra Costa Under Spanish, Mexican, and American Rule.* Oakland, 1876. $30.

HALLUM, John. *Biographical and Pictorial History of Arkansas. Vol. 1.* (All published.) Albany, 1887. $32.50.

HAMILTON, Alexander. *A Full Vindication of the Measures of the Congress, from the Calumnies of Their Enemies.* 35 pp. New York, 1774. 1st ed. Half morocco, $135.

HAMILTON, Alexander, John Jay, and James Madison. *The Federalist, The New Constitution, Written in the Year 1788.* Washington, 1818. $50. [For 1st ed., see *GIYA*.]

HAMILTON, The Rev. William and the Rev. S. M. Irvin. *An Ioway Grammar.* No place [Wolf Creek, Neb.], 1848. $625 (auction record).

HAMMOND, George Peter (ed.). *Noticias De California.* San Francisco, 1958. One of 400. $25.

HANCOCK, R. R. *Hancock's Diary: or, a History of the 2d Tennessee Confederate Cavalry.* 2 vols. in 1. Nashville, 1887. Covers dull, worn, $40.

HAND Book to the Gold Fields of Nebraska and Kansas (A). Map. 113 pp., paperbound. Chicago, 1859. (By William N. Byers and John H. Kellom.) 1st ed. $300 to $600, possibly more.

HAND-Book of Ness County, the Banner County of Western Kansas. 36 pp., paperbound. Chicago, 1887. Covers soiled, $45.

HARDEE, William J. *Rifle and Light Infantry Tactics.* 2 vols. Memphis, 1861. $50.

HARDING, George L. *Don Augustin V. Zamorano, Statesman, Soldier, Craftsman, and California's First Printer.* Los Angeles, 1934. $75.

HARE, George H. *Guide to San Jose and Vicinity.* 2 maps. 85 pp., paperbound. San Jose, 1872. $100.

HARGRAVE, Catherine Perry. *A History of Playing Cards.* Boston, 1930. In dust jacket, $70.

HARGRAVE, James. *The Hargrave Correspondence.* Map in pocket. Toronto, 1938. $25.

HARMAN, S. W. *Hell on the Border.* Portrait. Paperbound. Fort Smith, Ark., no date [1898]. 1st ed., green printed covers. $67.50 to $110.

HARPER, Henry H. *A Journey in Southeastern Mexico.* 100 pp., boards. New York, 1910. Uncut, $30.

HARRIS, Henry. *California's Medical Story.* Springfield, Ill., 1932. Uncut and unopened, $25.

HARRIS, Joel Chandler. *Daddy Jake the Runaway.* Pictorial glazed boards. New York, no date [1889]. 1st ed. $50. Another, dust soiled, $25.

HARRIS, Joel Chandler. *Tales of the Home Folks in Peace and War.* Boston, 1898. 1st ed. In dust jacket, $25.

HARRIS, Joel Chandler. *Uncle Remus: His Songs and His Sayings.* Vellum. New York, 1895. One of 250 on large paper, signed. Soiled, front inner hinge weak, $37.50. [For 1st ed., see *GIYA*.]

HARRISON, W. H. *A Discourse on the Aborigines of the*

Valley of the Ohio. Folding map. 51 pp., paperbound. Cincinnati, 1838. $75.

HARTE, Bret. *M'Liss.* (From *The Luck of Roaring Camp and Other Sketches.*) San Francisco, 1948. One of 300. In dust jacket, $30.

HARTLEY, Oliver C. *Digest of the Laws of Texas.* Philadelphia, 1850. Rebound, $35.

HARVEY, George. *Harvey's Scenes in the Primeval Forests of America.* 4 hand colored plates. Half morocco. No place [New York?], no date. $50.

HARVEY, Henry. *History of the Shawnee Indians.* Cincinnati, 1855. $27.50.

HASTAIN, E. *Township Plats of the Creek Nation.* Full limp morocco. Muskogee, 1910. $45. [For Cherokee township maps, see *Township Maps* in *GIYA.*]

HATFIELD, Edwin F. *History of Elizabeth, New Jersey.* 8 plates. New York, 1868. 1st ed. $25.

HAUPT, Gen. Herman. *Reminiscences of.* Milwaukee, 1901. Limited, autographed. $27.50.

HAVEN, Samuel. *A Guard Against Extremes Under Afflictive Providences.* 34 pp., paperbound. Portsmouth, 1767. $25.

HAWKER, Lieut. Col. P. *Instructions to Young Sportsmen.* Philadelphia, 1846. 1st Am. ed. $50 to $75.

HAWLEY, A. T. *The Climate, Resources, and Advantages of Humboldt County, etc.* 42 pp., paperbound. Eureka, 1879. $450.

HAWLEY, W. A. *The Early Days of Santa Barbara.* 5 plates. 105 pp., paperbound. New York, 1910. $45.

HAWTHORNE, Nathaniel. *Doctor Grimshawe's Secret.* Boston, 1883. 1st ed. Rubbed, slightly dust soiled, all edges uncut, $35.

HAWTHORNE, Nathaniel. *Grandfather's Chair*. Boston, 1841. 1st ed. $150. Another, binding faded, $30. Another, ex-library, $25. [Supersedes entry in *GIYA*.]

HAWTHORNE, Nathaniel. *Life of Franklin Pierce*. Boston, 1852. 1st ed., 1st issue. $35.

HAWTHORNE, Nathaniel. *Tanglewood Tales, for Girls and Boys*. Green cloth. Boston, 1853. 1st ed., 1st issue, with ads reading "In Press." In half morocco folding case, $67.50. [Supersedes entry in *GIYA*.]

HAY, John. *Jim Bludso of the Prairie Belle and Little Breeches*. 23 pp., paperbound. Boston, 1871. In slip case, $25.

HAYDEN, Ferdinand V. *Sun Pictures of Rocky Mountain Scenery*. 30 mounted photographs. ¾ morocco. New York, 1870. 1st ed. Autographed, $100. Another, $80.

HAYWOOD, John. *The Natural and Aboriginal History of Tennessee*. Nashville, 1823. 1st ed., with half title and errata leaf. Hinges strengthened, foxed, in slip case, $250.

HAZARD, Ebenezer. *Historical Collections. Vol. 1*. Boards. Philadelphia, 1792. Uncut, in slip case, (lacking Vol. 2), $35.

HAZARD, Thomas R. *The Jonny-Cake Letters*. 2 vols. Paperbound. Providence, 1882. 1st ed. Uncut, $50.

HAZEN, Gen. W. B. *A Narrative of Military Service*. Boston, 1885. Rubbed, numerous pencil notes, $30.

HAZEN, Gen. W. B. *Our Barren Lands*. 53 pp., paperbound. Cincinnati, 1875. $75. Another, ex-library, $25. [Supersedes entry in *GIYA*.]

HAZEN, Gen. W. B. *Some Corrections of "Life on the Plains."* (Cover title.) 18 pp., paperbound. St. Paul, 1875. $50.

HEADLEY, John W. *Confederate Operations in Canada and New York*. New York, 1906. Cover discolored, $40.

HEARN, Lafcadio. *Kwaidan*. Color plates. Printed silk, bound

Japanese style. Wrap-around silk case. New York, 1932. One of 1,500, signed. $25.

HEARNE, Samuel. *A Journey from Prince of Wales's Fort in Hudson's Bay to the Northern Ocean, in the Years 1769, 1770, 1771, and 1772.* Plates, folding maps. Toronto, 1911. One of 500. $30.

HEART of the West (The): An American Story. By an Illinoisan. Chicago, 1871. 1st ed. $35.

HECKEWELDER, John. *A Narrative of the Mission of the United Brethren Among the Delaware and Mohegan Indians.* 5 plates, 3 maps. Cleveland, 1907. One of 160. $57.50.

HEMINGWAY, Ernest. *A Farewell to Arms.* New York, 1929. 1st trade ed., 1st state, uncut. In dust jacket, $27.50. Another, frayed jacket, $12.50. [For signed, limited ed., see *GIYA.*]

HEMINGWAY, Ernest. *The Spanish Earth.* Cleveland, 1938. 1st ed., 1st issue. One of 1,000. $50.

HEMINGWAY, Ernest. *The Torrents of Spring.* New York, 1926. 1st ed. In dust jacket, $60.

HENRY, Alexander. *Travels and Adventures in Canada and the Indian Territories.* Boston, 1901. One of 700. $25. [For original ed., 1809, see *GIYA.*]

HENRY, Alexander and David Thompson. *New Light on the Early History of the Greater Northwest.* 3 vols. New York, 1897. Large paper, boards, $100. Regular ed., clothbound, $75.

HERBERT, Henry William. *The Quorndon Hounds.* Philadelphia, 1852. 1st ed., blue cloth. Bookplate, edges browned, in folding case, $200.

HESTON, James Franklin. *Moral and Political Truth.* Philadelphia, 1811. 1st ed. $30.

HEWITT, Randall H. *Notes By the Way. Memoranda of a Journey Across the Plains, etc.* 58 pp., paperbound. Olympia, 1863. 1st ed. $1,000 and up.

HIGBEE, Elias and R. B. Thompson. *The Petition of the Latter-Day Saints, etc.* 13 pp., sewed. Washington, 1840. $35.

HIGGINS, George. *"The King of Counties," Miami County.* 32 pp., paperbound. Paola, Kan., 1877. Small piece of front cover missing, affecting title, $50.

HILDRETH, Samuel P. *Genealogical and Biographical Sketches of the Hildreth Family.* Marietta, Ohio, 1840. $35.

HILDRETH, Samuel P. *Pioneer History.* Folding map. Half morocco. Cincinnati, 1848. 1st ed. $40. Another, foxed, $30.

HILLS, Chester. *The Builder's Guide.* 70 plates. 2 vols. in 1. Hartford, 1834. 1st ed. Hinges split, rubbed, foxed, $30.

HINMAN, Wilbur F. *The Story of the Sherman Brigade.* Alliance, O., 1897. Worn at ends, inner hinges taped, $25.

HINTS to My Countrymen. By an American. Boards. New York, 1826. (By Theodore Sedgwick.) 1st ed. Uncut, $35.

HISTORIA Cristiana de la California. Boards. Mexico, 1864. (By El Domingo.) $65.

HISTORICAL and Descriptive Review of the Industries of Tacoma, 1887. 108 pp., unbound. Los Angeles, 1887. $37.50.

HISTORY of Alameda County. Oakland, 1883. (By J. P. Munro-Fraser.) $100.

HISTORY of Amador County, California. Oakland, 1881. $150.

HISTORY of the Arkansas Valley, Colorado. Chicago, 1881. $27.50.

HISTORY of Black Hawk County, Iowa. Chicago, 1878. $27.50.

HISTORY of the Counties of Woodbury and Plymouth, Iowa. Chicago, 1890-91. $26.75.

HISTORY of Floyd County, Iowa. Chicago, 1882. $30.

HISTORY of Franklin, Jefferson, Washington, Crawford and Gasconade Counties, Missouri. Chicago, 1888. $35.

HISTORY of Franklin and Pickaway Counties, Ohio. No place, 1880. $30.

HISTORY of Howard and Cooper Counties, Missouri. St. Louis, 1883. $30.

HISTORY of the Indian Wars with the First Settlers of the United States (A). 2 plates. Paper covered boards. Rochester, 1828. (By Daniel C. Sanders.) 2d ed. Uncut, in morocco case, $75. [For 1st ed. of 1812, see *GIYA*.]

HISTORY of Jasper County, Missouri. Des Moines, 1883. $27.50.

HISTORY of Jo Daviess County, Illinois (The). Chicago, 1878. $25.

HISTORY of Little Goody Two-shoes (The). Printed by Isaiah Thomas. Worcester, MDCCLXXXVII (1787). (By Oliver Goldsmith?) 1st Worcester ed. Foxed, $250. Another, auction price, $190.

HISTORY of Marin County, California. San Francisco, 1880. $200. Rebound, $100.

HISTORY of Mendocino County. San Francisco, 1880. $150.

HISTORY of Milam, Williamson, Bastrop, Travis, Lee and Burleson Counties, Texas. Chicago, 1893. Worn, title page lacking, $60.

HISTORY of Montana, 1739-1885. Folding map. Half morocco. Chicago, 1885. (By M. A. Leeson.) $90.

HISTORY of Napa and Lake Counties, California. San Francisco, 1881. Rebound, $30.

HISTORY of Ontario County, New York. Philadelphia, 1876. Slightly shaken, $52.50.

HISTORY of Pike County, Illinois; History of Illinois. Chicago, 1880. New spine, $28.75.

HISTORY of Pike County, Missouri. Des Moines, 1883. Mended, title page and one page of contents missing, $27.50.

HISTORY of Sangamon County, Illinois. Chicago, 1881. $28.75.

HISTORY of Southeastern Dakota. Sioux City, 1881. Spotted, $27.50.

HISTORY of the Steam-Boat Case (A), Lately Discussed by Counsel Before the Legislature of New Jersey. 48 pp., unbound. Trenton, 1815. $50.

HISTORY of Texas (A), or The Emigrant's Guide to the New Republic, by a Resident Emigrant. New York, 1844. (By the Rev. A. B. Lawrence.) $35.

HISTORY of the United States for 1796 (The). Philadelphia, 1797. (By James Thomson Callender.) Half morocco, $32.50.

HISTORY of Wabasha County, Minnesota. Compiled by Franklyn Curtiss-Wedge and others. Winona, 1920. $27.50.

HISTORY of Walworth County, Wisconsin. Chicago, 1882. New spine, $32.50.

HISTORY of Waukesha County, Wisconsin. Chicago, 1880. New spine, $32.50.

HISTORY of Wayne County, New York. Philadelphia, 1877. $47.50.

HITTELL, John S. *The Commerce and Industry of the Pacific Coast of North America.* Folding colored map, plates. San Francisco, 1882. $25.

HITTELL, John S. *A History of the City of San Francisco.* San Francisco, 1878. $50.

HITTELL, Theodore H. (ed.). *The Adventures of James Capen Adams, Mountaineer and Grizzly Bear Hunter, of California*. San Francisco, 1860. Spine chipped, $37.50. Boston, 1861. Waterstains on a few pages, $25.

HODDER, James. *Hodder's Arithmetick*. Boston, 1719. 1st ed. Frontispiece and last leaf of text in facsimile, lacking front flyleaves, calf binding rubbed, $87.50.

HODGE, Gene Meany. *The Kachinas Are Coming*. 18 color plates. Los Angeles, 1936. $25.

HODGSON, Joseph. *The Cradle of the Confederacy*. Mobile, 1876. 1st ed. $25.

HOGG, Thomas E. *The Fate of Marvin and Other Poems*. Houston, 1873. $27.50.

HOLBROOK, John Edwards. *Ichthyology of South Carolina. Vol. 1*. (All published.) 28 plates. ¾ morocco. Charleston, 1860. $65.

HOLDEN, William Curry. *The Spur Ranch*. Boston, 1934. 1st ed. $35.

HOLDING, The Rev. C. B. *Green Bluff. A Temperance Story*. St. Louis, 1874. 1st ed. Binding faded, foxed, $37.50.

HOLE in the Wall; or a Peep at the Creed-Worshippers. 3 plates. 36 pp., paperbound. No place, 1828. 1st ed. Spine torn, $35.

HOLLISTER, Uriah S. *The Navajo and His Blanket*. 8 color plates. Denver, 1903. $35. Binding slightly soiled, $30.

HOLLOWAY, W. L. *Wild Life on the Plains*. St. Louis, 1891. 1st ed. $35.

HOLMES, Mrs. Mary J. *Cousin Maude, and Rosamond*. 2 vols. in 1. New York, 1860. 1st ed. $40.

HOLMES, Oliver Wendell. *The Autocrat of the Breakfast Table*. Boston, 1853. 1st ed. $50 to $60.

HOLMES, Oliver Wendell. *Francis Parkman.* 4 pp., leaflet. No place, no date [Boston, 1894]. 1st ed. One of 50. In slip case, $60.

HOLY Bible (The). Printed and sold by R. Aitken. Philadelphia, MDCCLXXXII (1782). $1,000 and up. Another: Printed by Isaiah Thomas. Worcester, 1791. Worn, foxed, $32.50.

HOME on a Furlough: A Sketch of Real Life. Paperbound. Springfield, 1864. 1st ed. $60.

HOMES in Texas on the Line of the International and Great Northern Railroad. 79 pp., paperbound. No place, no date [Chicago, 1879]. (By N. W. Hunter.) $25.

HONIG, L. C. *Westpoint, Gateway to the Early West.* North Kansas City, 1950. One of 525, signed. $35.

HONORED in Verse: The Tributes of a Galaxy of American Poets. (On the Death of President Garfield.) 8 pp. Boston, 1881. Spine torn, $32.50.

HOOKER, W. A. *The Horn Silver Mine. Report.* (Cover title.) 5 tinted views, colored map. 32 pp., paperbound. New York, 1879. $60.

HOPKINS, Gerard T. *A Mission to the Indians, from the Indian Committee of Baltimore Yearly Meeting, to Fort Wayne in 1804.* Paperbound. Philadelphia, 1862. $75.

HOPKINS, Samuel. *Historical Memoirs, Relating to the Housatunnuk Indians.* Boston, 1753. $250.

HOUSMAN, A. E. *A Shropshire Lad.* Boards, vellum back. New York, 1897. 1st Am. ed. $75.

HOUSTON, Sam. *Speech of . . . Exposing the Malfeasance and Corruption of John Charles Watrous, Judge of the Federal Court of Texas, and his Confederates.* Frontispiece. New York, 1860. $75.

HOUSTOUN, Mrs. Matilda C. *Texas and the Gulf of Mexico.*

Frontispiece of Santa-Anna. Philadelphia, 1845. 1st Am. ed. $25.

HOWARD, Benjamin. *A Report of the Decisions of the Supreme Court . . . in the Case of Dred Scott vs. John F. A. Sandford.* Paperbound. New York, 1857. $25.

HOWARD, J. Q. *The Life of Abraham Lincoln.* 102 pp., paperbound. Columbus, 1860. 1st ed., 1st issue, buff paper covers, 8 unnumbered pages of ads. $100 to $150.

HOWARD, O. O. *Account of Gen. Howard's Mission to the Apaches and Navajos.* 12 pp., paperbound. No place, no date. Back cover missing, in protective binder, $25.

HOWARD, O. O. *My Life and Experiences Among Our Hostile Indians.* 2 plates. Hartford, no date [1907]. $35.

HOWARD, O. O. *Nez Perce Joseph.* Boston, 1881. $25.

HOWARD, William. *Narrative of a Journey to the Summit of Mont Blanc.* Boards. Baltimore, 1821. 1st ed. Rubbed, foxed, lacking frontispiece, $32.50.

HOWE, Octavius T., M.D., and F. C. Mathews. *American Clipper Ships, 1833-58.* 114 plates. 2 vols. Vol. 1, marbled boards. Vol. 2, cloth. Salem, 1926-27. $62.

HOWELL, William C. *Recollections of Life in Ohio.* Cincinnati, 1895. 1st ed. $25.

HOWELLS, William D. *Lives and Speeches of Abraham Lincoln and Hannibal Hamlin.* Columbus, 1860. 2d ed., with errata slip on page 74. $35.

HOWES, Wright. *U.S.-iana (1700-1950).* New York, 1954. 1st ed. $50.

HUBBARD, Elbert. *A Message to Garcia.* East Aurora, 1899. 1st ed. One of 925. $25.

HUBBARD, John Niles. *Sketches of Border Adventures in*

the Life and Times of Maj. Moses Van Campen. Bath, N.Y., 1842. 2d ed. Half calf, $25. [For 1st ed., 1841, see *GIYA*.]

HUGHES, John T. *Doniphan's Expedition*. Cincinnati, 1848. 2d ed. $25. 3d ed., same date, with map and portrait of Doniphan, spine worn, $32.50. Another, 144 pp., paperbound, undated, with "Volunteer" frontispiece, 4th ed.(?), $27.50. [For 1st ed., 1847, see *GIYA*.]

HUMFREVILLE, J. Lee, *Twenty Years Among Our Savage Indians*. 250 engravings. Hartford, 1897. 1st ed. Very fine copy, $40. Another, $27.50.

HUMPHREYS, David. *A Poem, on the Happiness of America*. 15 pp., paperbound. Portsmouth, 1790. Name on title page, $38.50.

HUNLANISKI, F. J. (ed.). *History of Contra Costa County, California*. Berkeley, 1917. $35.

HUNTER, Alexander. *Johnny Reb and Billy Yank*. New York, 1905. $30.

HUNTER, J. Marvin (comp.). *The Trail Drivers of Texas*. 2 vols. No place, no date [San Antonio, 1920-23]. 1st ed. $75 to $100.

HUNTER, William S., Jr. *Hunter's Ottawa Scenery*. Ottawa, 1855. $30.

HUNTER, William S., Jr. *Hunter's Panoramic Guide from Niagara Falls to Quebec*. 66 pp., with picture map. Montreal, 1860. $37.50.

HURST, Samuel H. *Journal-History of the 73d Ohio Volunteer Infantry*. Chillicothe, 1866. Cover faded, $25.

HUTCHINS, Thomas. *An Historical Narrative and Topographical Description of Louisiana and West-Florida*. 95 pp. Philadelphia, 1784. 1st ed. Rebound in ¾ morocco, writing on back of title page, $225. [See *GIYA* for 1904 reprint.]

HUTTON, Joseph. *The Wounded Hussar*. Unbound. New York, 1809. 1st ed. $45.

HUXLEY, Aldous. *Leda*. New York, 1929. One of 364, signed, $25.

HYDE, George E. *The Early Blackfeet and Their Neighbors*. 45 pp., paperbound. Denver, 1933. One of 75. $50.

HYDE, George E. *The Pawnee Indians*. Parts 1 and 2. 54 pp. and 50 pp., each paperbound. Denver, 1934. Limited to 100. $50.

HYDE, George E. *Rangers and Regulars*. 47 pp., paperbound. Denver, 1933. $50.

HYDE, S. C. *Historical Sketch of Lyon County, Iowa*. Map. 40 pp., paperbound. Lemars, 1872. In slip case, $40.

I

I KUNSTITUSHUN i Micha i nan vlhpisa Chickasha, Okla i nan apesa yvt apesa tokmak oke. ("Chickasaw People, Their Constitution and Their Law 1857-59. 1867-68. 1870-72.") Translated from English to Chickasaw by Allen Wright. Chickasha, 1872. $100.

IDAHO: A Guide in Word and Picture. (WPA). Caldwell, 1937. $25.

IDE, Simeon. *The Conquest of California: A Biography of William B. Ide*. Map. No place, no date [San Francisco, 1944]. One of 500. Uncut, $25. [For 1st ed., 1880, see *GIYA*, page 130.]

IDE, William B. *Who Conquered California?* Boards. Claremont, N.H., no date [1880?]. 1st ed. $150. Other copies, $95 and $100.

IDLE Man (The). Edited by Richard Henry Dana, Sr. 6 parts

in 1. Morocco. New York, 1821-22. 1st ed. (Contains 5 Bryant poems.) Rubbed, $27.50.

ILLINOIS in 1837; A Sketch, etc. Folding colored map. Boards. Philadelphia, 1837. (By Samuel A. Mitchell.) 1st ed., 1st issue, with "animals" misspelled on title page. Backstrip worn, $25.

ILLUSTRATED Album of Biography of Pope and Stevens Counties, Minnesota. Chicago, 1888. New spine, $32.50.

ILLUSTRATED Historical Atlas of the State of Indiana. Chicago, 1876. $40 to $50.

ILLUSTRATED History of Los Angeles County (An). Chicago, 1889. $125.

ILLUSTRATED History of San Joaquin County (An). Chicago, 1890. $100.

IN MEMORIAM: Harry Elkins Widener. Morocco, uncut. No place, 1912. (By Dr. A. S. W. Rosenbach.) $55.

INDEX to the Final Rolls of Citizens and Freedmen of the Five Civilized Tribes in Indian Territory. No place, 1906. $50.

INDIAN Treaties and Laws and Regulations Relating to Indian Affairs, etc. Boards. Washington City, 1826. Rebacked, uncut, $32.50.

INDIANOLA Scrap Book. (Articles by H. E. Bolton and others.) Victoria, 1936. $50.

INDIANS (The): or, Narratives of Massacres and Depredations on the Frontier, etc. By a Descendant of the Huguenots. Unbound. Rondout, N.Y., 1846. (By Johannes H. Bevier.) In slip case, $50. Another $60. [See author entry in *GIYA*.]

INDUSTRIAL Prodigy of the New Southwest (The). 157 pp., paperbound. Muskogee, Indian Territory, no date [about 1902]. $32.50.

INFERNO from La Divina Commedia (The). (Dante Alighieri). Translated by Henry F. Cary. Blake engravings. New York, 1931. One of 1,200, boxed. $60.

INGERSOLL, Ernest. *An Island in the Air.* New York, 1905. 1st ed. In dust jacket, $25.

INGERSOLL, Luther A. *Ingersoll's Century Annals of San Bernardino County, 1769 to 1904.* Morocco. Los Angeles, 1904. $35.

INGRAHAM, Joseph Holt. *Pierce Fenning, or, The Lugger's Chase.* 95 pp., unbound. Boston, 1846. 1st ed. $75.

INGRAHAM, Joseph Holt. *The Prince of the House of David.* New York, 1855. 1st ed. $25.

INMAN, Col. Henry (ed.). *Buffalo Jones' 40 Years of Adventure.* 43 plates. Topeka, 1899. $47.50. Other copies, $25 and $37.50.

INQUIRIES, Respecting the History, Traditions, Languages, Manners, Customs, Religion, etc., of the Indians. Detroit, 1823. (By Lewis Cass.) Photostatic reproduction, $27.50.

INVESTIGATION (An) of That False, Fabulous and Blasphemous Misrepresentation of Truth, Set Forth by Thomas Paine, in His Two Volumes, Entitled "The Age of Reason," etc . . . By a Delaware Waggoner. 192 pp., paperbound. No place, no date. (By David Nelson.) Uncut, $50.

IRVING, Washington. *The Legend of Sleepy Hollow.* Rackham illustrations, 8 color plates. Philadelphia, no date. 1st Am. ed. One of 125 on large paper, signed by artist. $37.50.

IVES, Lieut. Joseph C. *Colorado River of the West.* 2 folding maps, 7 color plates. Washington, 1861. $25.

IVINS, Virginia W. *Pen Pictures of Early Western Days.* No place, no date [1905]. $30. 1908 [Keokuk, Iowa], 2d ed. $25. [See *GIYA.*]

J

JACKSON, A. W. *Barbariana: or Scenery, Climate, Soils and Social Conditions of Santa Barbara City and County.* 48 pp., paperbound. San Francisco, 1888. $60.

JACKSON, Andrew. *To the Citizens of Pennsylvania.* 12 pp., paperbound. No place, no date [Washington, 1834]. Rebound in leather (front loose), original covers bound in, $27.50.

JACKSON, George *Sixty Years in Texas.* No place, no date [Dallas, 1908]. $75.

JACKSON, Col. Oscar L. *The Colonel's Diary.* No place, no date [Sharon, Pa., 1922?]. Spine dull, $25.

JACKSON, Pearl Cashell. *Texas Governors' Wives.* Soft leather. Austin, no date [1905]. $35.

JAMES, Edwin (ed.). *Account of an Expedition from Pittsburgh to the Rocky Mountains.* 3 vols. (including atlas). Boards and paper labels, uncut. Philadelphia, 1823. 1st ed. In slip cases, labels defective, $200. Another set, text vols. rebound in ¾ morocco, atlas in original boards, $250. Another set, less fine, $75. [Supersedes entry in *GIYA*.]

JAMES, Frank. *The Only True History of the Life of Frank James, Written by Himself.* 134 pp., paperbound. No place no date [Pine Bluff, 1926]. Stained, spine worn, $27.50.

JAMES, Henry, Jr. *A Bundle of Letters.* Paperbound. Boston, no date [1880]. 1st ed., state A, with comma after "Jr." on front cover. $50.

JAMES, Henry, Jr. *A Passionate Pilgrim and Other Tales.* Boston, 1875. 1st ed., terra-cotta cloth. Uncut, $35.

JAMES, Gen. Thomas. *Three Years Among the Indians and Mexicans.* 130 pp., paperbound. Waterloo, Ill., 1846. 1st ed.

Copy with paper covers supplied, $2,600 (auction price). New copy: up to $5,000? St. Louis, 1916. One of 365. $65 and $60. Another, shaken, $60. [Supersedes entry in *GIYA*.]

JANEWAY, James. *A Token for Children*. Printed by Benjamin Franklin. Philadelphia, MDCCXLIX (1749). Price: Find it and name it. (One copy of this item known.) Boston, 1771, 156 pp., unbound, $50.

JANSON, Charles Williams. *The Stranger in America*. Philadelphia, 1807. Rebound in calf, worn, hinges cracked, $37.50.

JEFFERS, Robinson. *The Loving Shepherdess*. Boards. New York, 1956. 1st ed. One of 115. In slip case, $50.

JEFFERS, Robinson. *Poems*. San Francisco, 1928. 1st ed. One of 310, signed. $27.50.

JENKS, Ira C. *Trial of David F. Mayberry for the Murder of Andrew Alger, etc.* 48 pp., paperbound. Janesville, Wis., 1855. $150.

JENNINGS, N. A. *A Texas Ranger*. New York, 1899. 1st ed. $40.

JEPSON, Willis L. *The Silva of California*. Paperbound. Berkeley, 1910. $25.

JERMAN, John. *The American Almanack for the Year of Christian Account 1731*. Philadelphia, no date. $350 (auction price, 1954).

JEWITT, John R. *Journal Kept at Nootka Sound*. Boards. Boston, 1931. One of 300. $25.

JINGLE, Bob. *The Association, &C. of The Delegates of the Colonies, at the Grand Congress, Held at Philadelphia, Sept. 1, 1774, Versified, and Adapted to Music, Calculated for Grave and Gay Dispositions*. No place [New York], 1774. 1st ed. Removed from binding, $110.

JOAQUIN (the Claude Duval of California); or The Marauder of the Mines. Paperbound. New York, 1888. (By Henry L. Williams.) 1st ed. $50. Clothbound, same date, 2d ed. $25.

JOHN Leech On My Shelves. No place, 1930. One of 155. Boxed, $27.50.

JOHNSON, Crisfield (comp.). *History of Cuyahoga County, Ohio.* Double column pages. Half morocco. Cleveland, 1879. Rubbed, $42.50.

JOHNSON, Don Carlos. *A Brief History of Springville, Utah.* Paperbound, errata slip. Springville, 1900. 1st ed. $30.

JOHNSON, Edwin F. *Railroad to the Pacific, Northern Route.* 2 folding maps, 8 plates. New York, 1854. Rebound, profile map repaired, $35.

JOHNSON, Joseph. *The Memorial of the Chamber of Commerce and of the Citizens of Charleston, Against the Tariff on Woollen Goods.* 16 pp. Charleston, 1827. Half morocco, $35.

JOHNSON, Rossiter. *Phaeton Rogers: A Novel of Boy Life.* New York, 1881. 1st ed. $125.

JOHNSON, Sidney S. *Some Biographies of Old Settlers, etc.* Vol. 1. (All published?). Tyler, Tex., 1900. $35.

JOHNSON, Mrs. Susannah. *A Narrative of the Captivity of Mrs. Johnson.* Windsor, 1807. 2d ed. $32.50. [For 1st ed., see title entry in *GIYA*.]

JOHNSON, Theodore T. *Sights in the Gold Region, and Scenes by the Way.* New York, 1849. 1st ed. $27.50 and $32.50.

JOHNSTON, Carrier Polk and W. H. S. McGlumphy. *History of Clinton and Caldwell Counties, Missouri.* Topeka, 1923. $25.

JOHNSTON, Charles. *Narrative of the Incidents Attending the Capture, Detention, and Ransom of Charles Johnston, etc.* Boards, uncut. New York, 1827. $55. [Supersedes title listing in *GIYA*.]

JOHNSTON, Lieut. Col. J. E., and others. *Reports of the Secretary of War, with Reconnaissances of Routes from San*

Antonio to El Paso, etc. 2 folding maps, 72 plates. Washington, 1850. 1st ed. In ¾ morocco, $47.50. Another, binding worn, back cover loose, $27.50.

JOHNSTON, Mary. *To Have and to Hold.* Red cloth. Boston, 1900. One of 250, uncut. $35 to $50.

JONES, Anson B. *Memoranda and Official Correspondence Relating to the Republic of Texas, Its History and Annexation.* New York, 1859. $25.

JONES, Charles C., Jr. *Historical Sketch of the Chatham Artillery.* 3 maps. Albany, Ga., 1867. Ex-library, cracked endpapers, cover discolored and worn. $35. (Large paper copies issued also.)

JONES, The Rev. David. *A Journal of Two Visits Made to Some Nations of Indians on the West Side of the River Ohio, in the Years 1772 and 1773.* Paperbound. New York, 1865. One of 50 on large paper. Rebound in half morocco, covers bound in, uncut, $37.50.

JONES, U. J. *History of the Early Settlement of the Juniata Valley.* Philadelphia, 1856. $25.

JORDAN, Gen. Thomas and J. P. Pryor. *The Campaigns of Lieut.-Gen. N. B. Forrest.* New Orleans, 1868. Rebound in buckram, $30.

JOURNAL of the Convention to Form a Constitution for the State of Wisconsin: Begun and Held at Madison on the 5th Day of October, 1846. Calf-backed boards. Madison, 1847. 1st ed. Binding repaired, foxed, $47.50. Another, rebound, $45.

JOURNAL of the Expedition of Dragoons under the Command of Col. Henry Dodge to the Rocky Mountains During the Summer of 1835. 2 folding maps. Paperbound. No place, no date [Washington, 1836]. (By Lt. G. P. Kingsbury.) Morocco (rehinged), original covers bound in, $85. [See also Nolie Mumey entry.]

JOURNAL . . . House of Representatives of the Mass.-Bay. Begun and Held at Harvard College . . . 27th May, 1772. Unbound, unstitched, uncut. Boston, 1772. $65.

JOURNAL of the Proceedings of the Congress, Held at Philadelphia, Sept. 5, 1774. Paperbound. Philadelphia, 1774. 1st ed., 1st issue, with the first seal of the Confederate States. $150.

JOURNAL of the Senate . . . 1st Session . . . 3d Congress, Begun and Held . . . Philadelphia, Dec. 2, 1793. Philadelphia, 1793 (actually 1794). Uncut, stitching missing, $26.50.

JOURNAL of a Tour Around Hawaii, the Largest of the Sandwich Islands. Map. Boston, 1825. (By William Ellis.) 1st ed. $35.

JOUTEL'S Journel of LaSalle's Last Voyage. Chicago, 1896. Caxton Club reprint, boxed. Unopened, $25.

JOYCE, James. *Ulysses.* Matisse illustrations. New York, 1935. One of 1,500, boxed. $135.

JURIDICA Demonstración de la Justicia que Assiste a D. Joseph Lorenz de Rada, etc. 246 pp., paperbound. Mexico, 1742. $900.

K

KA Euanelio a Mataio. (Together with *Marako* and *Ioane.*) Gospels of Matthew, Mark, and John in Hawaiian. 3 vols., sewed. Rochester, 1828-29. $75.

KANE, Thomas L. *The Mormons.* 92 pp., paperbound. Philadelphia, 1850. 2d ed. $35.

KANSAS City und sein Deutschthum im 19 Jahrhundert. Cleveland, 1900. Spine badly chipped, $35.

KEATS, John. *John Keats Unpublished Poem to His Sister Fanny April, 1818.* Boston, 1909. 1st ed. One of 489 on vellum. $25.

KELLEY, Joseph (Bunco). *Thirteen Years in the Oregon Penitentiary*. 142 pp., paperbound. Portland, 1908. 1st ed. $25.

KELLOGG, H. S. *Life of Mrs. Fmily J. Harwood*. Albuquerque, 1903. $125. (Yes, "Fmily" is what it says.)

KELLY, Charles. *Old Greenwood. The Story of Caleb Greenwood, Trapper, Pathfinder and Early Pioneer of the West*. Salt Lake City, 1936. One of 350. $60 (California dealer). $37.50 (New York dealer).

KELLY, Charles. *Salt Desert Trails*. Salt Lake City, 1930. $25.

KELLY, Charles and Maurice L. Howe. *Miles Goodyear, First Citizen of Utah*. Salt Lake City, 1937. One of 350. $60 (California dealer). $37.50 (New York dealer).

KELLY, Jonathan F. *The Humors of Falconbridge*. Philadelphia, no date [1856]. 1st ed. $25.

KEMP, Louis Witz. *The Signer of the Texas Declaration of Independence*. Houston, 1944. 1st ed. $30.

KENDALL, George Wilkins. *Narrative of the Texan Santa Fe Expedition*. 5 plates, folding map. 2 vols. New York, 1856. 7th ed. Foxed, in folding case, $125.

KENDALL, Joseph. *A Landsman's Voyage to California*. Portrait. Marbled boards. San Francisco, 1935. One of 200. $25.

KENNEDY, James Harrison. *A History of the City of Cleveland*. Cleveland, 1896. $27.50.

KENNEDY, William. *Texas; The Rise, Progress and Prospects of the Republic of Texas*. Folding maps. 118 pp., paperbound. Fort Worth, 1925. $25. [For an earlier version, 1844, see *GIYA*.]

KEY, Eugene George. *Mars Mountain*. 142 pp., boards. Everett, Pa., no date [1934]. In dust jacket, up to $200 (?). [According to fantasy expert Mel Korshak. Don't ask me why; it's unbelievably amateurish.]

KEYNES, Goeffrey. *A Bibliography of William Blake.* New York, 1921. One of 250. Uncut, $100.

KILBOURN, John. *The Ohio Gazetteer, or Topographical Dictionary.* Columbus, 1816. 2d ed. Old decorative paper covers, $25. [For 6th ed., see *GIYA.*]

KIMBALL, Fiske. *Thomas Jefferson, Architect.* Boston, 1916. One of 350. Ex-library, binding soiled, $32.50.

KING, Frank M. *Longhorn Trail Drivers.* Pasadena, 1940. 1st ed. One of 400, signed. $42.50.

KINGSBURY, Jedidiah. *A New Improved Dictionary for Children.* Boards. Boston, 1822. 1st ed. $25.

KIP, Lawrence. *Army Life on the Pacific.* New York, 1859. 1st ed. $25.

KIP, Lawrence. *The Indian Council in the Valley of the Walla-Walla, 1855.* 32 pp., paperbound. San Francisco, 1855. $225.

KIPLING, Rudyard. *Letters to the Family.* Paperbound. Toronto, 1908. 1st ed. Spine chipped, in slip case, $37.50.

KLONDYKE Mines and the Golden Valley of the Yukon (The). 24 pp., paperbound (self wrappers). No place, 1897. $60.

KNIGHT, William Allen. *The Song of Our Syrian Guest.* 14 pp., green imitation leather covers. Boston, no date [1903]. 1st ed., 1st issue, with announcement of *The Love Watch* for "early in 1904" on next to last page. $35.

KONINGSMARKE, the Long Finne: A Story of the New World. 2 vols., boards. New York, 1823. (By James K. Paulding.) 1st ed., uncut, $50.

KOREN, E. *Fra Pioneertiden.* Decorah, 1914. $35.

KUNZ, George Frederick and Charles Hugh Stevenson. *The Book of the Pearl.* New York, 1908. 1st ed. $25.

KUYKENDALL, Judge W. L. *Frontier Days.* No place [Denver?], 1917. $30.

L

LABOULAYE, Edward. *Laboulaye's Fairy Book.* Translated by Mary L. Booth. New York, 1867. 1st ed. $32.50.

LA BREE, Ben (ed.). *The Confederate Soldier in the Civil War, 1861-1865.* Louisville, 1897. Spine fraying, $55. Rebound in buckram, $30.

LA CROIX, Arda. *Billy the Kid.* Paperbound. New York, 1907. Rebound in cloth, $30.

LAFITTE; or The Pirate of the Gulf. 2 vols. Clothbound, paper labels. New York, 1836. (By Joseph Holt Ingraham.) 1st ed. Particularly fine, $100. Another, the same, $75.

LA FRENTZ, F. W. *Cowboy Stuff.* Boards. New York, 1927. 1st ed., 1st issue, 49 plates. One of 500. $75. Another, $60. 2d issue, 50 plates, $75.

LA GUERRA de Tejas sin Máscara. 20 pp. Mexico, 1845. In new paper covers, $125.

LAKESIDE LIBRARY (The). Vol. 4, No. 82. 36 pp. Chicago, 1877. "People's ed." (Contains H. N. Maguire's "The Black Hills and American Wonderland.") Corners of three leaves torn, $40.

LAMAR, Mirabeau B. *Verse Memorials.* New York, 1857. Inscribed, $150. (This, from the catalogue of a Texas dealer, appears to be out of line.)

LAMBOURNE, Alfred. *The Old Journey: Reminiscences of Pioneer Days.* 18 plates. No place, no date [Salt Lake City, 1897]. $27.50.

LANCASTER, Joseph. *The British System of Education.* 5 plates, frontispiece. Georgetown, 1812. 1st ed. $32.50.

LANCASTER, R. A., Jr. *Historic Virginia Homes and Churches.* Philadelphia, 1915. Limited ed. Shaken, $40.

LANG, H. O. (ed.). *History of the Willamette Valley.* Portland, 1885. $30. [Supersedes entry in *GIYA*.]

LANG, Col. William W. *A Paper on the Resources and Capabilities of Texas.* 19 pp., paperbound. No place [New York], 1881. 1st ed. $45. 2d ed., 31 pp., paperbound, New York [1881], $35.

LANG, Col. William W. *The Relative Increase of Population and Production.* 8 pp., sewed. New York, 1881. $35.

LANGFORD, Nathaniel Pitt. *Vigilante Days and Ways.* 15 plates. 2 vols. Boston, 1890. $50 and $55. Signed, $65.

LANGLEY, Henry G. *The San Francisco Directory for the Year 1858.* San Francisco, 1858. Cover worn, 3 leaves defective, $38.50.

LANGSTON, Mrs. George. *History of Eastland County, Texas.* Dallas, 1904. $30.

LANMAN, James H. *History of Michigan.* Folding map. New York, 1839. $25. Signed, $35.

LANTHORN Book (The). New York, 1898. One of 12 (of an ed. of 125) signed by contributors, including Stephen Crane. Rebacked, $57.50.

LAPHAM, I. A. and F. Randall. *Report of a Committee Appointed by the Trustees of the Town of Milwaukee, Relative to the Commerce of That Town and the Navigation of Lake Michigan.* 12 pp., sewed. Milwaukee, 1842. Uncut, $250.

LARDNER, Ring W. *Gullible's Travels.* Indianapolis, no date [1917]. 1st ed. In dust jacket, $25.

LARKIN, Thomas O., and others. *California in 1846.* San Francisco, 1934. One of 550. $25.

LAROQUE, Francois A. *Journal of . . . from the Assiniboine to the Yellowstone, 1805.* 82 pp., paperbound. Ottawa, 1910. $45.

LARRANCE, Isaac. *Post Office Chart.* Maps (2 each) of 10 states. 47 pp., printed in red and blue. Cincinnati, 1860. $60.

LAST Hours of Charles R. S. Boyington (The). 44 pp., paperbound. Mobile, 1835. $45.

LATOUR, A. Lacarriere. *Historical Memoir of the War in West Florida and Louisiana in 1814-15.* With an atlas. 2 vols. Philadelphia, 1816. Rebound, $75.

LAURENS, Henry. *The Army Correspondence of Col. John Laurens in the Years 1777-8.* New York, 1867. One of 75. $25.

LA VERDAD Desnuda sobre la Guerra de Tejas, O sea contestación al Folleto Titulado; La Guerra de Tejas sin Máscara. 42 pp., sewed. Mexico, 1845. $125.

LAW of Descent and Distribution Governing Lands of the Creek Nation, As Held by C. W. Raymond, Judge of the U. S. Court for the Western District of the Indian Territory. 14 pp., paperbound. No place, 1903. $100.

LAWS of the Choctaw Nation, Made and Enacted by the General Council from 1886 to 1890. (In English and Choctaw.) Atoka, Indian Territory, 1890. $25.

LAWS and Decrees of the State of Coahuila and Texas, in Spanish and English. Houston, 1839. Hinges repaired, $125.

LAWS Relating to Internal Improvement in the State of Michigan. 16 pp., sewed. Detroit, 1837. $25.

LAWS of the State of New York, etc. 2 vols. in 1, calfbound. New-York, 1789. Rebacked, $100.

LAWS of the Territory of Kansas, Passed at the 2d Session, etc. Lecompton, no date [1857]. $40.

LAWS of the Territory of New Mexico. 71 pp., paperbound. Santa Fe, 1862. Backstrip worn, waterstains, $65.

LAWS of the Territory of the United States North-West of the Ohio, Adopted . . . at a Session Beginning on Friday, the XXIX Day of May, 1795. No place [Cincinnati], no date [about 1880]. New buckram, $27.50.

LAZCANO, Francisco Xavier. *Exortación Evangelica para Excitar en Todos los Fieles Cristianos, etc.* 33 pp., vellum. Mexico, 1760. $750.

LEA, Lt. Albert M. *Notes on the Wisconsin Territory.* Map. Paperbound. Philadelphia, 1836. 1st ed. New cloth, original covers pasted on, map lacking, $75.

LECKENBY, Charles H. (comp.). *The Tread of Pioneers.* Steamboat Springs, Colo., 1945. $40.

LE CONTE, Joseph. *A Journal of Ramblings Through the High Sierras of California.* 9 mounted photos. San Francisco, 1875. $60.

LEE, J. D. *J. D. Lee's Behjendelse.* 36 pp., paperbound. Salt Lake City, 1877. $40.

LEE, John D. *The Journals of . . . 1846-47 and 1859.* Salt Lake City, 1938. One of 250. $32.50 and $75. [Supersedes entry in *GIYA*.]

LEE, L. P. *History of the Spirit Lake Massacre!* 48 pp., paperbound. New Britain, 1857. $25.

LEE, Nelson. *Three Years Among the Camanches.* 2 plates. 224 pp., paperbound and clothbound. Albany, 1859. 1st ed. Paperbound, $150 to $250. Clothbound, $150 or more.

LEE, Susan P. *Memoirs of William Nelson Pendleton, by His Daughter.* Philadelphia, 1893. $40.

LEESE, Jacob P. *Historical Outline of Lower California.* 46 pp., paperbound. New York, 1865. $40.

LEONARD, Irving (trans.). *The Mercurio Volante of Don Carlos De Signuenza y Gongora, etc.* Los Angeles, 1932. In dust jacket, $25.

LEONARD, Zenas. *Narrative of the Adventures of, etc.* Clearfield, Pa., 1839. 1st ed. Up to $5,000 in original cloth binding. Repaired copy, $4,600 (auction price). Rebound, $2,900 (auction price). Cleveland, 1904. $25. [Supersedes entry in *GIYA*.]

LESSONS for Youth. Selected for the Use of Schools. Philadelphia, 1799. 1st ed. $42.50.

LESTER, J. C. and D. L. Wilson. *The Ku Klux Klan: Its Origin, Growth and Disbandment.* New York, 1905. $30.

LETTER From a Clergyman in Town (A); Vindicating Himself Against the Malevolent Aspersions of a late Pamphleteer Letter-Writer. No place [Philadelphia], 1764. Half morocco, $35.

LETTER of J. C. Fremont to the Editors of the National Intelligencer, Communicating Some General Results of a Recent Winter Expedition Across the Rocky Mountains, etc. 7 pp., binder's cloth. No place, no date [Washington, 1854]. $25.

LETTERS from An American Farmer. Philadelphia, 1793. (By Michel Crevecoeur.) $25.

LETTERS of Jonathan Oldstyle, Gent. Paperbound. New York, 1824. 1st ed. (By Washington Irving.) In folding case, $40.

LEVY, Daniel. *Le Français en Californie.* ¾ morocco. San Francisco, 1884. $32.50.

LEWIS, E. J. *Hints to Sportsmen.* Philadelphia, 1851. $25.

LEWIS, J. O. *The Aboriginal Port Folio.* 72 colored portraits. Paperbound. Philadelphia, 1835. Rebound in decorated leather, front cover bound in and 3 ad leaves included, $750.

LEWIS, Meriwether and William Clark. *History of the Expedition Under the Command of Capts. Lewis and Clark, to the Sources of the Missouri.* Maps, charts. 2 vols., boards.

Philadelphia, 1814. 1st ed., 1st issue, with page 89 unnumbered. Rebound in green leather, original covers bound in each volume, $1,750. Another set, less fine $1,000. [Supersedes entry in *GIYA*.]

LEWIS W. S. and P. C. Phillips (eds.). *The Journal of John Work*. Cleveland, 1923. $25.

LEY y Reglamento Aprobado de la Junta Directiva y Económica del Fondo Piadoso de Californias. 20 pp. Mexico, 1833. Calfbound, gilt-stamped, $250.

LIFE and Adventures of Bronco John. His Second Trip Up the Trail. By Himself. 32 pp., paperbound. No place, no date [Valparaiso, Ind., 1908.] $25.

LIFE and Adventures of Charles Anderson Chester, the Notorious Leader of the Philadelphia "Killers." Paperbound. Philadelphia, 1850. 1st ed. $35.

LIFE and Adventures of John A. Murrell (The), the Great Western Land Pirate. Paperbound. New York, 1848. Uncut, $85.

LIFE History of Mrs. Annie St. John. Containing Her Marriage, Seduction of Her Sister by Her Own Husband, Subsequent Divorce, etc. Marbled boards, cloth back. New York, 1872. Worn, stained, $15.

LIFE of Maj.-Gen. Harrison (The). Portrait, plates. Boards. Philadelphia, 1840. $25.

LIFE in the New World; or Sketches of American Society. New York, no date [1844]. (By Karl Postl.) 1st ed. Rubbed, $37.50.

LIFE of Thomas W. Gamel (The). 32 pp., paperbound. No place, no date [1932]. $30.

LIFE, Travels, Voyages, and Daring Engagements of Paul Jones (The). Albany, 1809. 3d Am. ed. Rubbed, $27.50.

LIFE and Writings of Maj. Jack Downing, of Downingville (The), Away Down East in the State of Maine. Boston, 1833. (By Seba Smith.) 1st ed. Rubbed, shaken, $50.

LINCOLN, Abraham. *By the President of the United States of America. A Proclamation.* General Orders No. 1. War Department, Washington, Jan. 2, 1863. 3 printed pages, 4-page section. (Emancipation Proclamation.) 1st ed. $200.

LINCOLN, Abraham and Stephen A. Douglas. *Political Debates.* Columbus, 1860. 1st ed., 1st issue, with no ads, no rule on copyright page, and signature "2" at foot of page 13. $30, $45, $60.

LINCOLN Centennial Medal (The). Presenting the Medal of Abraham Lincoln by Jules Edouard Roine Together With Papers on the Medal, etc. New York, 1908. Boxed, $25.

LINCOLN, Mrs. D. A. *Mrs. Lincoln's Boston Cook Book.* Boards. Boston, 1884. 1st ed. $450 (catalogue price, with her *Boston School Kitchen Text-Book,* 1887, thrown in).

LINDBERGH, Charles A. *"We."* New York, 1927. Author's Autograph ed. In original board container, $50.

LINSLEY, D. C. *Morgan Horses.* New York, 1857. 1st ed. $25.

LITTLE, James A. *Biographical Sketch of Feramorz Little, Written Under the Patronage of His Family, by His Brother.* Morocco. Salt Lake City, 1890. Backstrip worn and partly lacking, hinges weak, $27.50.

LITTLE, James A. *From Kirtland to Salt Lake City.* Salt Lake City, 1890. 1st ed. $25 and $35.

LITTLE, James A. *What I Saw on the Old Santa Fe Trail.* 127 pp., paperbound. Plainfield, Ind., no date [1904]. $60. Another, $40.

LITTLEHEART, Oleta. *The Lure of the Indian Country.* Moccasin-skin binding. Sulphur, Okla., 1908. Signed presentation copy, $40.

LIVINGSTON, Luther S. *Franklin and His Press at Passy.* New York, 1914. One of 300 for the Grolier Club. $40.

LOCKE, John. *A Letter Concerning Toleration.* Stitched, uncut. Boston, 1743. 3d ed. (1st Am. ed.) Stitching torn, $50.

LOCKWOOD, Frank C. *The Apache Indians.* New York, 1938. 1st ed. In dust jacket, $30. Another, lacking jacket, $25.

LOCKWOOD, Frank C. *Arizona Characters.* Los Angeles, 1928. Limited ed. $30.

LOMAS, Thomas. *Recollections of a Busy Life.* No place, no date [Cresco, Iowa, 1923]. $100. Rebound in morocco, $85. [Supersedes "Loomis" entry in *CIYA.*]

LONDON, Jack. *The Cruise of the Dazzler.* New York, 1902. 1st ed., 1st issue, white binding, with "Published October, 1902" on copyright page. $100 to $150. Copies less fine, $60 to $100. [Supersedes entry in *GIYA.*]

LONDON, Jack. *The God of His Fathers.* New York, 1901. 1st ed. $25.

LONE Star Guide Descriptive of Countries on the Line of the International and Great Northern Railroad of Texas (The). Folding map and table, plates. 32 pp., paperbound. St. Louis, no date [about 1877]. (By H. M. Hoxie.) $35.

LONG Island Atlas. Published by Beers. No place, 1873. $40.

LONGFELLOW, Henry W. *Ballads and Other Poems.* Marbled boards, morocco back and corners, marbled edges. Cambridge, 1842. 1st ed., 1st issue, with small "t" in "teacher" in last line of page 88 and with the quotes at end of line 1, page 34, scratched out. $150.

LONGFELLOW, Henry W. *The Belfry of Bruges and Other Poems.* Boards, gilt top, uncut. Cambridge, 1846. 1st ed. $37.50.

LONGFELLOW, Henry W. *Evangeline, A Tale of Acadie.* Gray or yellow boards, paper labels. Boston, 1847. 1st ed.,

1st issue, with "Long" for "Lo" in line 1, page 61. $250 or more. Rebound, $150. "Lo" issue, 2d issue, same date, up to $100 or more. Defective copies, $40 to $80. Signed copies, either issue, worth more. [Supersedes entry in *GIYA*.]

LONGFELLOW, Henry W. *Saggi de Novellieri Italiani d'ogni secolo.* Boston, 1832. 1st ed., with half-title and errata slip. Uncut, $35.

LOOKING-Glass for Presbyterians (A). Philadelphia, 1764. Half morocco, bookplate, $50.

LORANT, Stefan (ed.). *The New World: the First Pictures of America, etc.* New York, no date [1946]. Boxed, $25.

LORENZANA, Francisco Antonio. *Historia de Nueva-España.* Maps. Mexico, 1770. $350.

LOST "Spade" (The); or The Grave Digger's Revenge. 16 pp., paperbound. New York, 1864. 1st ed. Back cover missing, $65.

LOUGHBOROUGH, J. *The Pacific Telegraph and Railway.* 2 folding maps. 80 pp., unbound. St. Louis, 1849. $400.

LOVE of Admiration, or Mary's Visit to B——. A Moral Tale. By a Lady. Unbound. New Haven, 1828. 1st ed. $35.

LOVECRAFT, H. P. *Beyond the Wall of Sleep.* Sauk City, 1943. $35.

LOVECRAFT, H. P. *The Outsider and Others.* Sauk City, 1939. In dust jacket, $35.

LOVECRAFT, H. P. *The Shunned House.* 59 pp. Athol, Mass., 1928. 1st ed. Unbound, $90.

LOWELL, Amy. *Dream Drops.* Boston, no date [1887]. 1st ed. $75.

LOWELL, James Russell. *Poems. Second Series.* Cambridge, 1848. Uncut, $25.

LUCE, Edward S. *Keoghe, Comanche and Custer.* No place, 1939. Limited, signed ed. In dust jacket, $45.

LUKE Darrell, The Chicago Newsboy. Chicago, 1865. 1st ed. Bottom of spine frayed, $47.50.

LUKE, L. D. *Adventures and Travels in the New Wonder Land of Yellowstone Park.* Utica, 1886. $25.

LUNDY, Benjamin. *The Life, Travels and Opinions of.* Colored folding map. Philadelphia, 1847. 1st ed. In ¾ morocco, $45. Another, foxed, $40.

LUXAN, Diego Perez de. *Expedition Into New Mexico Made by Antonio de Espejo, 1582-1583.* Translated by George Peter Hammond and Agapito Rey. Los Angeles, 1929. $50. Another, $30.

LYFORD, W. G. *The Western Address Directory.* Baltimore, 1837. $25.

LYKKEJAEGER, Hans. *Luck of a Wandering Dane.* Boards. Philadelphia, 1885. Covers loose, $45.

LYMAN, Albert. *Journal of a Voyage to California, and Life in the Gold Diggings.* Paperbound. Hartford, 1852. Chipped, in folding box, $150. Another, $90. [Supersedes entry in *GIYA.*]

Mc

McAFEE Brothers. *Tehama County: Geography, Topography, Soil, Climate, Productions, etc.* 32 pp., paperbound. No place, no date [San Francisco, 1881]. $50.

McCLINTOCK, James. *Pioneer Days in the Black Hills.* Deadwood, 1939. $40.

McCLORMICK, Hon. Richard. *Arizona: Its Resources and Prospects.* Folding map. 22 pp., paperbound. New York, 1865. $25.

McCLURE, J. B. *Edison and His Inventions.* (Includes " 'Uncle Remus' and the Phonograph," by Joel Chandler Harris.) Chicago, 1879. 1st ed., 1st state, with no reviews of this book in the ads and with "with copious illustrations" in one line on title page. $25.

McCONKEY, Mrs. Harriet E. (Bishop). *Dakota War Whoop; or, Indian Massacres and War in Minnesota.* 6 portraits. St. Paul, 1863. 1st ed. $75. Another, green morocco, $35.

McCONNELL, H. H. *Five Years a Cavalryman.* Text on pink paper. Jacksboro, Tex., 1889. $25 and $32.50.

McCONNELL, Joseph Carroll. *The West Texas Frontier. Vol. 1.* (All published.) No place, 1933. $35.

McCOY, Isaac. *History of the Baptist Indian Missions.* Washington, 1840. $40.

McCOY, Isaac. *Remove Indians Westward.* (Caption title). 48 pp., sewed. No place [Washington], 1829. $35. [For related item, see author listing in *GIYA*.]

McCRACKEN, Harold. *The Charles M. Russell Book.* Leatherbound. New York, 1957. One of 250, signed, boxed. $100.

McCRACKEN, Harold (ed.). *Frederic Remington's Own West.* New York, 1960. One of 167, signed, boxed. $50.

McCRACKEN, Harold. *George Catlin and the Old Frontier.* Colored plates. Pigskin, buckram box. New York, 1959. One of 250, with extra color plate tipped in at front. $67.50.

McDANIELD, H. F. and N. A. Taylor. *The Coming Empire.* New York, no date [1877]. 1st ed. $25.

McDONALD, Archibald. *Peace River: A Canoe Voyage from Hudson's Bay to Pacific, by the late George Simpson . . . in 1828.* Edited by Malcolm McLeod. Folding map. 119 pp., paperbound. Ottawa, 1872. 1st ed. $150. Another, covers bound in, $125.

McDONALD, John. *Biographical Sketches of Gen. Nathaniel Massie, Gen. Duncan McArthur, Capt. William Wells, and Gen. Simon Kenton.* Cincinnati, 1838. $75.

McFADDEN, William S. *Corvallis to Crescent City, California, in 1874.* 44 pp., mimeographed paperbound. (WPA.) No place, no date [1937]. $25.

McGILLYCUDDY, Julia B. *McGillycuddy Agent: A Biography of Dr. Valentine T. McGillycuddy.* Stanford, no date [1941]. In dust jacket, $25.

McGOWAN, Ned. *Narrative of.* Boards. San Francisco, 1917. One of 200. $25.

McGUFFEY, William H. *The Eclectic Fourth Reader.* 3/4 red morocco. Cincinnati, 1837. 1st ed. Rubbed, $45.

McGUFFEY, William II. *Revised and Improved Third Reader.* Boards. Cincinnati, 1838. $45.

McILVAINE, William. *Sketches of Scenery and Notes of Personal Adventures in California and Mexico.* San Francisco, 1951. One of 400. $25. [For 1st ed., 1850, see GIYA.]

McKAY, Richard C. *South Street, A Maritime History of New York.* New York, 1934. One of 200, signed, boxed. $50.

McKEE, James Cooper. *Narrative of the Surrender of a Command of U. S. Forces at Fort Fillmore, N. M., in July A. D. 1861.* 30 pp., paperbound. New York, 1881. 2d ed. $45.

McKENNEY, Thomas L. *Sketches of a Tour to the Lakes.* Boards, paper label. Baltimore, 1827. 1st ed. Uncut, $45.

McKIM, Randolph H. *A Soldier's Recollections: Leaves from the Diary of a Young Confederate.* New York, 1911. $30.

McKINSTRY, George H., Jr. *Thrilling and Tragic Journal Written by . . . While on a Journey to California in 1846-47.* Broadside folded to book size, original printed paper covers. West Hoboken, no date [1920]. One of 65. $30.

McKNIGHT, Charles. *Old Fort Duquesne: or, Captain Jack, the Scout.* Pittsburgh, 1873. 1st ed. $25.

McMURRAY, W. J. *History of the 20th Tennessee Regiment Volunteer Infantry, C.S.A.* Nashville, 1904. $27.50.

McWILLIAMS, John. *Recollections of.* Princeton, no date [1919]. 1st ed. $27.50 and $25.

M

MACARIA: or, Altars of Sacrifice. 183 pp., paperbound. Richmond, 1864. (By Augusta Jane Evans Wilson.) 1st ed. $350 or more.

MacCABE, Julius P. B. *Directory of the City of Detroit.* Printed boards. Detroit, 1837. 1st ed. $150.

MACKENZIE, Alexander. *Voyages from Montreal, on the River St. Lawrence, Through the Continent of North America.* Folding map. New York, 1802. 1st Am. ed. $25. Philadelphia, 1802, boards, uncut, with penciled index on blank pages at end, $50.

MacLEISH, Archibald and others. *"What is America's Foreign Policy."* 12 pp., mimeographed. State Dept. press release. No place [Washington], 1945. $45.

MacNUTT, Francis A. *Bartholomew de Las Casas, His Life, Apostolate, and Writings.* Cleveland, 1909. $25.

MACON, T. J. *Reminiscences of the 1st Company of Richmond Howitzers.* Richmond, no date [about 1909]. $50.

MADISON, James. *Communications from the American Ministers at Ghent.* 74 pp., sewed. Washington, 1814. 1st ed., with final signature "10," which is "frequently lacking." $35.

MADISON, James. *Communications from the Plenipotentiaries of the U. S. Negotiating Peace with Great Britain.* 28 pp., sewed. Washington, 1814. $25.

MADISON, James. *Message from the President of the United*

States, Recommending an Immediate Declaration of War Against Great Britain. 12 pp., sewed. Washington, 1812. $60.

MADRID Y ORMACHEA, German. *Historia Christiana de la California.* 238 pp., paperbound. Mexico, 1864. $45.

MAGEE, Dorothy and David. *Bibliography of the Grabhorn Press, 1940-1956.* San Francisco, 1957. One of 225. $85.

MAGOFFIN, Susan Shelby. *Down the Santa Fe Trail and Into Mexico.* Edited by Stella M. Drumm. New Haven, 1926. 1st ed. In dust jacket, $37.50. Another, lacking jacket, $25.

MAGOUN, F. Alex. *The Frigate Constitution and Other Historic Ships.* Salem, 1928. In dust jacket, $57.50.

MAHAN, Dennis Hart. *Summary of the Course of Permanent Fortification, etc.* Boards. West Point, 1850. 1st ed. $50.

MAHONEY, J. W. *The Cherokee Physician, or Indian Guide to Health.* Asheville, N.C., 1849. 2d ed. $75.

MAJOR Jones' Courtship; or Adventures of a Christmas Eve. 61 pp., paperbound. Savannah, 1850. (By William Tappan Thompson.) Name on cover, $27.50.

MAJOR Jones' Sketches of Travel, Comprising the Scenes, Incidents, and Adventures in his Tour from Georgia to Canada. Philadelphia, 1848. (By William Tappan Thompson.) 1st ed. $95.

MALONE, James. *The Chickasaw Nation.* Louisville, 1922. Enlarged ed. $30.

MANIFIESTO del Crongreso General en el Presente Año. 20 pp., paperbound. Mexico, 1836. $60.

MANNING, Wentworth. *Some History of Van Zandt County, Texas. Vol. 1.* (All published.) Des Moines, no date [1871]. $35.

MARCY, Randolph B. *Exploration of the Red River of Louisiana.* Washington, 1854. $25.

MARCY, Randolph B. *The Prairie Traveler: A Hand-Book for Overland Expeditions.* Maps, 31 illustrations. New York, 1859. 1st ed. $25. Another, "good but not fine," $25.

MARIGNY, Bernard. *Réflexions sur la Campagne du Gen. Jackson en Louisiane en 1814-15.* 51 pp., sewed. Nouvelle-Orleans, 1848. $30.

MARKOE, Peter. *The Reconciliation; or the Triumph of Nature: A Comic Opera, in Two Acts.* Philadelphia, 1790. 1st ed. Removed from another binding, $27.50.

MARKS, Elias, M.D. *The Aphorisms of Hipprocrates.* Boards, paper label. New York, 1818. 1st ed. $32.50.

MARQUIS, Thomas B. *Memoirs of a White Crow Indian.* (Thomas H. LeForge). New York, 1928. 1st ed. $25 and $30.

MARRANT, John. *A Narrative of the Life of.* 48 pp., paperbound. Halifax, 1812. Rebound in calf, paper covers bound in, uncut, $35.

MARSHALL, Humphrey. *Arbustrum Americanum: The American Grove, an Alphabetical Catalogue of Forest Trees and Shrubs, Natives of the American United States.* Paperbound. Philadelphia, 1785. 1st ed. Uncut, $150.

MARSHALL, Jabez P. *Memoirs of the Late Rev. Abraham Marshall.* Boards. Mount Zion, Ga., 1824. Worn, front hinge broken, $45.

MARTELL, Martha. *Second Love.* New York, 1851. 1st ed. $27.50.

MARTIN, Luther. *The Genuine Information, Delivered to the Legislature of the State of Maryland, etc.* 93 pp. Philadelphia, MDCCLXXXVIII (1788). Half calf, uncut, $175.

MARTINEZ CARO, Ramon. *Verdadera Idea de la Primera Campana de Tejas y Sucesos Ocurridos despues de la acción de San Jacinto.* Boards. Mexico, 1837. $175.

MASON, Dr. Philip. *A Legacy to My Children.* Connersville, Ind., 1868. $25.

MASSON, L. R. *Les Bourgeois de la Compagnie du Nord-Ouest.* Folding map. 2 vols. Quebec, 1889. $75.

MASTERS, Edgar Lee. *Spoon River Anthology.* New York, 1915. 1st ed., 1st issue, 7/8 inches across top. In dust jacket, $90. Other copies, $65, $50, and $42.50. [Supersedes entry in *GIYA*.]

MATHER, Samuel. *An Apology for the Liberties of the Churches in New England.* Errata leaf. Boston, 1738. Hinges cracked, worn, $38.50.

MATHER, W. W. *Second Annual Report of the Geological Survey of the State of Ohio.* 19 plates. Unbound. Columbus, 1838. Uncut and unopened, $50.

MATSELL, George W. *Vocabulum; or, The Rogue's Lexicon.* New York, 1859. 1st ed. $50.

MAVERICK, Samuel Augustus. *Notes on the Storming of Bexar in the Close of 1835.* Edited by F. C. Chabot. 32 pp. No place, no date. One of 100. $35.

MAXIMILIAN, Prince of Weid. *The Atlas Volume.* To accompany his *Travels in the Interior of North America, 1832-1834.* 81 plates, folding map in color. Cleveland, 1906. $75.

MAYNARD, Charles J. *Directory of the Birds of Eastern North America.* 25 hand colored plates. West Newton, Mass., 1907. $25. [For earlier ed., see *GIYA*.]

MAYNARD, G. W. *Report on the Property of the Alice Gold and Silver Mining Co., Butte.* Maps, plates. 28 pp., paperbound. New York, 1882. $25.

MEANY, Edmond S. *Origins of Washington Geographic Names.* Seattle, 1923. $50.

MEANY, Edmond S. *Washington from Life.* 9 plates. Seattle, 1931. $25.

MELLICK, Andrew D. *The Story of an Old Farm.* Somerville, 1889. $25.

MELVILLE, Herman. *Redburn.* New York, 1849. 1st ed. $50 to $100.

MEMORIAL *to the President and Congress for the Admission of Wyoming Territory to the Union.* 75 pp., paperbound. Cheyenne, 1889. $42.50.

MENCKEN, H. L. *Menckeniana: A Schimpflexikon.* Vellum. New York, 1928. 1st ed. One of 80, signed, boxed. $25.

MENTUIG, Padre Jean. *Rudo Ensayo, Tenative de Una Provencional Descripción Geographica de la Provincia de Sonora.* Translated by Buckingham Smith. San Augustin [St. Augustine—printed in Albany], no date [1863]. 1st ed. Limited ed., one of 10 large paper copies. $250. Regular issue, same date, $100. [Supersedes title entry in *GIYA*.]

MERRILL, Rufus. *Indian Anecdotes.* 7 wood engravings. 16 pp., paperbound. Concord, no date [about 1850]. $25.

MESSAGE *from the President of the United States, Communicating Discoveries Made in Exploring the Missouri, Red River, and Washita by Capts. Lewis and Clark, Dr. Sibley, and Mr. Dunbar, etc.* 2 folding tables. 171 pp., paperbound. Washington, 1806. (By Thomas Jefferson.) $300 and $275. New York, 1806. Paperbound, $165.

MESSAGE *from the President of the United States, in Compliance with a Resolution of the Senate Concerning the Fur Trade and Inland Trade to Mexico.* Washington, 1832. (By Andrew Jackson.) 1st ed. $50.

MESSAGE *of the President of the United States in Relation to the Indian Difficulties in Oregon . . . March 29, 1848.* (Caption title.) No place, no date [Washington, 1848]. (By James K. Polk.) Uncut, unopened, $30.

METRICAL *Description of a Fancy Ball Given at Washing-*

ton, 9th April, 1858, (A). Washington, 1858. 1st ed. (By Albert Pike.) $25.

MEXICO in 1842 . . . to Which is Added, An Account of Texas and Yucatan, and of the Santa Fe Expedition. Folding map. New York, 1842. (By George F. Folsom or Charles J. Folsom?) 1st ed. $40. Another, $50.

MEXICO, Its Social Evolution. L. Justus Sierra, editor. 3 vols., leatherbound. Mexico, 1900. (Weighs 30 pounds!) $100.

MEXICO and the United States: An American View of the Mexican Question. By a Citizen of California. 33 pp., paperbound. San Francisco, 1866. $45.

MILLAY, Edna St. Vincent. *Fatal Interview.* Boards. New York, 1931. 1st ed. One of 36 on Japan vellum. In slip case, $50.

MILLAY, Edna St. Vincent. *A Few Figs from Thistles.* Paperbound. New York, 1921. 2d ed. Covers worn, $25. [For 1st ed., see *GIYA*.]

MILLAY, Edna St. Vincent. *Renascence and Other Poems.* New York, 1917. 1st ed., 1st issue. One of 15 on Japan vellum, boards. $950 (1960 auction record). Another auction price, earlier, $575. Regular issue, black cloth, on "Glaslan" watermarked paper: In dust jacket, up to $150; signed, in dust jacket, $200 (auction record, 1960); unsigned, lacking jacket, $50 to $100. [Supersedes entry in *GIYA*.]

MILLER, Benjamin S. *Ranch Life in the Southwest.* New York, 1896. $75.

MILLER, Henry. *Account of a Tour of the California Missions, 1856.* 59 pp., boards. San Francisco, 1952. One of 375, boxed. $38.50.

MILLER, Lewis B. *Saddles and Lariats.* Boston, 1912. 1st ed. $25.

MILLER, T. L. *History of Hereford Cattle.* Chillicothe, Mo., 1902. $75. [Supersedes entry in *GIYA*.]

MILTON, John. *An Old Looking-Glass for the Laity and Clergy.* 74 pp., paperbound. Philadelphia, 1770. 1st Am. ed. $50.

MINERS and Business Men's Directory. Paperbound. Columbia, 1856. $1,100 (auction price, 1959).

MINUTES of Conferences Held at Easton, in October, 1758, with the Chief Sachems and Warriors of the Mohawks, Oneidoes, Onondagoes, Cayugas, Senecas, Tuscaroras, Delawares, Mohickons, and Pumptons. Printed by Benjamin Franklin. 31 pp., folio. Philadelphia, 1758. Title supplied in facsimile, full calf binding, $750.

MITCHEL, Jonathan. *Nehemiah on the Wall in Troublesom Times.* Cambridge, 1671. $300 to $400.

MITCHEL, Martin. *History of the County of Fond Du Lac.* Fond Du Lac, 1854. $50.

MITCHELL, John D. *Lost Mines of the Great Southwest.* No place, no date [Phoenix, 1933]. 1st ed. $40.

MITCHELL, Joseph. *The Missionary Pioneer.* Boards. New York, 1827. $125.

MITCHELL, Margaret. *Gone With the Wind.* New York, 1936. 1st ed., 1st issue, with "May, 1936" on copyright page. In dust jacket, $35 to $50. Another, autographed, $45. Lacking dust jacket, $10 to $25.

MITCHELL, S. Weir. *Hugh Wynne, Free Quaker.* 2 vols., gray boards, white cloth backs, paper labels, uncut. New York, 1897. 1st ed., with last word of page 64, Vol. 1, being "in" and line 16 on page 260, Vol. 2, reading "before us." One of 60 on large paper, boxed. $65 to $100.

MITCHELL, Samuel Augustus. *Traveller's Guide Through the United States, etc.* Map. Philadelphia, no date [1836]. $35. New York, 1851. $25.

MITCHELL, W. H. *Geographical and Statistical Sketch of*

the Past and Present of Goodhue County. 191 pp., paperbound. Minneapolis, 1869. $45.

MOMAN Pruiett, Criminal Lawyer. No place, no date [Oklahoma City, 1945]. $40.

MONETTE, John W. *History of the Discovery and Settlement of the Valley of the Mississippi.* New York, 1846. $37.50.

MONSIGNY, Madame. *Mythology: or, A History of the Fabulous Deities of The Ancients.* Randolph, N.H., 1809. 1st Am. ed. $27.50.

MONTANA, Its Climate, Industries and Resources. 74 pp., paperbound. Helena, 1884. $35.

MONTGOMERY, Cora. *Eagle Pass; or, Life on the Border.* New York, 1852. 1st ed. $37.50.

MOORE, Clement C. *Christmas Carol. The Visit of Saint Nicholas.* [Broadside; text printed in blue.] Philadelphia, no date [1842]. $35.

MOORE, Edward A. *The Story of a Cannoneer Under Stonewall Jackson, etc.* New York and Washington, 1907. Cover waterstained, interior crinkled, $35.

MOORE, Marianne. *Marriage. Manikin Number Three.* 10 pp., paperbound. New York, no date [1923]. 1st ed. $35.

MOORE, Thomas. *The Common-Wealth of Utopia.* Philadelphia, 1753. 1st Am. ed. $50.

MOORE, Thomas. *Epistles, Odes and Other Poems.* Philadelphia, 1806. (By Joseph Dennie.) 1st ed. $30.

MORAN, Thomas. *The Yellowstone National Park, and the Mountain Regions of Idaho, Nevada, Colorado and Utah.* 15 plates of water color sketches. Half red morocco. Boston, 1876. Corners scuffed, $275.

MORDECAI, Alfred. *A Digest of the Laws Relating to the*

Military Establishment of the United States. Washington, 1833. $45.

MORGAN, Dale L. and Carl I. Wheat. *Jedediah Smith and His Maps of the American West.* Folding maps. San Francisco, 1954. One of 530. $120.

MORGAN, Dick T. *Manual of the U. S. Homestead and Townsite Laws.* 144 pp., paperbound. Guthrie, Okla., 1893. $75.

MORGAN, Lewis. *The American Beaver and His Works.* Map, 23 plates. Philadelphia, 1868. 1st ed. Chip on spine, $30.

MORISON, Stanley. *Fra Luca de Pacioli of Borgo S. Sepolcro.* Boards. New York, 1933. One of 390. $25.

MORRELL, Z. N. *Flowers and Fruits from the Wilderness.* Boston, 1872. 1st ed. $27.50.

MORRIS, G. F. *Portraitures of Horses.* No place, 1952. $40.

MORRIS, William and Emery Walker. *Printing.* Boards. Park Ridge, Ill., 1903. Unopened. $25.

MORSE, Jedidiah. *Elements of Geography.* 2 folding maps. Unbound. Boston, 1795. 1st ed. $67.50.

MORSE, Jedidiah. *A Report to the Secretary of War . . . on Indian Affairs, etc.* Colored folding map. New Haven, 1822. Rebound in calf, $30.

MORTON, Nathaniel. *The New-England's Memorial.* Plymouth, 1826. Foxed, flyleaves missing, $37.50.

MOURELLE, Francisco Antonio. *Voyage of the Sonora in the 2d Bucareli Expedition, to Explore the Northwest Coast.* Translated by Daines Barrington. 2 maps. Boards. San Francisco, 1920. One of 230. $40.

MOWRY, Sylvester. *Memoir of the Proposed Territory of Arizona.* Map in some copies. 30 pp., paperbound. Washington,

1857. $60 to $100. Copy in new boards, map in facsimile, covers missing, waterstained, $40.

MUMEY, Nolie. *History of the Early Settlements of Denver (1599-1860).* Map. Boards, vellum back. Glendale, 1942. One of 500, signed. $42.50 and $40.

MUMEY, Nolie. *James Pierson Beckwourth, 1856-1866.* Folding map. Denver, 1957. One of 500. $25.

MUMEY, Nolie. *John Williams Gunnison, (1812-1853).* Colored portrait, plates, folding map. Boards. Denver, 1955. One of 500. $25.

MUMEY, Nolie. *March of the First Dragoons to the Rocky Mountains in 1835.* Errata slip, plates, folding map. Boards. Denver, 1957. One of 350. $25 and $30. (See also *Journal of the Expedition of Dragoons, etc.*)

MUMEY, Nolie. *Old Forts and Trading Posts of the West. Vol. 1.* Denver, 1956. One of 500. $25.

MUMEY, Nolie. *Pioneer Denver, Including Scenes of Central City, Colorado City, and Nevada City.* Folding plates. Boards. Denver, 1948. One of 240, signed. $32.50 and $35.

MUMEY, Nolie. *The Teton Mountains.* Boards. Denver, 1947. 1st ed. One of 700. $50 and $45.

MURPHY, Jerre C. *The Comical History of Montana.* 332 pp., paperbound. San Diego, 1912. $25.

MURRAY, Keith A. *The Modocs and Their War.* Norman, no date [1959]. 1st ed. (saved from fire by being sent out for review). Unbound, $30. (Bound second printing, same date, is worth only $5.)

MURRAY, Mrs. Louis L. *Incidents of Frontier Life.* Goshen, Ind., 1880. $40.

MUSEUM (The). Vol. 1. (26 numbers, all published). Boards. Hartford, 1825. (Contains first printing of "Lafitte, or The Baratarian Chief.") $42.50.

MYERS, Frank. *Soldiering in Dakota.* 60 pp., paperbound. Huron, 1888. In morocco case, $450.

MYSTERIES and Miseries of San Francisco (The), By a Californian. New York, no date [copyright 1853]. 1st ed. Rebound in ¾ morocco, internal waterstains, $175.

N

NAPTON, W. B. *Over the Santa Fe Trail, 1857.* 99 pp., paperbound. Kansas City, 1905. $25.

NARRATIVE of the Capture and Burning of Fort Massachusetts, etc. Albany, 1870. (By the Rev. John Norton.) One of 100. $25.

NARRATIVE of the Capture and Providential Escape of Misses Frances and Almira Hall, etc. 24 pp., including plate. No place [St. Louis?], 1832. 1st ed. $100.

NARRATIVE of Late Massacre (A), in Lancaster County, of a Number of Indians, Friends of the Province, by Persons Unknown. No place [Philadelphia], 1764. (By Benjamin Franklin.) $90.

NARRATIVE and Report of the Causes and Circumstances of the Deplorable Conflagration at Richmond. Sheep and oak boards. No place [Richmond?], 1812. $40.

NARRATIVE of Some of the Adventures, Dangers, and Sufferings of a Revolutionary Soldier (A). Hallowell, Me., 1830. (By James Sullivan Martin.) $50. Inscribed, $75.

NARRATIVE of the Suppression by Col. Burr (A), of the "History of the Administration of John Adams," etc. New York, 1802. (By James Cheetham.) 1st ed. Unbound, $25.

NARRATIVE of the Tragical Death of Mr. Darius Barber and His Seven Children, etc. 24 pp., paperbound. Boston, no date [about 1818]. $130 and $150. Estimated price for perfect copy: $300 or more.

NATIONAL Elgin Watch Co.'s Illustrated Almanac for 1875 (The). (Includes "My Rococo Watch," by Louisa May Alcott.) Paperbound. Chicago, no date [1874]. 1st ed. $27.50.

NAVAL Monument (The). 25 plates. Errata slip. Boston, 1816. (By Abel Bowen.) 1st ed. $45.

NAVIGATOR (The). Containing Directions for Navigating the Monongehela, Allegheny, Ohio, and Mississippi. Boards. Pittsburgh, 1811. (By Zadok Cramer.) 7th ed. $77.50. Another, chipped, $47.50. [For other eds., see *GIYA*.]

NEAL, John. *The Moose-Hunter; or, Life in the Maine Woods.* Paperbound. New York, no date [1864]. 1st ed., 1st issue, with No. 73 announced on the inside of the front cover. Back cover chipped, $35.

NEVERS, William. *Memoir of Col. Samuel Nevers.* 80 pp., paperbound. Norway, Me., 1858. 1st ed. $25.

NEW Empire (The): Oregon, Washington, Idaho. Folding map. 103 pp., paperbound. Portland, 1888. $25.

NEW England Primer (The), or, an Easy and Pleasant Guide to the Art of Reading. Paper covered thin wooden boards. No place [New-England], no date [not after 1796]. Cover cracked and mended, $185. Leominster, Mass., 1804. $32.50. [For others, see *GIYA*.]

NEW Guide of the Conversation in Portuguese and English (The). Boston, 1883. 1st ed. (Has introduction by Mark Twain.) Unbound sheets, in slip case, $25. (Bound copies presumably much less.)

NEW Ritual for "Sam" (A): Written by One Connected with the Cincinnati Times, and Dedicated to "Sam's" Numerous Friends. 47 pp., paperbound. Cincinnati, 1855. 1st ed. $48.50.

NEW Spain and the Anglo-American West. Edited by Herbert E. Bolton. 2 vols. No place, no date [Los Angeles, 1932]. One of 500, boxed. $75.

NEW Testament of Our Lord and Saviour Jesus Christ, Translated into the Choctaw Language. New York, 1854. 2d ed. $35.

NEW Topographical Atlas of St. Lawrence County, New York. Colored maps and plans. Published by Beers. Philadelphia, 1865. $25.

NEW-YORK Book of Poetry. New York, 1837. $25.

NEW YORK and Oro-Fino Gold and Silver Mining Co. of Idaho. 31 pp., paperbound. New York, 1865. $35.

NEWMARK, Harris. *Sixty Years in Southern California, 1853-1913.* Boston, 1930. 3d ed. $25 and $30.

NEWTON, J. H. and C. G. Nichols and A. G. Sprankle. *History of the Pan-handle . . . West Virginia.* Wheeling, 1879. $40.

NIAGARA Book (The). A Complete Souvenir of Niagara Falls. Buffalo, 1893. 1st ed., 1st issue, with Mark Twain contribution. $150.

NICHOLS, Beach. *Atlas of Schuyler County, New York.* 21 maps in color, 31 leaves. Philadelphia, 1874. Spine chipped, $42.50.

NOEL, Theophilus. *Autobiography and Reminiscences of.* Chicago, 1904. $37.50 and $25.

NOMENCLATURA Brevis Angelo-Latino in Usum Scholarum. Boston, 1752. (By Francis Gregory.) 2d Am. ed. Two leaves split, $25.

NORRIS, J. Wellington. *General Directory and Business Advertiser of the City of Chicago for the Year 1844.* Paperbound. Chicago, 1844. Binding defects, $475 (auction record). [Supersedes entry in *GIYA.*]

NORRIS, Thomas Wayne (book catalogue). *A Descriptive and Priced Catalogue . . . of California and the Far West.* Oakland, 1948. $25.

NORTH, Thomas. *Five Years in Texas; or, What You Did*

Not Hear During the War, etc. Cincinnati, 1870. Spine frayed, $25.

NORTHERN Route to Idaho (The). 8 pp., clothbound. St. Paul, no date. Auction prices: $225 and $400.

NORTHERN Traveller (The). New York, 1826. (By Theodore Dwight, Jr.) 2d ed. $30.

NOTICE sur la Rivière Rouge dans le Térritoire de la Baie-D'Hudson. 32 pp., paperbound. Montreal, 1843. (By Alex Tache?) Rebound in new cloth, portion of original cover stuck to title page, $650.

NOTICIA breve de la Expedición Militar de Sonora y Cinoloa, su Éxito Feliz, y Ventajoso Estado en que por Consecuencia de ella se han Puesto Ambar Provincias. 12 pp., paperbound. Mexico, 1927. (By Jose De Galvez.) (Reprint of Mexico, 1771, ed.) $60.

NOTICIAS of the Port of San Francisco in Letters of Miguel Costanso, Fray Juan Crespi and Fray Francisco Palou in the Year 1772. 22 pp., boards. No place [San Francisco], 1940. $35.

NOURSE, Hon. C. C. *Iowa and the Centennial.* 42 pp., paperbound. Des Moines, 1876. $30.

NOVUM Testamentum. Juxta Exemplar Joannis Millii Accuratissime Impressum. Worcester, 1800. Spine chipped, $27.50.

NOWLIN, William. *The Bark Covered House.* Detroit, 1876. Signed presentation copy, $350. Unsigned, $250 to $300.

NOYES, Alva J. *In the Land of Chinook, or the Story of Blaine County.* 24 plates. Helena, no date [1917]. 1st ed. $25, $27.50, and $32.50.

NUTTALL, Thomas. *The Genera of North American Plants.* 2 vols. in 1. Philadelphia, 1818. 1st ed. $45.

O

OATES, Gen. William C. *The War Between the Union and the Confederacy and Its Lost Opportunities, etc.* New York and Washington, 1905. Rebound in buckram, $50.

O'BEIRNE, H. F. *Leaders and Leading Men of the Indian Territory.* (History of the Choctaws and Chickasaws.) Chicago, 1891. $35.

OEHLER, Andrew. *The Life, Adventures, and Unparalleled Sufferings of.* Trenton, 1811. 1st ed. In slip case, $25.

OFFICIAL and Historical Atlas Map of Alameda County. Oakland, 1878. $125.

OFFICIAL Record from the War Department of the Proceedings of the Court Martial Which Tried, and the Orders of Gen. Jackson for Shooting the Six Militia Men, etc. 32 pp., sewed. Washington, 1828. $45.

OFFICIAL Report of the Trial of Laura D. Fair, for the Murder of Alex. P. Crittenden. San Francisco, 1871. $35.

OFFICIAL Reports of the Debates and Proceedings in the Constitutional Convention of the State of Nevada . . . July 4, 1864, etc. San Francisco, 1866. $25.

OGDEN, Peter Skeene. *Traits of American Indian Life and Character.* San Francisco, 1933. One of 550. $30.

OLDHAM, Williamson S. and George W. White. *Digest of the General Statute Laws of the State of Texas.* Austin, 1859. Rebound, $35.

OLIVER, John W. (pub.). *Guide to the New Gold Region of Western Kansas and Nebraska.* Folding map. 32 pp., paperbound. New York, 1859. $2,800. (This rare item was discovered by a "Gold in Your Attic" column reader and sold to a Chicago book dealer, who catalogued it at this price.)

OLMSTED, Henry K. *Genealogy of the Olmsted Family in America, 1632-1912.* New York, 1912. $30.

OLNEY, J. (ed.). *The Easy Reader; or Introduction to the National Preceptor.* Boards, calf back. New-Haven, 1833. 1st Am. ed. $25.

ON The Just Shaping of Letters. From *The Applied Geometry of Albrecht Dürer.* Translated by R. T. Nichol. Marbled boards. New York, 1917. One of 218. $45.

ONE Thousand Valuable Secrets, in the Elegant and Useful Arts. Leatherbound. Philadelphia, 1795. 1st Am. ed. $27.50.

O'NEILL, Eugene. *Before Breakfast.* Paperbound. New York, 1916. 1st separate ed. $35.

O'NEILL, Eugene. *Gold.* Boards. New York, no date [1920]. 1st ed. $25.

O'NEILL, Eugene. *The Hairy Ape, Anna Christie, The First Man.* Boards. New York, no date [1922]. 1st ed. In dust jacket, $25.

O'NEILL, Eugene. *Thirst and Other One Act Plays.* Boston, no date [1914]. 1st ed., 1st issue, hyphen missing at end of 9th line, page 115. In dust jacket, $100 and more. Lacking dust jacket, $35 to $75. [Supersedes entry in *GIYA*.]

ONLY Authentic Life of Abraham Lincoln, Alias "Old Abe." (Ridiculing him.) 16 pp., paperbound. No place, no date [New York, 1864]. $60.

ONTWA, the Son of the Forest. A Poem. Boards. New York, 1832. (By Henry Whiting.) $45.

OPTIC, Oliver. *The Boat Club; or, The Bunkers of Rippleton.* Boston, 1855. (By William T. Adams.) 1st ed. $55. Another, $25.

ORANGE County History Series. 2 vols., boards. Santa Ana, no date [1931 and 1932]. $60.

ORDEAL (The): A Critical Journal of Politicks and Literature. 26 numbers. Printed and edited by Joseph T. Buckingham. Boston, 1809. $45.

ORDER of the Governor in Council, for Further Regulating the Inland Navigation from the United States by the Port of St. Johns. No place, no date [Quebec, 1800]. Unbound, $37.50.

ORDER of the Governor in Council, of the 7th July 1796, for the Regulation of Commerce Between This Province and the United States of America. Quebec, 1796. (Including a second title page in French and a blank leaf at end.) Unbound, $55.

ORDINANCES of the Town of Berkeley, Alameda County, California, etc. (The). 24 pp., paperbound. Berkeley, 1882. $45.

OREGON: Agricultural, Stock Raising, Mineral Resources, Climate, etc. (Published by U.P.R.R.) 68 pp., paperbound. Council Bluffs, 1888. $30.

ORIGINAL Charades. Oblong. Cambridge, 1839. 1st ed. $25.

ORR, N. M. *The City of Stockton.* 64 pp., paperbound. Stockton, 1874. $60.

ORR and Ruggles. *San Joaquin County.* Map, plates. 130 pp., paperbound. Stockton, 1887. $75.

ORTÉGA, José. *Historia del Nayarit, Sonora, Sinaloa y Ambas Californias.* Mexico, 1887. $35.

ORTÉGA, Luis. *California Hackamore (La Jaquima).* Sacramento, 1948. 1st ed. $25.

ORTON, Richard H. *Records of California Men in the War of the Rebellion, 1861-1867.* Sacramento, 1890. Spine worn, $25.

OSBORN, H. S. *Plants of the Holy Land.* Philadelphia, 1860. $35.

OTHERS: An Anthology of the New Verse. Edited by Alfred Kreymborg. New York, 1917. 1st ed. $30.

OTIS, James. *Jenny Wren's Boarding-House.* Boston, no date [1893]. (By James Otis Kaler.) 1st ed., blue or brown cloth, gold stamped. $25.

OUR Great Indian War. The Miraculous Lives of Mustang Bill and Miss Marion Fannin, etc. 78 pp., paperbound. Philadelphia, no date [1876?]. $100.

OUR Kith & Kin, or, a History of the Harris Family, 1754-1895. No place, no date [Philadelphia, 1895]. $30.

OUTLINE Descriptions of the Posts in the Military Division of the Missouri, etc. Folding map. Chicago, 1876. ¾ morocco, scuffed, $75.

OUTLINE Description of U. S. Military Posts and Stations in the Year 1871. Washington, 1872. Cloth covers defective, $30.

OWEN, Richard E. and E. T. Cox. *Report on the Mines of New Mexico.* 59 pp., paperbound. Washington, 1865. 1st ed. $35.

OWEN, Robert Dale. *A Brief Practical Treatise on the Construction and Management of Plank Roads.* Plate. New Albany, Ind., 1850. $50.

P

PADILLIA, Nicolas Lopez. *Manifiesto, Dirigido a Exponer a el Publico las Utilidades, que le Resultaran de la Formación de una Compañia para el Estabecimiento de Fabricas.* 12 pp. Guadalajara, 1773. $350.

PAGE, Thomas Nelson. *In Ole Virginia.* New York, 1887. 1st ed., 1st issue. $25.

PAINE, Thomas. *The Age of Reason.* New York, 1794. 1st ed., with copyright notice. $30.

PAINE, Thomas. *The Decline and Fall of the English System of Finance.* Unbound. Philadelphia, 1796. Uncut, $25.

PALMER, Harry. *Base Ball: The National Game of the Americans.* 69 pp., paperbound. Chicago, 1888. $25.

PALMER, Joel. *Journal of Travels Over the Rocky Mountains, to the Mouth of the Columbia River, etc.* Paperbound. Cincinnati, 1847. 1st ed., with date 1847 on paper cover not overprinted or changed. In folding box, $900. Cleveland, 1906. Edited by R. G. Thwaites. $25.

PALMER, John. *Awful Shipwreck. An Affecting Narrative of the Unparalleled Sufferings of the Crew of the Ship Francis Spaight.* 24 pp., paperbound. Boston, 1837. 1st ed. $50.

PALOU, Francisco. *The Expedition into California of the Venerable Padre Junipero Serra and His Companions in the Year 1769.* Translated by Douglas S. Watson. San Francisco, 1934. $35.

PALOU, Francisco. *Relación Historica de la Vida y Apostólicas Tareas del Venerable Padre Fray Junipero Serra.* Folding map. Mexico, 1787. $450. Another, $250. [Supersedes entry in *GIYA*.]

PAREDES y Arrillaga, Mariano. *Manifiesto del Exmo. Sr. Presidente Interino de la Republica Mexicana.* 19 pp., paperbound. No place [Mexico], 1846. $60.

PARK Hotel (The). Travelers' Guide for 1872. Containing a Brief History of the City of Madison and Its Attractions. 128 pp., paperbound. Madison, 1872. $25.

PARK, Robert Emory. *Sketch of the 12th Alabama Infantry.* Richmond, 1906. Paper covers bound in cloth, $50.

PARKER, A. A. *Trip to the West and Texas.* Colored folding

map, 3 plates. Concord, 1836. 2d ed. $50. Lacking map, $35. [For 1st ed., 1835, see *GIYA*.]

PARKER, Dorothy. *After Such Pleasures.* New York, 1933. 1st ed. One of 250. $25.

PARKER, Samuel. *Journal of an Exploring Tour Beyond the Rocky Mountains . . . 1835-37.* Map. Ithaca, 1842. $30.

PARKER, Solomon. *Parker's American Citizen's Sure Guide.* Sag-Harbor, 1808. $27.50.

PARKMAN, Francis. *The Oregon Trail.* Calfbound and clothbound. Boston, 1892. 1st ed., with Frederick Remington illustrations. Calfbound, in dust jacket, $100. Clothbound, in dust jacket, $60. Another, lacking jacket, $35.

PASTIME of Learning (The), with Sketches of Rural Scenes. 4 colored botanical plates. Boards. Boston, 1831. 1st ed. $25.

PATTERSON, Samuel. *Narrative of the Adventures and Sufferings of.* Rhode Island, 1817. 1st ed., 114 pp., $25 to $100. Palmer, Mass., 1817, 1st ed., 2d issue, 144 pp., $100. [Supersedes entry in *GIYA*.]

PATTON, The Rev. W. W. and R. N. Isham. *U. S. Sanitary Commission, No. 38: Report on the Condition of Camps and Hospitals at Cairo. . . . Paducah and St. Louis.* 12 pp., stitched. 1st ed. $25.

PEABODY, Joel R. *A World of Wonders.* Boston, 1838. 1st ed. $25.

PECK, John M. *A Gazetteer of Illinois.* Jacksonville, 1834. $25.

PEEK, Peter V. *Inklings of Adventure in the Campaigns of the Florida Indian War.* 727 pp., in double columns, pictorial paper covers. Schenectady, 1860. 1st ed. $350. [Cataloguer says: "So far as we can trace, the only known copy." Library of Congress has one, according to Wright Howes' *U.S.-iana.* I offer $500 to any buyer of *More Gold in Your Attic* (not a dealer) who finds a hitherto unknown and complete copy of Peek (not in a dealer's hands) and mails it to me with his bill by January, 1963.]

PENA, Juan Antonio De La. *Derrotero de la Expedición en la Provincia de los Texas, etc.* Plates of the Presidios of Pilar, Dolores, San Antonio de Bejar, and Bahia de Espiritu Santo (Goliad). 29 pp., boards. Mexico, 1722. Some leaves silked (mended), $3,250.

PENDLETON, Nathaniel Greene. *Military Posts—Council Bluffs to the Pacific Ocean.* (Caption title.) Folding map. No place, no date [Washington, 1843]. ¾ morocco, $37.50.

PENN, William. *Essays on the Present Crisis in the Present Condition of the . . . Indians.* Boston, 1829. (By Jeremiah Evarts.) Rebound, $27.50.

PENNELL, Joseph. *The Glory of New York.* 24 color reproductions. New York, 1927. One of 355. In dust wrapper, boxed, $27.50.

"PEOPLE'S Reville" (The), Souvenir Hill City, Graham County, Kansas. (Cover title.) 112 pp., paperbound. Topeka, 1906. $30.

PEPPER, Capt. George W. *Personal Recollections of Sherman's Campaigns in Georgia and the Carolinas.* Zanesville, 1866. Worn, foxed, $30.

PERKINS, Charles Elliott. *The Pinto Horse.* Santa Barbara, 1927. 1st ed. Signed by author, $25.

PERSONAL Reminiscences of a Maryland Soldier. Baltimore, 1898. (By G. W. Booth.) Signed, $75.

PETER Parley's Tales About Great Britain, Including England, Wales, Scotland. Folding map. Baltimore, 1832. (By Samuel G. Goodrich.) Worn, $25.

PETERS, De Witt C. *Life and Adventures of Kit Carson, the Nestor of the Rocky Mountains.* 10 plates. New York, 1858.

1st ed. $50 to $70. Rebound, $25 and $30. [Supersedes entry in *GIYA*.]

PETERS, Fred J. *Railroad, Indian and Pioneer Prints by N. Currier and Currier and Ives.* New York, 1930. One of 500, boxed. $25.

PETERS, Harry T. *America on Stone.* New York, 1931. One of 676, boxed. $75.

PETERS, Harry T. *California on Stone.* New York, 1935. One of 501. In dust jacket, boxed, $45 and $60.

PETTER, Rodolphe. *English-Cheyenne Dictionary.* Kettle Falls, 1913-15. $150.

PHILIP Dru, Administrator. New York, 1919. (By Col. E. M. House.) 1st ed. $25.

PHILLIPS, D. L. *Letters from California.* Springfield, 1877. $25.

PHILLIPS, Samuel. *The History of Our Lord and Saviour Jesus Christ Epitomiz'd: In a Catechetical Way.* Boston, 1738. 1st ed. Few headings shaved, pages 33-36 lacking, $42.50.

PIERCE, N. H. and N. E. Brown. *The Free State of Menard.* Menard, 1946. 1st ed. $25.

PIERSON, B. T. *Directory of the City of Newark for 1838-9.* Boards. Newark, 1838. Rebacked, $37.50.

PIGMAN, Walter Griffith. *Journal.* Edited by Ulla Staley Fawkes. Boards. Mexico, Mo., 1942. $30.

PIKE County Puzzle, Vol. 1, No. 1. 4 pp. (Burlesque of country newspaper.) Camp Interlaken, Pa., 1894. (By Stephen Crane.) $90.

PIKE, Zebulon. *An Account of Expeditions to the Sources of the Mississippi.* 4 maps, 2 charts. Boards. Philadelphia, 1810. Rebacked, $350. [Supersedes entry in *GIYA*.]

PILOT Knob. Mendota. 23 pp., paperbound. No place, no date [St. Paul, 1887]. (By Gen. H. H. Sibley.) $45.

PINKERTON, William A. *Train Robberies, Train Robbers, and "Hold-up" Men.* Paperbound. Chicago and New York, 1907. $65.

PIONEER History of Custer County and Short Sketches of Early Days in Nebraska. Broken Bow, 1901. (By S. D. Butcher.) $35.

PIONEER Life in Kentucky. A Series of Reminiscential Letters from Daniel Drake, M.D., of Cincinnati to His Children. Cincinnati, 1870. $35.

PIONEERING the Plains. Journey to Mexico in 1848. The Overland Trip to California. 113 pp., paperbound. Kaukana, Wis., 1924. (By Alexander W. McCoy.) $75. Another, covers bound in, $45.

PITMAN, Benn. *The Assassination of President Lincoln and the Trial of the Conspirators.* Cincinnati, 1865. New buckram, $25.

PLAN de una Compañia de Accionistas para Fomentar con Actividad el Beneficio de las Ricas Minas de Sonora y Restablecer las Pesqueria de Perlas en el Golfo de Californias. 8 pp., Mexico, 1771. In slip case, $350.

PLUMBE, John, Jr. *Sketches of Iowa and Wisconsin.* Folding map on thin paper. 103 pp., paperbound. St. Louis, 1839. $725 (auction record, 1958). Another, rebound in boards, lacking map and title page, $250.

POE, Edgar Allan. *The Conchologist's First Book.* Boards. Philadelphia, 1839. 1st ed., with colored plates, which designate 1st state. $50. [Supersedes entry in *GIYA*.]

POE, Edgar Allan. *Eureka: A Prose Poem.* New York, 1848. 1st ed. $45. Another, $30. [Supersedes entry in *GIYA*; note correct date, 1848, not 1838 (typographical error).]

POE, Edgar Allan. *The Journal of Julius Rodman.* Colored illustrations. Boards. San Francisco, 1947. One of 500. $37.50.

POE, Edgar Allan. *The Literati.* Marbled boards. (Also was issued in cloth.) New York, 1850. 1st ed. $175.

POE, Sophie A. *Buckboard Days.* Caldwell, 1936. 1st ed. $25 and $30.

POEM (The) Which the Committee of the Town of Boston Had Voted Unanimously to Be Published with the Late Oration, etc. 30 pp., paperbound. Boston, 1772. (By James Allen.) 1st ed. $110.

POEMS Chiefly in the Scottish Dialect. By a Native of Scotland. Washington, Pa., 1801. (By David Bruce.) 1st ed. $225.

POEMS, on Several Occasions. Written in Pennsylvania. Frontispiece. Philadelphia, 1786. (By William Moore Smith.) 1st ed. Foxed, names on endleaf, binding repaired, $33.50.

POETRY for Children, Entirely Original. Boston, 1812. (By Charles Lamb.) 1st. Am. ed. Calf binding worn, $100.

POLITICIAN Out-Witted (The), a Comedy in Five Acts. Written in the year 1788. By an American. New York, 1789. (By Samuel Low.) 1st ed. Removed from another binding, $32.50.

POLLEY, J. B. *A Soldier's Letters to Charming Nellie.* New York and Washington, 1908. $37.50.

POOLE, Ernest. *The Harbor.* New York, 1915. 1st ed. $60.

POOR, M. C. *Denver, South Park and Pacific.* Denver, 1949. In dust jacket, $100 to $125.

PORTFOLIO (The). Vol. 19. Philadelphia, 1825. (Contains "Letters from the West: The Missouri Trapper.") Front cover loose, spine torn, $47.50.

PORTRAIT and Biographical Album of Henry County, Iowa. Chicago, 1888. Break in spine, $30.

PORTRAIT and Biographical Album of Jo Daviess County, Illinois. Chicago, 1889. $25.

PORTRAIT and Biographical Album of Otoe and Cass Counties, Nebraska. Chicago, 1889. Hinges broken, $27.50.

PORTRAIT and Biographical Album of Will County, Illinois. Chicago, 1890. $27.50.

PORTRAIT and Biographical Record of Dickinson, Saline, McPherson and Marion Counties, Kansas. Chicago, 1893. $32.50.

PORTRAIT and Biographical Record of Sheboygan County, Wisconsin. Chicago, 1894. $30.

POSTSCRIPT to the Statement Respecting the Earl of Selkirk's Settlement Upon the Red River, in North America. 28 pp. (195-222), plain paper covers, uncut. No place, no date [Montreal, 1818]. (By John Halkett.) $300.

POTTER, Jack. *Lead Steer and Other Tales.* Paperbound. Clayton, N.M., 1939. $30. Signed, $35.

POUND, Ezra. *Lustra.* New York, 1917. 1st ed. One of 60. Unopened, $85.

POUND, Ezra. *Provença: Poems Selected from "Personae," "Exultations" and "Canzoniere."* Boards. Boston, no date [1910]. 1st ed. Unopened, in dust wrapper, $30.

POWELL, H. M. T. *The Santa Fe Trail to California, 1849-1852.* Edited by Douglas S. Watson. San Francisco, no date [1931]. $350.

POWELL, J. W. *Canyons of the Colorado.* Meadville, Pa., 1895. Soiled, $35.

POWER of Sympathy (The): or, The Triumph of Nature. 2 vols. in 1. Boston, 1789. (By William Hill Brown.) 1st ed. Back cover loose, frontispiece torn, $275. Another, modern boards, tears in text repaired, bookplates, some foxing, in slip case, $350.

PRÉCIS Touchant la Colonie du Lord Selkirk, sa Destruction en 1815 et 1816, et le Massacre du Gouverneur Semple et de son Parti. Boards, uncut. Montreal, 1818. (By John Halkett.) $100.

PRESIDENT Lincoln Campaign Songster (The). 72 pp. New York, no date [1864]. Tears on title page repaired, new boards, calf back, $27.50.

PRESTON, Lieut.-Col. William. *Journal in Mexico. Morocco.* No place, no date. $62.50.

PRICE, George F. *Across the Continent with the 5th Cavalry.* New York, 1883. $25.

PRICHARD, G. W. *Bureau of Immigration, of the Territory of New Mexico.* Report of San Miguel County. Folding view. 30 pp., paperbound. Las Vegas, 1882. $45.

PRIEST, Josiah. *Stories of the Revolution.* Folding plate. 32 pp. Albany, 1836. Half calf, uncut, $50.

PRIEST, Josiah. *A True Narrative of the Capture of David Ogden.* (Cover title.) Woodcut. Self wrappers. Lansingburgh, 1840. 1st ed. $75.

PRINCE, Thomas. *A Chronological History of New-England. Vol. 1.* Boston, 1736. 1st ed. Foxed. $25. [For the complete set, see G1YA.]

PRINDLE, Cyrus. *Memoir of the Rev. Daniel Meeker Chandler.* Middlebury, 1842. $42.50.

PRITTS, J. *Mirror of Olden Time Border Life.* Abingdon, Va., 1849. $35.

PROCEEDINGS of a Convention to Consider the Opening of the Indian Territory, Held at Kansas City, Mo., Feb. 8, 1888. 80 pp., paperbound. Kansas City, 1888. $35.

PROCEEDINGS of the Executive of the United States Respecting the Insurgents (The). Philadelphia, 1795. 1st ed. $32.50.

PROCEEDINGS of the 1st Annual Session of the Territorial Grange of Montana. Diamond City, 1875. $300.

PROCEEDINGS of a General Meeting Held at Chester Courthouse, Nov. 18, 1831. 16 pp., sewed, uncut. Columbia, S.C., 1832. $45.

PROGRESSIVE Men of Southern Idaho. Chicago, 1904. 1st ed. Leather binding cracked, $35.

PROSCH, J. W. *McCarver and Tacoma.* 2 plates. Seattle, no date [1906]. 1st ed. $25 and $27.50.

PROSE and Poetry of the Live Stock Industry of the United States. Vol. 1. (All published.) Leatherbound. Denver and Kansas City, no date [1905]. (By James W. Freeman.) 1st ed. $450. Another, $350. Rebacked, last leaf repaired, $400. New York, 1959. One of 550. $85.

PROSPECTUS of the Port Folio [New Series], a Monthly Miscellany, etc. 11 pp., stitched. Philadelphia, 1809. (By Joseph Dennie.) 1st ed. $45.

PROTEST of the Columbia Typographical Society . . . Against the Washington Institute. 21 pp., unbound. Washington, 1834. 1st ed. $45.

PSALMS, Hymns, and Spiritual Songs (The), of the Old and New Testament, Faithfully Translated into English Metre. (Revised Bay Psalm Book.) Boston, 1758. Edited by Thomas Prince. 1st Prince ed. $135.

PUBLIC and General Statute Laws of the State of Illinois (The). Chicago, 1839. 1st ed., 1st issue, with printer's credit line, "Printed and bound by O.C.B. Carter & Co., Roxbury, Mass." missing from title page. $150 or more. Later issue, $15 to $25.

PULTZ, Gustav von. *What the Wood Whispers to Itself.* Translated by E.E.H. New York, 1870. 1st ed. $25.

PUT'S Golden Songster. 64 pp., paperbound. San Francisco, no date [1858]. $25.

PYLE, Howard. *The Price of Blood.* Boards. Boston, 1899. 1st ed., first binding, with unlettered spine. $45.

PYRNELLE, Louise-Clarke. *Diddie, Dumps, and Tot, or Plantation Child-Life.* New York, 1882. 1st ed. $122.50.

R

R. B. ADAM Library Relating to Dr. Samuel Johnson and His Era (The). 3 vols. Buffalo, 1929. 1st ed. One of 500. In dust wrappers, $75.

RADICAL Reconstruction on the Basis of One Sovereign Republic. 17 pp., sewed. Sacramento, 1867. $45.

RAHT, Carlysle Graham. *The Romance of Davis Mountains and Big Bend Country.* Map, 13 plates. El Paso, no date [1919]. 1st ed. $35.

RAILROAD to San Francisco. (Caption title.) No place, no date [1849]. (By P. P. F. DeGrand.) $25.

RAINE, William MacLeod. *Cattle Brands. A Sketch of Bygone Days in the Cow-Country.* 8 pp., paperbound. Boston, no date [1920]. 1st ed. $27.50.

RAMSEY, Alex. *Message of the Governor in Relation to a Memorial from Half-breeds of Pembina.* 4 pp. St. Paul, 1849. In morocco case, $450.

RAMSEY, J. G. M. *Annals of Tennessee.* Map. Chattanooga, 1926. $40. [For 1860 ed., see *GIYA*.]

RAND, Thomas. *The Voice of the Turtle.* 52 pp., unbound. No place (Wrentham, Mass.), 1802. 1st ed. $37.50.

RANSOM, Will. *Private Presses and Their Books.* New York, 1929. One of 1,200. $25.

RAPPORT sur Les Missions du Diocèse de Québec, No. 7. Paperbound. Quebec, 1847. In slip case, $45.

RAUNICK, Selma M. and Margaret Schade. *The Kothmanns of Texas, 1845-1931.* Austin, 1931. $35.

RAVEN, Ralph. *Golden Dreams and Leaden Realities.* New York, 1853. (By George Payson.) 1st ed. Foxed, $37.50.

REAGAN, John H. *Memoirs, with Special Reference to Secession and the Civil War.* New York and Washington, 1906. Cover spotted, $25.

RECIO, Jesus T. *Tomochie! Episodios de la Compana de Chihuahua, 1893.* Rio Grande City, 1894. $100.

RÉCIT des Événemens qui out en Lieu sur le Térritoire des Sauvages. Boards. Montreal, 1818. (By Simon McGillivray.) $150.

REDFIELD, Levi. *A True Account of Some Memorable Events and Remarkable Occurrences in the Life of Levi Redfield, Late of Connecticut.* 24 pp., sewed. Norwich, no date [1798]. $50.

REDHEAD, H. W. *The Horseman.* Cleveland, 1855. $35.

REED, S. G. *A History of the Texas Railroads.* Houston, no date [1941]. 2d ed. $25.

REFORMED Practice of Medicine (The). 2 vols. in 1, boards. Boston, 1831. Rubbed, foxed, $27.50.

REGLAMENTO, e Instruccion para los Presidios que se Han de Formar en la Linea de Frontera de la Nueva Espana. 132 pp. Mexico, 1773. Modern vellum, $2,750. Another ed., 30 pp., paperbound, Mexico, 1834. $350.

REGULATIONS and List of Premiums of the Jerauld County Agricultural and Industrial Society for the First Fair to be Held at Wessington Springs, D.T. 16 pp., paperbound. Wessington Springs, 1884. $45.

REID, A. J. *The Resources and Manufacturing Capacity of the Fox River Valley.* Folding map and panorama, plates. 56 pp., paperbound. Appleton, 1874. $25.

REID, John C. *Reid's Tramp, or A Journal of the Incidents of Ten Months Travel Through Texas, New Mexico, etc.* Selma, Ala., 1858. $1,000 and up. (Auction record: $1,100, in 1958.)

REID, Samuel C., Jr. *The Scouting Expeditions of McCulloch's Texas Rangers.* Philadelphia, 1859. $27.50.

RELATION des Jésuites Contenant ce qui s'est Passé le Plus Remarquable dans les Missions des Pères de la Compagnie de Jésus dans la Nouvelle-France. 3 vols., morocco. Quebec, 1858. $100.

RELIEF Business Directory. Names and New Locations in San Francisco, Oakland, Berkeley and Alameda of 4,000 San Francisco Firms and Business Men. 64 pp., paperbound. Berkeley, May, 1906. $35.

REMARKS Upon the Delineated Presbyterian Play'd Hob With; or Clothes for a Stark Naked Author. 8 pp. Philadelphia, 1764. Half morocco, $45.

REMARKS on a Late Protest Against the Appointment of Mr. Franklin an Agent for This Province 7 pp. Philadelphia, 1764. (By Benjamin Franklin.) Bound together with William Smith's *An Answer to Mr. Franklin's Remarks on a Late Protest.* 22 pp. Philadelphia, 1764. Half morocco, $50.

REMARKS on a Late Publication in the Independent Gazetteer; with a Short Address to the People of Pennsylvania, etc. 72 pp. Philadelphia, 1783. Half morocco, $25.

REMARKS on the Quaker Unmask'd; or Plain Truth Found to Be Plain Falsehood. 8 pp. Philadelphia, no date [1764]. Morocco, cut close, affecting text, $27.50.

REMINGTON, Frederic. *Drawings.* Suede folio. New York,

1897. One of 250 signed copies. Hinges cracked, binding worn, $75.

REMINGTON, Frederic. *Frontier Sketches.* 15 plates. Chicago, 1898. 1st ed. $30.

REMINGTON, Frederic. *Men with the Bark On.* New York, 1900. $25.

REMINGTON, Frederic. *Sundown Leflare.* New York, 1899. $25.

REMINISCENCES of a Campaign in Mexico. Nashville, 1849. (By John B. Robertson.) 1st ed. Spine chipped, light foxing, stains, autographed, $75.

REMSBURG, John E. and George J. *Charley Reynolds, Soldier, Hunter, Scout and Guide.* Kansas City, 1931. One of 175. $37.50.

RENFROW, W. C. *Oklahoma and the Cherokee Strip.* Folding map. 16 pp., paperbound. Chicago, 1893. $35.

REPLY to Gen. Joseph Reed's Remarks on a Late Publication in the Independent Gazetteer (A). Philadelphia, 1783. (By John Cadwalader.) Half morocco, $25.

REPORT of the Board of Canal Commissioners, to the General Assembly of Ohio, etc. Sewed. Columbus, 1824. Uncut, $75. [For 1825 report, see *GIYA.*]

REPORT of the Board of Directors of Internal Improvements of the State of Massachusetts, on the Practicability and Expediency of a Railroad from Boston to the Hudson River, and from Boston to Providence. 6 folding plans. Boston, 1829. 1st ed. $85.

REPORT of the Secretary of the Interior, Communicating . . . The Report of J. Ross Browne, on the Late Indian War in Oregon and Washington Territories. 66 pp. Washington, 1858. 1st ed. New paper covers, $35.

REPORT on [sic] *the Secretary of the Navy, etc.* (December,

1864.) Half morocco. Washington, 1864. Inscribed, "Compliments of the Secretary of the Navy." $45.

REPORT from a Select Committee of the House of Representatives, on the Overland Emigration from Minnesota to British Oregon. St. Paul, 1858. Rebound in new cloth, $450.

REPORTS of the Committee of Investigation Sent in 1873, by the Mexican Government, to the Frontier of Texas. 3 folding maps. Leatherbacked boards. New York, 1875. $65.

RESIGNATION: An American Novel by a Lady. 2 vols., marbled boards, calf backs. Boston, 1825. (By Sarah Ann Evans.) 1st ed., with errata leaf in Vol. 1. $115.

RESOURCES of Arizona (The). 71 pp., paperbound. No place, no date [Florence, Ariz., 1881]. (By Patrick Hamilton.) 1st ed. $27.50.

RESOURCES and Development of the Territory of Washington. Folding map. 72 pp., unbound. Seattle, 1886. $35.

RESPONSE a une Addresse de la Chambre des Communes, en date du 23 Avril 1869, Demandant un Rapport Indiquant le Progrès qui ont été faits dans L'Ouverture d'une Communication entre Fort William et l'Établissement de la Rivière-Rouge . . . Par Orde Hector L. Langevin, Secrétaire d'Etat. 8 pp., half morocco. Ottawa, 1869. $25.

REVIEW of the Constitution Proposed by the Late Convention Held at Philadelphia, 1787; by a Federal Republican. 39 pp. Philadelphia, MDCCLXXXVII (1787). Half calf, uncut, $150.

REYNOLDS, J. N. *Voyage of the United States Frigate Potomac.* New York, 1835. Repaired and worn, $30.

REYNOLDS, John. *My Own Times.* Portrait. Illinois [Belleville], 1855. 1st ed. $125 and $110. Another, rebound in polished calf, $100.

REYNOLDS, John. *Sketches of the Country on the Northern*

Route from Belleville, Ill., to the City of New York, and Back by the Ohio Valley. Belleville, 1854. 1st ed. $200. Another, foxed, $130. Another, foxed, $100.

RHAPSODY (A). A Poem. 19 pp., unbound. New York, 1789. 1st ed. $185.

RHODES, Eugene Manlove. *The Little World Waddies.* Chico, Calif., no date [1946]. 1st ed. $30.

RHODES, John. *The Surprising Adventures and Sufferings of.* Newark, 1799. Covers loose, $25.

RHODES, W. H. *The Indian Gallows and Other Poems.* No place, 1846. $47.50.

RICE County: Its Resources, etc. 20 pp., paperbound. Faribault, Minn., 1860. $125.

RICH, Edward R. *Comrades Four.* New York and Washington, 1907. Top of spine torn, $40.

RICHARDS, T. *Georgia Illustrated.* 44 pp. Penfield, 1842. $75.

RICHARDS, Thomas Addison. *The Romance of American Landscape.* 16 engravings. Morocco. New York, no date [1854]. 1st ed. $27.50.

RICHARDSON, Maj. J. *Eight Years in Canada.* Montreal, 1847. $40.

RICHARDSON, Rupert N. *The Comanche Barrier to South Plains Settlement.* Glendale, 1933. $25.

RICHEY, James H. *A Trip Across the Plains in 1854.* 8 pp., paperbound. No place, no date [Richey, Calif., 1908]. $25.

RICHMOND During the War; Four Years of Personal Observation. New York, 1867. (By Sally A. Brock.) Rebound in buckram, $35.

RICHTOFEN, Walter Baron Von. *Cattle-Raising on the Plains of North America.* New York, 1885. 1st ed. $25.

RINGWALT, J. Luther. *American Encyclopedia of Printing.* Philadelphia, 1871. $25.

ROBB, John S. *Streaks of Squatter Life, and Far-West Scenes.* Philadelphia, 1847. 1st ed. Modern boards, $95.

ROBERTS, Kenneth. *Oliver Wiswell.* New York, 1940. 1st ed., limited. $25.

ROBERTS, W. H. *Northwestern Washington.* Folding map. 52 pp., paperbound. Port Townsend, 1880. $150.

ROBERTSON, John W. *Francis Drake and Other Early Explorers Along the Pacific Coast.* 28 maps. San Francisco, 1927. $45.

ROBINSON, Edwin Arlington. *The Man Who Died Twice.* New York, 1924. 1st ed., signed. Uncut and unopened, $25.

ROBINSON, J. A. *The White Rover.* 100 pp., paperbound. New York, no date. $35.

ROBSON, John S. *How a One Legged Rebel Lives.* Paperbound. Richmond, 1876. New buckram, paper covers bound in, $60.

RODD, Rennell. *Roseleaf and Appleleaf.* Philadelphia, 1882. 1st ed., India paper deluxe issue. $25.

RODENBOUGH, T. F. *Uncle Sam's Medal of Honor.* New York, 1886. 1st ed. $25.

RODRIGUEZ DE SAN MIGUEL, Juan. *Documentos Relativos al Piadoso Fondo de Misiones para Conversión y Civilización de las Numerosas Tribus Barbaras de la Antigua y Nueva California.* 60 pp. Mexico, 1845. Full calf, $350.

RODRIGUEZ DE SAN MIGUEL, Juan. *Rectificación de Graves Equivocaciónes en que Inciden los Sonores Terceros Poseedores de Bienes del Fondo Piadoso de Californias, etc.* 16 pp., sewed. Mexico, 1845. In morocco case, $200.

RODRIGUEZ DE SAN MIGUEL, Juan. *Segundo Cuaderno de Interesantes Documentos Relativos a los Bienes del*

Fondo Piadoso de Misiones, para Conversión y Civilización de las Tribus Barbaras de las Californias. 32 pp., paperbound. Mexico, 1845. $350.

ROE, Azel Stevens. *James Montjoy: or I've Been Thinking.* 2 parts, paperbound. New York, 1850. 1st ed. $50.

ROGERS, A. N. *Communication Relative to the Location of the U.P.R.R. Across the Rocky Mountains Through Colorado Territory.* Paperbound. Central City, 1867. Lacking back cover, $325.

ROLLINS, Phillip Ashton (ed.). *The Discovery of the Oregon Trail.* New York, 1935. $30.

ROLLINSON, John K. *History of the Migration of Oregon-Raised Herds to Mid-Western Markets. Wyoming Cattle Trails.* Plates, maps, colored frontispiece by Remington. Caldwell, 1948. Limited, signed ed. $25.

ROLLINSON, John K. *Hoofprints of a Cowboy and a U.S. Ranger.* Caldwell, 1941. In dust jacket, $25.

ROMANCE of Indian History; or, Thrilling Incidents in the Early Settlement of America. 24 pp., paperbound. New York, no date [185-?]. (By Adam Poe.) $35.

ROOD, Hosea W. *Story of the Service of Co. E.* Milwaukee, 1893. Front hinge cracked, $25.

ROOSEVELT, Franklin D. *The Democratic Book, 1936.* Paperbound. No place, 1936. Limited ed., signed by F.D.R. Leatherbound, with original covers bound in, $35.

ROOSEVELT, Theodore. *Letter of . . . Accepting the Republican Nomination for President of the United States.* 32 pp., self wrappers. No place [New York], 1902. 1st ed. $35.

ROOT, Henry. *Personal History and Reminiscences.* San Francisco, 1921. One of 100, signed. $30 and $25.

ROOT, Riley. *Musical Philosophy.* 20 pp., paperbound. Galesburg, 1866. $32.50.

ROSS, Mrs. William P. *The Life and Times of Hon. William P. Ross.* No place [St. Louis, Mo., or Fort Smith, Ark.?], no date [about 1893]. $25.

ROUX, Antoine. *A Collection of Pictures Painted by . . . and His Sons.* Text by Bres and Gaubert, translated by Alfred Johnson. Boards. Salem, 1925. One of 97 on large paper, boxed, $40.

ROWLAND, Benjamin. *The Wall-Paintings of India.* 30 colored plates. Boston, 1938. $45.

ROWLANDSON, Mrs. Mary. *A Narrative of the Captivity, Sufferings, and Removes, of.* Stitched, unbound. No place, no date [Leominster, Mass., 1794]. Uncut, title page repaired, small tears in last leaf, $75.

RUA, Hernando De La. *Constituciones, y Leyes Municipales de esta Provincia del S. Evangelio.* 32 pp. Mexico, 1667. Modern vellum, $750.

RUBESAMEN, Fred. *Grenzerleben, Bilder and Skizzen aus dem "Wilden Western."* Chicago, 1892. $45.

RUDD, Dan A. and Theo Bond. *From Slavery to Wealth: The Life of Scott Bond.* Madison, Ark., 1917. 1st ed. Rubbed, soiled, $25.

RUINED Deacon (The): A True Story. By a Lady. Paperbound. Boston, 1834. (By Mary L. Fox.) $75.

RULES for the Government of the Council of Wisconsin Territory. 10 pp., paperbound. Madison, 1843. $45. Madison, 1845, 11 pp., paperbound, $40.

RULES for the Government of the House of Representatives of Wisconsin Territory. 10 pp., paperbound. Madison, 1845. $75.

RULES and Orders of the House of Representatives of the Territory of Washington, 1864-5. 32 pp., paperbound. Olympia, 1864. $30.

RULES, Regulations, and By-Laws of the Board of Commissioners to Manage the Yosemite Valley and Mariposa Big Tree Grove. 23 pp., paperbound. Sacramento, 1885. $27.50.

RULES and Regulations of the Utah and Northern Railway, for the Government of Employees. Calfbound. Salt Lake City, 1879. $27.50.

RUPPIUS, Otto. *Das Vermächtniss des Pedlars. Roman aus dem Amerikanischen Leben.* Half morocco. St. Louis, 1859. $50.

RUPPIUS, Otto. *Der Prairie-Teufel. Roman aus dem Amerikanischen Leben.* Half morocco. St. Louis, 1861. $75 and $37.50.

RUPPIUS, Otto. *Geld und Geist. Roman aus dem Amerikanischen Leben.* Morocco. St. Louis, 1860. $50.

RUSSELL, Charles M. *Good Medicine.* Introduction by Will Rogers. New York, 1929. 1st ed. $30.

RUSSELL, Charles M. *Pen Sketches.* Leatherette, oblong. Great Falls, Mont., no date [1898]. 1st ed. $200. Holliday sale auction record, $310.

RUSSELL, Charles M. *Trails Plowed Under.* New York, 1927. 1st ed. In dust jacket, $25.

RUTTENBER, E. M. *History of the County of Orange: With a History of the Town and City of Newburgh.* Plates, maps. Newburgh, 1875. 1st ed. $30.

RUXTON, George F. *Adventures in Mexico and the Rocky Mountains.* New York, 1848. 1st Am. ed. $32.50.

S

SABIN, Edwin. *Kit Carson Days (1809-1868).* Chicago, 1919. 2d ed. $28.50. New York, 1935. 2 vols. One of 250. $35.

SABINE and Rio Grande Railroad Co. Memorial of Duff Green, President. 50 pp. Washington, 1860. $35.

SAGE, Rufus B. *Wild Scenes in Kansas and Nebraska, the Rocky Mountains, Oregon, California, Mexico, Texas, and the Grand Prairies.* Philadelphia, 1855. 3d ed. $25.

SALAZAR Ylarregui, Jose. *Datos de los Trabajos Astronomics y Topograficos, Dispuestos en Forma de Diario.* 2 folding maps. Mexico, 1850. $250.

SALPOINTE, Bishop J. B. *A Brief Sketch of the Mission of San Xavier del Bac with a Description of Its Church.* 20 pp., paperbound. San Francisco, 1880. $45.

SALPOINTE, Bishop J. B. *Soldiers of the Cross.* Portrait, 45 plates. Banning, Calif., 1898. 1st ed. $60. Another, inner hinge cracked, $25.

SAN BERNARDINO County, California. Ingersoll's Century Annals of 1769-1904. Los Angeles, 1904. $25.

SAN FRANCISCO Bay and California in 1776. Maps and facsimiles. 7 pp., boards. Providence, 1911. (By Pedro Font.) One of 125. $75.

SAN FRANCISCO Board of Engineers: Report Upon the City Grades. 27 pp., paperbound. San Francisco, 1854. $60.

SANDBURG, Carl. *The People, Yes.* New York, no date [1936]. 1st ed. One of 270 on large paper, signed. In slip case, $25.

SANDBURG, Carl. *Rootabaga Stories.* New York, no date [1922]. 1st ed. In dust jacket, $25 to $30.

SANDBURG, Carl. *Smoke and Steel.* Green boards. New York, 1920. 1st ed. In dust jacket, $25.

SANDERS, Daniel C. *A History of the Indian Wars with the First Settlers of the United States.* Montpelier, Vt., 1812. 1st ed. Worn, blank leaf missing, in slip case, $75.

SANDERS, Capt. John. *Memoirs on the Military Resources on the Valley of the Ohio.* 19 pp., unbound. Pittsburgh, 1845. $75. Another edition, with a review exhibiting the functions and relations of forts and ships by Lt. James L. Mason. 24 pp., unbound. Washington, 1845. $50.

SANDS, Frank. *A Pastoral Prince: The History and Reminiscences of J. W. Cooper.* Santa Barbara, 1893. $75.

SANSOM, Joseph. *Sketches of Lower Canada, Historical and Descriptive.* Frontispiece view of Quebec. Boards. New York, 1817. 1st ed. Uncut, spine repaired, $45.

SANTLEBEN, August. *A Texas Pioneer.* New York, 1910. $32.50.

SARA, Col. Delle. *Silver Sam; or, the Mystery of Deadwood City.* 166 pp., paperbound. New York, no date [1877]. $35.

SARINANA y Cuenca, Isidro. *Oración Funebre, que Dixo el Doctor D. Ysidro Sarinana y Cuenca Chantre de la Santa Iglesia Metropolitana de Mexico.* 25 pp. Mexico, 1681. $500 to $600.

SAVAGE, Timothy (pseud.). *The Amazonian Republic, Recently Discovered in the Interior of Peru.* Boards, paper label. New York, 1842. $75.

SAWYER, Eugene. *The Life and Career of Tiburcio Vasquez.* Oakland, 1944. One of 500. $35.

SAWYER, Lorenzo. *Way Sketches.* New York, 1926. One of 385. $25.

SCAMMON, Charles M. *The Marine Mammals of the Northwestern Coast of North America.* 27 plates. San Francisco, 1874. $100.

SCHARF, J. Thomas. *History of Delaware, 1609-1888.* 2 vols. Philadelphia, 1888. Rebound, $60.

SCHARMANN, H. B. *Scharmann's Overland Journey to Cali-*

fornia. No place, no date [New York, 1918]. Signed presentation copy, $50.

SCHMITZ, Joseph M. *Texan Statecraft, 1836-1845.* San Antonio, 1941. One of 200. $25.

SCHOEPF, Johann David. *Travels in the Confederation.* Translated and edited by Alfred J. Morrison. Portrait, 2 facsimiles. 2 vols. Philadelphia, 1911. $50.

SCHOOLCRAFT, Henry R. *Information Respecting the History, Condition, and Prospects of the Indian Tribes of the United States.* 6 vols., half morocco. Philadelphia, 1853. Reprint ed. $150. [For 1st ed., see *GIYA.*]

SCHOOLCRAFT, Henry R. *Narrative of an Expedition Through the Upper Mississippi to Itaska Lake, etc. . . . in 1832.* Folding map. New York, 1834. In ¾ leather, $25.

SCHOOLCRAFT, Henry R. *Personal Memoirs of a Residence of 30 Years with the Indian Tribes.* Philadelphia, 1851. $25.

SCHRANTZ, Ward L. *Jasper County, Missouri, in the Civil War.* Carthage, 1923. $32.50.

SCHURZ, William L. *Santa Rita, the University of Texas Oil Discovery.* 43 pp. No place [Austin?], 1943. 1st ed. $25.

SCHWETTMANN, Martin W. *The Manila Galleon.* New York, 1939. 1st ed. $40.

SCOTFORD, John. *The Judd Family.* Ann Harbor, 1869. 1st ed. $35.

SCOTT, The Rev. W. A. (ed.). *The Pacific Expositor. Vol. 1.* (Apparently all published.) San Francisco, 1859-60. Original wrapper bound in, $35.

SCRIBLER (The), Being a Letter From a Gentleman in Town to His Friend in the Country, etc. 24 pp. No place [Philadelphia], 1764. Half morocco, $45.

SCRIPPS, J. L. *The Undeveloped Northern Portion of the American Continent.* 20 pp., paperbound. Chicago, 1856. $75.

SEDGWICK, John. *Correspondence of.* 2 vols. No place [New York], 1902-3. 1st ed. One of 300. $50.

SEELIGSON, Mrs. Leila. *A History of Indianola.* 16 pp., paperbound. Cuero, no date [1930-31]. $25.

SELECT Translations and Imitations from the French of Marmontell and Gresset. By an Officer of the Army; who Fought for America, Under Gen. Wolfe, at the Taking of Quebec. New York, 1801. 1st ed. Defective, $45.

SERIES of Miscellaneous Letters (A), from a Father to His Children. 144 pp. South Hanover, Iowa, 1835. $35.

SEWELL, Anna. *Black Beauty.* Paperbound. Boston, 1890. 1st Am. ed. $25.

SEYMOUR, Capt. *The Isthmian Routes.* 27 pp., sewed. New York, 1863. $150. Another copy, $95. Another, $35.

SHARON Against Terry. In the Circuit Court of the United States, 9th Circuit, District of California. San Francisco, no date. Worn, $75.

SHAW, Edward. *Civil Architecture.* 97 plates. Calf. Boston, no date [1832]. 2d ed. Lacking endleaves, foxed, $25.

SHAW, Edward. *Rural Architecture.* 52 plates. Boston, 1843. 1st ed. Rubbed, $25.

SHERIDAN, Philip H. *Outline Descriptions of the Posts in the Military Division of the Missouri, etc.* Folding map. Chicago, 1872. Most of paper label on spine missing, $50.

SHERMAN, Roger. *An Astronomical Diary, or, An Almanack for . . . 1760.* Boston, 1760. Bound in modern cloth, dampstained, $25.

SHERWELL, Samuel. *Old Recollections for an Old Boy.* New York, 1923. 1st ed. $45.

SHIELDS, G. O. *The Battle of the Big Hole.* New York, 1889. 1st ed. $25.

SHINN, Charles Howard. *Pacific Rural Handbook.* San Francisco, 1879. $25.

SHIPMAN, Mrs. O. L. *Taming the Big Bend.* Folding map, 4 plates. No place [Austin?], no date [1926]. $35.

SHOEMAKER, James. *Directory of the City of Mankato, and Blue Earth County.* Boards. Mankato, 1888. $40.

SHORT Abridgement of Christian Doctrine (A). 16 pp., leather. No place, no date [Mexico, 1787]. $60.

SHORT Account of Algiers (A) . . . *With a Concise View of the Origin of the Rupture Between Algiers and the United States.* Folding map. Philadelphia, 1794. (By Mathew Carey.) 1st ed. Unbound, $25.

SHORT Narrative of the Horrid Massacre in Boston (A), Perpetrated in the Evening of the 5th Day of March, 1770. Boston, 1770. (By James Bowdoin?) 1st ed., 3d issue, 48 and 88 pp. Half calf, $125.

SIGUENZA y Gongora, Carlos de. *Trofeo de la Justicia Espanola en el Castigo de la Alevosia Francesa que al Abrigo de la Armada de Barlovento, etc.* 100 pp. Mexico, 1691. Full crushed levant binding (Riviere), $2,500.

SILLIMAN, Benjamin. *Report Upon the Oil Property of the Philadelphia and California Petroleum Co.* Maps. 36 pp., paperbound. Philadelphia, 1865. $200.

SILVER Mines of Virginia and Austin, Nevada. 19 pp., paperbound. Boston, 1865. $75.

SIMPSON, Elizabeth M. *Bluegrass Houses and Their Traditions.* Lexington, 1932. $25.

SIMPSON, Gen. James H. *Coronado's March in Search of the Seven Cities of Cibola.* Map. 34 pp., paperbound. Washington, 1884. $45.

SIMPSON, James H. *Journal of a Military Reconnaissance, from Santa Fe, N.M., to the Navajo Country.* Folding map, 75 plates, 23 colored. Philadelphia, 1852. $35 and $45.

SIMPSON, Capt. James H. *Report of Explorations Across the Great Basin of the Territory of Utah, etc.* Folding map, plates, errata leaf. Washington, 1876. $35.

SIMPSON, James H. *Report from the Secretary of War . . . and Map of the Route from Fort Smith, Ark., to Santa Fe, N.M.* 4 folding maps. ¾ morocco. No place, no date [Washington, 1850]. Hinges cracked, $25.

SIRINGO, Charles A. *A Cowboy Detective.* Clothbound. Chicago, 1912. 1st ed., 1st issue, pub. by Conkey. $30. Paperbound, 2d issue, same date, pub. by Ogilvie, $30.

SIRINGO, Charles A. *History of "Billy the Kid."* 142 pp., paperbound. No place [Santa Fe], 1920. 1st ed. $60 and $55.

SIRINGO, Charles A. *Riata and Spurs.* 16 plates. Boston, 1927. 1st ed., 1st issue, with "1927" on title page. $25 and $30.

SIRINGO, Charles A. *A Texas Cowboy.* Chicago, 1886. 1st ed., 2d issue, 347 pp. $27.50. [For 1st issue and a reprint, see *GIYA*.]

SITGREAVES, Lorenzo. *Report of an Expedition Down the Zuni and Colorado Rivers.* 79 plates, folding map. Washington, 1853. 1st ed. Rebacked, ex-library, $27.50.

SIXTY Years of the Life of Jeremy Levis. 2 vols., boards, cloth backs, paper labels. New York, 1831. (By Laughton Osborn.) 1st ed. Uncut, $65.

SKETCH of the Geographical Rout of a Great Railway . . . Between the Atlantic States and the Great Valley of the Mississippi. Folding map. 16 pp., half cloth. New York, 1829. (By William C. Redfield.) 1st ed. $50.

SKETCHES of Springfield, etc. By a Citizen. 49 pp., plus 21 pp. of ads, paperbound. Springfield, Ohio, no date [1852]. $60.

SKETCHES of the West, or the Home of the Badgers. Folding map. 48 pp., paperbound. Milwaukee, 1847. (By J. B. Grinnell.) $200. Another, lacking map and covers, bound in half morocco, $45.

SLOCUM, Joshua. *Voyage of the Destroyer from New York to Brazil.* 47 pp., paperbound. Boston, 1894. 1st ed. Edges chipped, $50.

SMEDLEY, William. *Across the Plains in '62.* Map. Boards. No place, no date [Denver, 1916]. Author's photograph, signed, mounted on half title, $70.

SMITH, Adam. *An Inquiry into the Nature and Causes of the Wealth of Nations.* 3 vols. Philadelphia, 1789. 1st Am. ed. $75.

SMITH, Buckingham (trans.). *Narratives of the Career of Hernando de Soto in the Conquest of Florida.* Folding map. Boards. New York, 1866. One of 75. $32.50, $50, and $60.

SMITH, Buckingham (trans.). *The Discovery of Florida.* San Francisco, 1946. One of 280. $25, $45, $65.

SMITH, Charles. *Universal Geography Made Easy; or, A New Geographical Pocket Companion.* New York, 1795. 1st ed. $55.

SMITH, Frank Meriweather (ed.). *San Francisco Vigilance Committee of '56.* 83 pp., paperbound. San Francisco, 1883. 1st ed. Cloth, original covers bound in, $28.50.

SMITH, Harry B. *A Sentimental Library.* No place [New York], 1914. 1st ed. $35.

SMITH, J. Calvin. *A New Guide for Travelers Through the United States With the Distances from Place to Place.* Folding map. New York, 1848. $27.50.

SMITH, J. Calvin. *The Western Tourist and Emigrant's Guide.* Colored folding map. New York, 1839. 1st ed. $37.50. New York, 1845. $35. [See title entry in *GIYA*.]

SMITH, J. R. *A Key to the Art of Drawing the Human*

Figure. 24 plates. Boards. Philadelphia, 1831. 1st ed. Text stained, binding loose, $30.

SMITH, Capt. James E. *A Famous Battery and Its Campaigns, 1861-64.* Washington, 1892. $27.50.

SMITH, Jerome V. C. *Natural History of the Fishes of Massachusetts.* Boston, 1833. 1st ed. Foxed, in slip case, $30.

SMITH, Joseph. *The Book of Mormon in Mormon Characters, or the Deseret Alphabet.* New York, 1869. $45. [For orthodox American eds., including the 1st, see *GIYA.*]

SMITH, Wallace. *Garden of the Sun: A History of the San Joaquin Valley, 1772-1939.* 558 pp. Los Angeles, no date [1939]. 1st ed. $50. Reprint ed., $10.

SMITH, William H. *Canadian Gazeteer.* Toronto, 1846. 1st ed., 1st issue, with numbers instead of place names on the map. $100. Later issues, same year, $75.

SMITH, William H. *History of Canada.* Folding table. 2 vols., boards, paper labels. Quebec, 1815. 1st ed. Uncut, $100.

SMITHSONIAN Institution. Annual Report of. Washington, 1871. $35.

SMITHWICK, Noah. *The Evolution of a State.* Austin, no date [1900]. 1st ed. $27.50.

SNELLING, William J. *The Polar Regions of the Western Continent Explored.* Boston, 1831. 1st ed. Foxed, front hinge cracked, rubbed, $75.

SOLIS, Father Antonio de. *Tesoro De La Iglesia Católica.* Vellum. Lima, 1650. Cover and title page repaired, $285.

SOME Account of the Work of Stephen J. Field, etc. No place [New York?], no date [1881]. (By Chauncey F. Black.) $40. [For a later edition, see *GIYA.*]

SOME Southwestern Trails. Essays by J. Evetts Haley and others. El Paso, 1928. Ltd. ed. $25.

SOUTH Carolina Jockey Club (The). Charleston, 1857. (By John B. Irving.) 1st ed. $37.50. Another, dampstained, $50.

SOUTHWORTH, S. S. *California for Fruit-Growers and Consumptives.* Folding map, plates. 108 pp., paperbound. Sacramento, 1883. $25.

SOWELL, A. J. *Early Settlers and Indian Fighters of Southwest Texas.* 12 plates. Austin, 1900. $150 and $100. Another, lightly damaged by smoke, $75.

SPARGO, John. *The Potters and Potteries of Bennington.* Boards. Boston, 1926. One of 800. $27.50.

SPAVERY (comp.). *The Harp of a Thousand Strings; or, Laughter for a Lifetime.* New York, no date [1858]. (By George Washington Harris.) 1st ed., with frontispiece in buff and black, imprints of both Craighead and Jenkins on copyright page, and perfect "y" in last word on page 55. $150.

SPEARS, John R. *Illustrated Sketches of Death Valley and Other Borax Deserts of the Pacific Coast.* Chicago, 1892. 1st ed. $50.

SPECIMENS: A Stevens-Nelson Paper Catalogue. Half goatskin. No place, no date [New York, 1953]. Boxed, $85.

SPILMAN, The Rev. T. E. *Semi-Centenarians of Butler Grove Township, Montgomery County, Illinois.* No place, no date. Spine taped, $27.50.

SPIRIT of '76 (The). Vol. 1. Frankfort, 1826. $185.

SPORTS of Childhood. 18 pp., paperbound. Northampton, no date [about 1830-40]. $42.50.

SPOTTS, D. L. *Campaigning with Custer.* Los Angeles, 1928. One of 800. $30.

SPRAGUE, Maj. J. T. *The Treachery in Texas.* 35 pp., paperbound. New York, 1862. $35.

SPRING, Agnes W. *Seventy Years: A Panoramic History of the Wyoming Stock Growers Association.* Stiff paper covers. No place [Cheyenne], 1942. 1st ed. $57.50 and $35.

SQUIRE, W. C. *Resources and Development of Washington Territory.* Folding map. 72 pp., paperbound. Seattle, 1886. $35.

STANLEY, David S. *Diary of a March from Fort Smith, Ark., to San Diego, Calif., Made in 1853.* 37 pp., multigraphed. No place, no date. In cloth case, $75.

STANLEY, F. *One Half Miles from Heaven, or, The Cimmaron Story.* 155 pp., paperbound. Denver, 1949. $30.

STATUTES of Columbia College in New-York (The). Folding chart. 18 pp., paperbound, stitched. New York, 1785. 1st ed. $150.

STEARNS, Charles. *Facts in the Life of Gen. Taylor.* 35 pp., unbound. Boston, 1848. $25.

STEELE, John. *In Camp and Cabin.* Paperbound. Lodi, Wis., 1901. 1st ed. In linen case, $130.

STEELE, Oliver G. *The Western Guide Book and Emigrants' Directory.* Map. Buffalo, 1836. 4th ed. $35.

STEELE, R. J., and others. *Directory of the County of Placer.* Boards. San Francisco, 1861. $200.

STEIN, Gertrude. *Things as They Are.* Pawlet, Vt., 1950. 1st ed. One of 516. $25.

STEIN, Gertrude and Virgil Thomson. *Four Saints in Three Acts. An Opera.* Boards. New York, no date [1948]. 1st ed. One of 30 on rag paper, signed, with sheet of music in ms. laid in. $50.

STEINBECK, John. *The First Watch.* Paperbound. Los Angeles, no date [1947]. 1st ed. One of 60. $25.

STEINBECK, John. *To a God Unknown.* New York, no date

[1933]. 1st ed., 1st issue, with Ballou imprint. In dust jacket, $30.

STEINBECK, John and Edward F. Ricketts. *Sea of Cortez.* New York, 1941. 1st ed. $25.

STEVENS, Capt. C. A. *Berdan's United States Sharpshooters, etc.* St. Paul, 1892. Worn, $40.

STEVENS and Conover. *Branch County Directory and Historical Record.* Ann Arbor, 1871. $45.

STEVENS, George W. *Adventures. American Anecdotes. Biographical, Historical and Descriptive.* Dansville, 1845. $75.

STEVENS, Isaac I. *Campaigns of the Rio Grande and of Mexico.* 108 pp., paperbound. New York, 1851. $45.

STEVENSON, Alexander, M.D. *The Life, Doings, Trials and Literary Career of.* 47 pp., paperbound. Pittsburgh, 1856. 1st ed. $25.

STEVENSON, B. F. *Letters From the Army.* Cincinnati, 1884. Rebound, $30.

STEVENSON, R. Randolph, M.D. *The Southern Side: or, Andersonville Prison.* Baltimore, 1876. Rebound, $30.

STEVENSON, Robert Louis. *Memoirs of Himself.* Boards. Philadelphia, 1912. 1st ed. One of 45. Uncut, in slip case, $60.

STILES, Ezra. *A History of Three of the Judges of King Charles I.* 8 plates. Hartford, 1794. 1st ed., 1st issue, with errata slip. $25 and $37.50. 1st ed., 2d issue, same date, lacking errata slip, $20 to $25.

STILLMAN, J. B. B. *The Horse in Motion.* Boston, 1882. 1st ed. $65.

STIPP, G. W. *The Western Miscellany.* Xenia, Ohio, 1827. Defective, $1,000 (auction price, 1958).

STOBO, Maj. Robert. *Memoirs of.* Folding plan. Pittsburgh, 1854. $37.50.

STOCKTON, Frank R. *The Floating Prince and Other Fairy Tales.* New York, 1881. 1st ed. $150.

STODDARD, Maj. Amos. *Sketches, Historical and Descriptive of Louisiana.* Philadelphia, 1812. Worn, $57.50.

STODDARD, Solomon. *Question Whether God Is Not Angry with the Country for Doing So Little Towards the Conversion of the Indians?* Boston, 1723. In full morocco binding by Riviere, $100.

STONE, Charles P. *Notes on the State of Sonora.* 28 pp., paperbound. Washington,1861. Presentation copy, $125.

STORIES from the Harvard Advocate. Half morocco. Cambridge, 1896. 1st ed. Uncut, $25.

STORY of Cripple Creek (A), The Greatest Gold Mining Camp on Earth. Folding map. 28 pp., paperbound. No place, no date [Denver, 1896]. $25.

STORY of Louis Riel, Rebel Chief (The). Toronto, 1885. (By J. E. Collins.) 1st ed. $35.

STOTZ, Charles Morse. *The Early Architecture of Western Pennsylvania.* Pittsburgh, 1936. $25.

STOWE, Harriet Beecher. *A Key to Uncle Tom's Cabin.* Paperbound and clothbound. Boston, 1853. 1st ed. Paperbound, $35. Clothbound, $6 and $8. [For *Uncle Tom's Cabin,* see *GIYA.*]

STRAHORN, Carrie A. *Fifteen Thousand Miles by Stage.* New York, 1911. 1st ed. $50. New York, 1915. 2d ed. $35. [See *GIYA.*]

STRAHORN, Robert E. *The Handbook of Wyoming, and Guide to the Black Hills and Big Horn Regions.* Paperbound. Cheyenne, 1877. 1st ed. $50. Another, clothbound, $35.

STRANG, James J. *The Book of the Law of the Lord.* 80 pp.

No place, no date [Kansas City, 1927]. Pencil notes on front flyleaf, $50.

STRANGER'S Guide to St. Louis, or What to See and How to See It, etc. Folding map. St. Louis, 1867. 1st ed. $25.

STRATTON, R. B. *Captivity of the Oatman Girls.* 3 plates. New York, 1858. 3d ed. $35. [For earlier eds., see *GIYA*.]

STREETER, Floyd Benjamin. *Prairie Trails and Cow Towns.* Boston, no date [1936]. 1st ed. $50 to $65. [Supersedes entry in *GIYA*.]

STRICKLAND, William. *Reports on Canals, Railways, Roads, and Other Subjects.* 58 plates. Philadelphia, 1826. $120.

STRICTURES Addressed to James Madison on the Celebrated Report of W. H. Crawford Recommending Intermarriage of Americans with the Indian Tribes. 22 pp., paperbound. Philadelphia, 1824. (By T. Cooper.) Uncut, $35.

STRICTURES of the Friendly Address Examined (The), and a Refutation of Its Principles Attempted. No place [New York], 1775. (By Thomas Bradbury Chandler.) 1st ed. $85.

STRICTURES on a Voyage to South America, as Indited by the "Secretary of the (Late) Mission" to La Plata, etc. By a Friend of Truth and Sound Policy. 108 pp., paperbound. Baltimore, 1820. Uncut, $45.

STRONG, Gen. W. E. *A Trip to the Yellowstone National Park in July, August, and September, 1875.* 2 maps, 7 portraits, 7 views. Morocco. Washington, 1876. $75.

STUBBS, Robert. *Browne's Cincinnati Almanac, for . . . 1811.* Cincinnati, no date [1810]. $75.

SULLIVAN, James. *Observations Upon the Government of the United States of America.* Pamphlet, removed. Boston, 1791. Foxed, writing, repairs to title page and binding, $30.

SULLIVAN, Maurice S. (ed.). *The Travels of Jedediah Smith.* Santa Ana, 1934. 1st ed. $75. [Supersedes Smith entry in *GIYA.*]

SUMMERFIELD, Charles. *The Rangers and Regulators of the Tanaha.* New York, 1856. 1st ed. Flyleaves and frontispiece stained, $25.

SUPERIOR Court of the City and County of San Francisco (In the) . . . *Sarah Althea Sharon, Plaintiff, vs. William Sharon, Defendant.* San Francisco, no date [about 1884]. $25.

SUTTER, John A. *New Helvetia Diary.* 2 color plates, facsimile, map. San Francisco, 1939. $37.50 and $25.

SUTTON, J. J. *History of the 2d Regiment, West Virginia Cavalry Vounteers.* Portsmouth, 1892. $25.

SWALLOW BARN, Or, A Sojourn in the Old Dominion. 2 vols. Boards. Philadelphia, 1832. (By John Pendleton Kennedy.) 1st ed. $50.

SWAMP Outlaws (The), or the Lowery Bandits of North Carolina. 84 pp., paperbound. New York, no date [1872]. Corner missing from two pages, $35.

SWISS Family Robinson (The). 2 vols. New York, 1832. (By Johann David Wyss.) 1st Am. ed. Front hinge of Vol. 1 partly cracked, $150.

T

TALBOT, Theodore. *The Journals of* . . . *1843 and 1849-52.* Edited by Charles H. Carey. Portland, 1931. 1st ed. $25.

TALES of the Northwest; or, Sketches of Indian Life and Character. By a Resident Beyond the Frontier. Boston, 1830. (By William J. Snelling.) Uncut, in slip case, spine remounted, faint stamp on title page, $100. Another, $125.

TALLAPOOSA Land, Mining and Manufacturing Co., Haralson County. Map. 32 pp., paperbound. Tallapoosa, 1887. $25.

TARASCON, Louis A. *The Opening of a Wagon Road from the River Missouri, North of the River Kansas, to the River Columbia.* 12 pp., morocco. Washington, 1824. $50.

TARKINGTON, Booth. *The Ohio Lady.* Paperbound. No place, 1916. $30.

TARRANT, Sgt. E. *The Wild Riders of the 1st Kentucky Cavalry.* Louisville, no date [1894]. Rebound in new cloth, title page ragged, paper yellowed, corners off several pages, $40.

TAYLOR, Amos. *A Narrative of the Strange Principles, Conduct, and Character of the . . . Shakers.* Worcester, MDCCLXXXII (1782). 1st ed. $100 and up.

TAYLOR, Benjamin F. (ed.). *Short Ravelings from a Long Yarn.* Santa Ana, 1936. 2d ed. $25.

TAYLOR, James W. *Northwest British America and Its Relations to the State of Minnesota.* St. Paul, 1860. $250.

TAYLOR, Joseph H. *Beavers—Their Ways and Other Sketches.* 20 plates. Washburn, N.D., 1904. 1st ed. Cover spotted, $30.

TAYLOR, Lee M. *The Texan: A Tale of Texas.* 106 pp. No place, 1908. With pp. 171-174 mutilated (as reported in all copies located), $50. (Let's find a copy *NOT* mutilated.)

TAYLOR, T. U. *Fifty Years on Forty Acres.* No place, 1938. 1st ed. $25.

TAYLOR, T. U. *Jesse Chisholm.* Bandera, no date [1939]. 1st ed. $25.

TAYLOR and Tallmadge. *The Bill to Authorize the People of Missouri to Form a Constitution and State Government.* 16 pp., sewed. No place, no date [1819]. $35.

TAYLOR, Zachary. *Letters of . . . from the Battle Fields of the Mexican War*. Rochester, 1908. One of 300. $25.

TEHAUNTEPEC Railway: Its Location Features and Advantages Under the LaSere Grant of 1869. Folding map. New York, 1869. $30.

TEMPLAR (The). To Which is Added Tales of the Passaic. By a Gentleman of New York. Hackensack, 1822. $150.

TERRITORY of Wyoming (The); Its History, Soil, Climate, Resources, etc. 84 pp., paperbound. Laramie City, 1874. (By J. K. Jeffrey.) 1st ed. In cloth case, $200. Another copy, $125. (These catalogue prices are later than a $210 auction price achieved by a lightly stained copy at the Bauer sale in 1958.)

TEXAS, the Home for the Emigrant, from Everywhere. Folding map. 43 pp., printed front paper cover. Houston, 1875. (By J. B. Robertson.) $45. St. Louis, 1876. Cover frayed, $25.

THADEUS Amat and Others Against Mexico. Argument for the Defense Before the Honorable Umpire. 50 pp., unbound. No place, no date [Washington, 1876]. Original signatures, unbound, unopened. $25.

THAYER, Mrs. J. *The Drunkard's Daughter*. Boston, 1842. 1st ed. Lacking end leaf, $25.

THISSELL, G. W. *Crossing the Plains in '49*. Oakland, 1903. 1st ed. $37.50.

THOMAS, Dylan. *Twenty-six Poems*. Boards. No place, no date [New York, 1949]. 1st ed. One of 140, signed, boxed. $75.

THOMAS, Henry W. *History of the Doles-Cook Brigade, Army of Northern Virginia*. Atlanta, 1903. Rebound in buckram, $35.

THOMAS, P. J. *Founding of the Missions*. Map, plates. San Francisco, 1877. $75.

THOMAS, Robert B. *(No. 1.) The Farmer's Almanac . . . 1793*. Boston, no date [1792]. 1st ed. Up to $100. Boston,

1816. 1st issue, with "Rain, hail, and snow" prediction for July 13. $150 and up. Complete run, all years: Up to $1,000.

THOMPSON, Capt. B. F. *History of the 112th Regiment of Illinois Volunteer Infantry, 1862-1865.* Toulon, 1885. Rebound, rubbed, paper brittle, $25.

THOMPSON, David. *David Thompson's Narrative of His Exploratons in Western America, 1784-1812.* Edited by J. B. Tyrell. Toronto, 1916. One of 550. $290. Another, $150. [Supersedes entry in *GIYA*.]

THOMPSON, Ed. Porter. *History of the Orphan Brigade.* Louisville, 1898. Rebound, $40.

THOMPSON, R. A. *Conquest of California.* 33 pp., paperbound. Santa Rosa, 1896. $30.

THOMPSON, Lieut. S. D. *Recollections with the 3d Iowa Regiment.* Cincinnati, 1864. Worn, cover dull, $25.

THOREAU, Henry. *Cape Cod.* Boston, 1865. 1st ed. $50.

THORNTON, J. Quinn. *Oregon and California in 1848.* Folding map. 2 vols. New York, 1849. 1st ed. $50, $62.50, $75. Another, foxed, spine of Vol. 1 chipped, $60. New York, 1855, 2 vols., $35.

THOUGHTS on the Destiny of Man. 96 pp., paperbound. Harmony, Ind., 1824. (By George Rapp.) $75.

THOUGHTS on the Proposed Annexation of Texas to the United States. 55 pp., paperbound. New York, 1844. (By Theodore Sedgwick.) $27.50.

THRALL, The Rev. Homer S. *A Pictorial History of Texas.* Folding map. Leather. St. Louis, 1879. 4th ed. $25.

THWAITES, Reuben Gold (ed.). *Atlas Accompanying the Original Journals of the Lewis and Clark Expedition, 1804-1806.* Facsimiles, 62 folding maps, 16 pp. text, boxed. New York, 1959. $35.

THWAITES, Reuben Gold (ed.). *Original Journals of The Lewis and Clark Expedition, 1804-1806.* 15 vols. New York, 1904-5. One of 50 on Japan vellum, $750. [For 8-vol. ed., see *GIYA.*]

TIMBERLAKE, Lieut. Henry. *Memoirs, 1756-1765.* Johnson City, Tenn., 1927. One of 35. $35.

TIMOTHY Crump's Ward. Boston, 1866. (By Horatio Alger, Jr.) 1st ed., published by Loring. $500 to $1,000.

TIPTON, R. B. *Directory of Marshalltown.* Boards. Marshalltown, Iowa, 1884. $35.

TITTSWORTH, W. G. *Outskirt Episodes.* No place, no date [Avoca, Iowa, 1927]. In dust jacket, $40. Another, lacking jacket, $40.

TO THE QUARTERLY and Monthly Meetings of Friends in Great Britain, Ireland, and America. 4 pp., leaflet. No place, no date [Philadelphia, 1751]. (Printed by Benjamin Franklin.) Repairs in folds, $950.

TODD, The Rev. John. *The Lost Sister of Wyoming.* Northampton, 1842. 1st ed. $25.

TOPOGRAPHICAL Description of the State of Ohio, Indiana Territory, and Louisiana (A). 5 plates. Boston, 1812. (By Jervis Cutler.) Original ed. $250. Others, $135 and $160. [Supersedes entry in *GIYA.*]

TOPONCE, Alexander. *Reminiscences of Alexander Toponce, Pioneer, 1839-1923.* Fabrikoid binding. 1st ed. No place, no date [Ogden, Utah, 1923]. $25.

TOPPING, E. S. *The Chronicles of the Yellowstone.* Folding map. St. Paul, 1883. $25, $30, $37.50.

TORNEL, Jose Maria (trans.). *Diario Historico del Ultimo Viaje que Hizo M. de La Sale Para Descubrir el Desembocadero y Curso del Missicipi.* Boards. New York, 1831. $75.

TOUR Through Upper and Lower Canada (A). By a Citizen of the United States. Litchfield, 1799. (By J. C. Ogden.) $65 and $60. Another, rebacked, $57.50.

TRAITS of American Indian Life. By a Fur Trader. San Francisco, 1933. (By Duncan Finlayson.) One of 500. Uncut, $27.50.

TRANSACTIONS of the Chicago Academy of Sciences. Vol. 1, Part 1, and Vol. 1, Part 2. Plates, lithographs, folding map, separate title page for Part 2. Chicago, 1867 and 1869. $125.

TRANSCRIPT of Record of Proceedings Before the Mexican and American Mixed Claims Commission with Relation to the "Pious Fund of the Californias." Washington, 1902. $60.

TRAUBEL, Horace L. (ed.). *At the Graveside of Walt Whitman: Harleigh, Camden, New Jersey, March 30th, and Sprigs of Lilac.* 37 pp., paperbound. No place [Philadelphia], 1892. 1st ed. $25.

TRAUBEL, Horace L. *Camden's Compliment to Walt Whitman.* Philadelphia, 1889. 1st ed. $25.

TRAVELS of Capts. Lewis and Clarke (The), by Order of the Government of the United States, Performed in the Years 1804-6, Being Upwards of 3,000 Miles, from St. Louis by Way of the Missouri and Columbia Rivers to the Pacifick Ocean. Folding map and 5 portraits of Indians. Philadelphia, 1809. $57.50. [Counterfeit ed. For authentic 1st ed., see entry under *Lewis and Clark.* Also, see *GIYA.*]

TRAVELS on the Western Slope of the Mexican Cordillera. 438 pp., paperbound. San Francisco, 1857. (By Marvin Wheat.) 1st ed. $65. Another, back cover missing, corner of front cover, title page, and leaf listing illustrations broken off, $45. [Supersedes entry under *Wheat* in *GIYA.*]

TREATY Between the United States and the Chasta and Other Tribes of Indians. Paperbound. No place, no date [Washington, 1855]. (By Joel Palmer.) $50.

TREATY Between the United States and the Comanche and Kiowa Tribes of Indians . . . *Proclaimed May 26, 1866.* 8 pp., folio. No place, no date [Washington, 1866]. $35.

TREATY Between the United States and the Creek and Seminole Tribes of Indians . . . *Ratified March 6, 1845.* 6 pp., folio. No place, no date [Washington, 1845]. $35.

TREATY Between the United States and the Klamath and Moadoc Tribes and Yahooskin Band of Snake Indians . . . *Proclaimed Feb. 17, 1870.* 8 pp., folio. No place, no date [Washington, 1870]. $35.

TREATY Between the United States and the Nez Perce Tribe of Indians . . . *Proclaimed April 20, 1867.* 10 pp., folio. No place, no date [Washington, 1867]. $25.

TREATY (The) Held with the Indians of the 6 Nations at Philadelphia in July, 1742. Philadelphia, MDCCXLIII (1743). (Printed by Benjamin Franklin.) $900 (auction price, 1954).

TREATY Held at the Town of Lancaster in Pennsylvania (A), by the Honourable the Lieutenant-Governor of the Province, etc. Philadelphia, 1744. Title page worn, stained, mounted on modern paper, as is last leaf; other repairs; modern brown paper covers, $185.

TRENT, Capt. William. *Journal of* . . . *from Logstown to Pickawillany, A.D. 1752.* Cincinnati, 1871. $25.

TRIAL of Daniel Isaac Eaton (The). New York, 1794. $37.50.

TRIAL of Impeachment of Levi Hubbell. Madison, 1853. Backstrip worn, $45.

TRIBES and Temples: A Record of the Expedition to Middle America Conducted by the Tulane University of Louisiana in 1925. 2 vols. New Orleans, 1926. $50.

TRIBUNE Book of Open Air Sports (The). Edited by Henry Hall. New York, 1887. $25.

TRIGGS, J. H. *History and Directory of Laramie City, Wyoming Territory.* 91 pp., paperbound. Laramie City, 1875. 1st ed. In folding case, $300.

TROLLOPE, Anthony. *The American Senator.* Green cloth. Detroit, 1877. Variant issue, "Craig & Taylor" on spine. Marginal defects in 4 leaves, $25.

TRUE and Impartial State of the Province of Pennsylvania (A). Philadelphia, 1759. Half morocco, $75.

TRUETT, Velma Stevens. *On the Hoof in Nevada.* Los Angeles, 1950. $25.

TRUMBULL, John. *M'Fingall: A Modern Epic Poem, in Four Cantos.* Paperbound, stitched. Hartford, 1782. 1st complete ed. Uncut, unopened, spine missing, $100.

TRUTH Will Out! The Foul Charges of the Tories Against the Editor of the Aurora Repelled by Positive Proof and Plain Truth, etc. No place, no date [Philadelphia, 1798]. (By William Duane.) 1st ed. Unbound, uncut and unopened, $35.

TUCKER, H. S. G. *Introductory Lecture Delivered by the Professor of Law in the University of Virginia, at the Opening of the Law School.* 24 pp. Charlottesville, 1841. $35.

TUCKER, Dr. J. C. *To the Golden Goal, and Other Sketches.* San Francisco, 1895. One of 50. $45.

TUFTS, James. *A Tract Descriptive of Montana Territory.* 15 pp., sewed. New York, 1865. $75.

TULLIDGE, Edward W. *The History of Salt Lake City and Its Founders.* Salt Lake City, no date [1886]. $25.

TURNER, Mary Honeyman Ten Eyck. *These High Plains.* Amarillo, 1941. One of 150. $37.50.

TURNER, T. G. *Gazetteer of the St. Joseph Valley, Michigan and Indiana, etc.* Chicago, 1867. Waterstained, $25.

TUTTLE, C. R. *History of Grand Rapids*. Grand Rapids, 1874. Hinge cracked, $27.50.

TWAIN, Mark. *The Adventures of Huckleberry Finn*. New York, 1885. (By Samuel Langhorne Clemens.) 1st ed., 1st issue. Original plate on page 283 bound in. ¾ morocco, rubbed, $175. [For 1st ed. points and other prices, see *GIYA*.]

TWAIN, Mark. *The Celebrated Jumping Frog of Calaveras County, and Other Sketches*. Edited by John Paul. New York, 1867. (By Samuel Langhorne Clemens.) 1st ed., 1st issue, red cloth, with perfect "i" in "this" in last line on page 198 and with page of yellow tinted ads preceding title page. $200. (Auction price, 1960, Arthur Swann's exceptionally fine copy, $270.) Another, rehinged, spine preserved, binding worn, $42.50. [Supersedes entry in *GIYA*.]

TWAIN, Mark. *Following the Equator*. Hartford, 1897. (By Samuel Langhorne Clemens.) 1st ed., 1st issue, with Hartford imprint only (New York added later). $25 to $40.

TWAIN, Mark. *Letters from the Sandwich Islands*. San Francisco, 1937. (By Samuel Langhorne Clemens.) 1st ed. One of 550. $30.

TWAIN, Mark. *Mark Twain's Sketches, New and Old*. Blue cloth. Hartford, 1875. (By Samuel Langhorne Clemens.) 1st ed., 1st issue, errata slip, with identical footnotes pp. 119 and 120. $50. Another, spine slightly frayed, $37.50. 2d issue, with footnote on p. 119 only, $10 to $15. [Not to be confused with paperbound *Mark Twain's Sketches* of 1874; see title entry in *GIYA*.]

TWAIN, Mark. *The Prince and the Pauper*. Boston, 1882. (By Samuel Langhorne Clemens.) 1st ed., 1st issue with imprint of Franklin Press at foot of copyright page. One of 15 (?) copies on China (India) paper. $600. 1st regular issue, $50 to $100. Worn copies, $10 up. Montreal, 1881. Paperbound (copyright ed.). $1,000. Boston, 1882. Prospectus for *The*

Prince and the Pauper, containing samples of text and binding styles. $25. [Supersedes entry in *GIYA.*]

TWAIN, Mark. *Tom Sawyer Abroad.* New York, 1894. (By Samuel Langhorne Clemens.) 1st ed. $40 to $50. [Supersedes entry in *GIYA.*]

TWAIN, Mark. *What Is Man?* Boards, leather label, uncut. New York, 1906. (By Samuel Langhorne Clemens.) 1st ed. One of 250, boxed. $75.

TWIN Cities Directory and Business Mirror for the Year 1860, Including the Cities of Davenport, Iowa; Rock Island, Ill., and Moline, Ill. Vol. 1. (E. Coy & Co.) Davenport, 1859. Backstrip lacking, $65.

TWO Years Before the Mast. New York, 1840. (By Richard Henry Dana, Jr.) 1st ed., 1st issue, tan printed cloth, with "Family Library. No. CVI" on spine, 105 titles listed on back cover, letter "i" dotted in word "in" on copyright page, and perfect type for running head on page 9. $600. [For other prices, see *GIYA.*]

TYLER, Sgt. Daniel. *A Concise History of the Mormon Battalion in the Mexican War.* No place [Salt Lake City], 1881 [actually 1882]. 1st ed. $50 to $100.

TYPES of Successful Men in Texas. Red leather. Austin, 1890. Spine worn, $25.

TYSON, Philip T. *Geology and Industrial Resources of California, etc.* Folding maps, charts, tables. Baltimore, 1851. With 37-page *Reports on the Geology and Topography of California* bound in, $30.

TYSON, Robert A. *History of East St. Louis.* Paperbound. Folding map and folding view of stock yards. East St. Louis, 1875. $100.

U

ULTIMAS Communicaciónes entre el Gobierno Mexicano y el Enviado Estraordinario, etc. 22 pp., paperbound. Mexico, 1846. $75.

UNITED States Enrollment Laws (The), for Calling Out the National Forces. Paperbound. New York, 1864. $27.50.

UNITED States "History" as the Yankee Makes and Takes It, By a Confederate Soldier. 99 pp., paperbound. Glen Allen, 1900. (By John Cussons.) Ex-library, new buckram, original covers patched, bound in, $25.

URREA, José. *Diario de las Operaciónes Militares de la División que al Mando del Gen. José Urrea hizo la Campaña de Tejas.* Victoria, Mexico, 1838. Rebound in full calf, $450.

V

VAGABOND (The). A New Story for Children. 16 pp., paperbound. Hartford, 1819. (By Samuel Griswold Goodrich.) 1st ed. $150.

VAIL, Isaac Newton. *Alaska: Land of the Nugget. Why?* 68 pp., paperbound. Pasadena, 1897. $25.

VAIL, Issac Newton. *Ophir's Golden Wedge.* 36 pp., paperbound. Pasadena, 1893. $25.

VAIL, Joseph. *Noah's Flood: A Poem.* 28 pp., paperbound. New London, 1796. Uncut, $45.

VAN BRAGHT, T. J. *Der Blutige Schauplatz oder Märtyrer Spiegel der Tauffs Gesinnten oder Wehrlosen Christen . . . bis auf das Jahr.* Leatherbound, metal corners. Ephrata, Pa., 1748-49. Worn, $75.

VAN CLEVE, Mrs. Charlotte O. C. *"Three Score Years and*

Ten"; *Life-Long Memories of Fort Snelling, Minn., and Other Parts of the West.* No place [Minneapolis], 1888. 1st ed. $25.

VANCOUVER, Capt. George. *Photostatic Facsimile Atlas to Vancouver's Voyages.* No place, no date. In ¾ morocco, $100.

VANDERBILT, William K. *Taking One's Own Ship Around The World.* 19 color plates, 112 photos. Half morocco. New York, 1929. One of 200, boxed. $65.

VANDERBILT, William K. *West Made East With the Loss of a Day.* 7 color plates, 13 charts. New York, 1933. One of 800. Presentation copy, $45.

VAN TRAMP, John C. *Prairie and Rocky Mountain Adventures.* 61 plates. Columbus, 1858. 1st ed. $25.

VAN VLIET, Gen. S. *Table of Distances in the Department of the Missouri.* 3 folding maps, folding table. 20 pp., paperbound. Washington, 1874. Unopened, $75.

VAUGHAN, Dr. John. *A Concise History of the Autumnal Fever, Which Prevailed in the Borough of Wilmington, in the Year 1802.* 32 pp., unbound. Wilmington, Del., 1803. 1st ed. $60.

VENEGAS, Miguel. *El Apostol Mariano Representado en la Vida del V.P. Juan Maria De Salvatierra, de la Compañia de Jesus, Fervoroso Missionero en la Provincia de Nueva-Espana, etc.* Vellum. Mexico, 1754. $450.

VERGARA, Agustin de. *Manifiesto que Saca a Luz, el Defensor de los Bienes del Marques de Villapuente, en Representación de la Marques a de las Torres, etc.* 138 pp., paperbound. Puebla de los Angeles, 1741. $1,200.

VICAR of Wakefield (The). 2 vols. in 1. Philadelphia, 1772. (By Oliver Goldsmith.) 1st Am. ed. $150.

VILLAGRA, Gaspar de. *History of New Mexico.* Translated by Gilberto Espinosa. Boards. Los Angeles, 1933. $35.

VINTON, John Adams. *The Vinton Memorial*. Boston, 1858. $25.

VISIT to Texas (A). Folding map, 4 engravings. New York, 1834. (By Col. W. W. Morris and Dr. M. [or E.] Fisk [e]?) 1st ed. $150 to $200. Spine worn, $100. New York, 1836. 2d ed. $75 to $100.

VOICE of the Fair. Vol. 1. Half morocco. Chicago, 1865. $100.

VOLTAIRE, Jean Francois Marie Arouet de. *Candide*. Translated by Richard Aldington. Rockwell Kent illustrations. New York, 1928. One of 95. $75.

VON ROSENBERG Family of Texas. No place, 1949. $25.

VOORHEES, Luke. *Personal Recollections of Pioneer Life on the Mountains and Plains of the Great West*. 75 pp., clothbound. Cheyenne, Wyo., 1920. $50.

VOYAGE to Mexico and Havanna (A); Including Some General Observations on the United States. By an Italian. New York, 1841. (By Charles Barinetti.) 1st ed. Worn, hinges partly split, lacking spine, $25.

W

WAGNER, Lieut. Col. A. L. and Comm. J. D. Kelley. *The United States Army and Navy*. 43 colored plates. Oblong folio, leatherette. Akron, 1899. $70. Another, rubbed, shaken, $25.

WAGNER, Henry R. *Bullion to Books*. Los Angeles, 1942. $35.

WAGNER, Henry R. (ed.). *California Voyages, 1539-1541*. San Francisco, 1925. $25.

WAGNER, Henry R. *The Cartography of the Northwest Coast of America to the Year 1800*. 2 vols. Berkeley, 1937. In dust jacket, boxed, $50.

WAGNER, Henry R. *Sir Francis Drake's Voyage Around the World.* Maps, plates. San Francisco, 1926. 1st ed. $25.

WAGSTAFF, A. E. (ed.). *Life of David S. Terry.* San Francisco, 1892. $45.

WAKEFIELD, Maj. Paul L. (comp.). *Campaigning Texas.* 156 pp., paperbound. Austin, 1932. One of 50. $50.

WALKER, Charles D. *Biographical Sketches of the Graduates and Élèves of the Virginia Military Institute Who Fell During the War Between the States.* Philadelphia, 1875. Spine worn, $30.

WALKER, Tacetta B. *Stories of Early Days in Wyoming Big Horn Basin.* Casper, no date (1936). $25.

WALL, Bernhardt. *Ten Etched Poems. First Series.* Boards, paper label. New York, 1924. 1st ed. One of 50 signed by the artist. Uncut, $30.

WALLA Walla County. Colored maps. Chicago, 1909. Worn, $25.

WALN, Robert. *American Bards. A Satire.* Philadelphia, 1820. $25.

WALTHER, C. F. and I. N. Taylor. *The Resources and Advantages of Nebraska.* 2 folding maps. 27 pp., paperbound. No place, no date [Omaha, 1871]. $45.

WAR History of the National Rifles, Co. A, 3d Battalion, District of Columbia Volunteers, of 1861. Errata slip. Wilmington, Del., 1887. $38.50.

WAR in Texas (The), etc. By a Citizen of the United States. Paperbound. Philadelphia, 1837. (By Benjamin Lundy.) 2d ed. ¾ morocco, original covers bound in, $30.

WARD, D. B. *Across the Plains in 1853.* 55 pp., paperbound. Seattle, no date [1911]. $90.

WARDER, T. B. and J. M. Catlett. *Battle of Young's Branch, or, Manassas Plain.* 2 folding maps. Paperbound. Richmond, 1862. 1st ed. A little torn, $25.

WARE, Eugene F. *The Indian War of 1864.* Topeka, 1911. 1st ed. $37.50.

WARE, Eugene F. *The Lyon Campaign in Missouri.* Topeka, 1907. Corners bent, $30.

WARNER and Foote. *Directory of Carroll County.* (Iowa). 48 pp., paperbound. Minneapolis, 1884. $35.

WARNER, Col. J. J., Benjamin Hayes, and Dr. J. P. Widney. *An Historical Sketch of Los Angeles County.* 88 pp., paperbound. Los Angeles, 1876. $65.

WARNER, M. M. *Warner's History of Dakota County, Nebraska.* Lyons, Neb., 1893. 1st ed. Inner hinge weak, $27.50.

WARNER, Matt and Murray E. King. *The Last of the Bandit Riders.* Caldwell, 1940. 1st ed. $50.

WARNER, Susan. *The Wide, Wide World.* 2 vols. New York, 1851. 1st ed., 1st state, brown cloth. $52.50.

WARREN, Edward. *A Doctor's Experiences in Three Continents.* Baltimore, 1885. $30. Worn, $25.

WARREN, Lieut. G. K. *The Report of the Secretary of War, etc.* 79 pp., maps. No place [Washington], 1855. $25.

WARREN, John C., M.D. *The Mastodon Giganteus of North America.* Boston, 1852. 1st ed. $25.

WARREN, Mrs. Mercy. *Poems, Dramatic and Miscellaneous.* Boston, 1790. 1st ed. $25.

WASHINGTON, George. *A Message of the President . . . Relative to France and Great Britain: Dec. 5, 1793.* Philadelphia, 1795. Foxed, $27.50.

WASHINGTON'S Ankunft in Elisium, eine Dialogi-kirte Elizze. 36 pp., paperbound. Lancaster, 1800. Chipped, $250.

WASSON, George S. and Lincoln Colcord. *Sailing Days on the Penobscot.* Salem, 1932. $25.

WATSON, Douglas S. (ed.). *California in the Fifties.* 50 views. Oblong folio. San Francisco, 1936. Limited ed. In dust jacket, $50 and $40.

WATTS, W. W. *Old English Silver.* 307 plates. New York, 1924. Uncut, unopened, in dust jacket, $32.50 and $40.

WAUGH, Lorenzo. *Autobiography of.* Oakland, 1883. 1st ed. $25.

WEBBER, Charles W. *The Hunter Naturalist; Romance of Sporting, and Wild Scenes and Wild Hunters.* Colored lithographs. Philadelphia, no date [1851]. $25.

"WEBFOOT." *Fore and Aft; Or, Leaves from the Life of an Old Sailor.* Boston, 1871. (By William D. Phelps.) 1st ed. $35.

WEBSTER, Noah. *A Compendious Dictionary of the English Language.* Hartford, 1806. 1st ed. $35 to $50.

WEBSTER, Noah. *A Dictionary of the English Language Compiled for the Use of Common Schools in the United States.* New Haven, 1807. 1st ed. Inkstained, $25. [For other Webster dictionaries, see *GIYA*.]

WEBSTER, Noah. *Dissertation on the English Language.* Boards. Boston, 1789. 1st ed. New replica calf back, $40.

WEBSTER, Noah. *Elements of Useful Knowledge. Vol. 1.* Hartford, 1802. 1st ed. $25.

WEGERSLEV, C. H. and Thomas Walpole. *Past and Present of Buena Vista County, Iowa.* Chicago, 1909. $30.

WELLMAN, Paul I. *The Callaghan, Yesterday and Today.* Map. 82 pp., paperbound. Encinal, Tex., no date. $35.

WEST, John C. *A Texan in Search of a Fight.* 189 pp., paperbound. Waco, 1901. $40. Rebound in buckram, $45.

WEST Shore (The). Vol. XIII. (January to December, 1887.) Half leather. Portland, 1887. $25.

WESTERN Agriculturist (The), and Practical Farmer's Guide. Folding plate. Cincinnati, 1830. $35.

WESTERNERS Brand Books. Denver: 1945 [1946], $25, $35, $60; 1946 [1947], $25, $35; 1947 [1949], $25; 1948 [no date], $25; 1949 [1950], $25; 1950 [1951], $25; 1951 [1952], $40; 1952 [1953], 1953 [no date], 1956 [1957], and later, $15 to $20, going up. Los Angeles: No. 2 [1949], $25; No. 4 [1950], $25; No. 5 [1953], $25; No. 7 [1957], $25. Chicago: Vol. 1 [1941], $25. [Supersedes *Brand Book* listings in *GIYA*.]

WESTON, Silas. *Four Months in the Mines of California; or, Life in the Mountains.* Paperbound. Providence, 1854. 2d ed. (of *Life in the Mountains*). In folding case, $110.

WESTON, Silas. *Life in the Mountains: or Four Months in the Mines of California.* Paperbound. Providence, 1854. 1st ed. $135.

WETHERILL, Samuel. *An Apology for the Religious Society, Called Free Quakers.* Paperbound. Philadelphia, no date [1798]. 1st ed. Uncut, $37.50.

WETMORE, Alphonso (comp.). *Gazetteer of the State of Missouri.* Folding map. St. Louis, 1837. 1st ed. $75. [For other, defective copies, see *GIYA*.]

WHARTON, Clarence. *Remember Goliad.* 61 pp., boards. Houston, 1931. One of 100. $75.

WHEAT, Carl I. *Mapping the Trans-Mississippi West. Vol. 1.* San Francisco, 1957. One of 1,000. $75 and going up. *Vol. 2 (Lewis and Clark to Fremont, 1804-1845).* 60 maps. San Francisco, 1958. $60.

WHEAT, Carl I. *Maps of the California Gold Region, 1848-1857.* 26 maps reproduced. San Francisco, 1942. $275.

WHEAT, Carl I. *The Pioneer Press of California.* Oakland, 1948. One of 450. $25.

WHEELER, Edward L. *Deadwood Dick's Doom; or, Calamity Jane's Last Adventure.* 16 pp., paperbound (self wrappers). New York, 1881. Unopened, $35.

WHEELER, William Ogden (comp.). *The Ogden Family in America.* Philadelphia, 1907. $25.

WHERE Men Only Dare to Go, or, The Story of a Boy Company, by an Ex-Boy. Richmond, 1885. (By Royall W. Figg.) $40.

WHITE, The Rev. George. *Statistics of the State of Georgia.* Map and errata leaf. Savannah, 1849. $25.

WHITE, John. *History of a Voyage to the China Sea.* Folding map, 6 plates. Half leather. Boston, 1823. 1st ed. Uncut, $30.

WHITE, John M. *The Newer Northwest.* 216 pp., paperbound. St. Louis, 1894. $65.

WHITE, Joseph M. *A New Collection of the Laws . . . of Great Britain, France and Spain.* 2 vols. Philadelphia, 1839. Worn, $50.

WHITE, Owen P. *Trigger Fingers.* New York, 1926. 1st ed. $45.

WHITEFIELD, G. *Three Letters from the Rev. Mr. G. Whitefield.* (Letters I and II to a Friend in London, Letter III to the Inhabitants of Maryland, Virginia, North and South Carolina.) 16 pp. Philadelphia, 1740. (Printed by Benjamin Franklin.) Half morocco, $135.

WHITMAN, Walt. *The Book of Heavenly Death.* (Compiled from *Leaves of Grass* by Horace Traubel.) Portrait. Portland, 1905. One of 50 on Japan vellum. In dust jacket, boxed (box torn), $25.

WHITMAN, Walt. *Notes and Fragments: Left by Walt Whitman and Now Edited by Richard Maurice Bucke.* No place, 1899. One of 225. $25.

WHITMAN, Walt. *November Boughs.* Limp red cloth. Philadelphia, 1888. 1st ed., large paper. $37.50. Another, inscribed by Whitman, $200.

WHITMER, David. *An Address to All Believers in Christ.* 75 pp., paperbound. Richmond, Mo., 1887. $55. [Supersedes listing in *GIYA*.]

WHITNEY, J. D. *The Auriferous Gravels of the Sierra Nevada of California.* Folding maps and plates. Cambridge, 1880. $50.

WHITNEY, J. H. E. *The Hawkins Zouaves.* New York, 1866. Worn, $25.

WHITTIER, John G. *Moll Pitcher, and the Minstrel Girl. Poems.* Paperbound. Philadelphia, 1840. Part of spine missing, $75. [See *GIYA* for 1st ed. (1832) of *Moll Pitcher.* This 1840 reprint includes the first book edition of "The Minstrel Girl."]

WHOLE Booke of Psalms (The). No place [Cambridge], 1640. (Translated by Richard Mather, John Eliot, and Thomas Weld and printed by Stephen Daye.) $151,000 (auction price, 1947). [Supersedes entry in *GIYA*.]

WIERZBICKI, F. P. *California As It Is and As It May Be, or a Guide to the Gold Regions.* San Francisco, 1933. One of 550. In dust jacket, $30.

WIGGIN, Kate Douglas. *Rebecca of Sunnybrook Farm.* Boston and New York, 1903. 1st ed., 1st issue, with publisher's imprint on spine in type only $\frac{1}{16}$ inches high. $25.

WILBUR, Marguerite Eyer (trans.). *The Indian Uprising in Lower California, 1734-1737, As Described by Father Sigismundo Taraval.* Los Angeles, 1931. $25.

WILDER, Thornton. *The Bridge of San Luis Rey.* Rockwell Kent lithographs. New York, 1929. One of 1,000, boxed, signed. $25.

WILKES, Charles. *Western America, Including California and*

Oregon. 3 maps. Paperbound. Philadelphia, 1849. $87.50. Another, $35.

WILKESON, Samuel. *Wilkeson's Notes on Puget Sound.* 47 pp., paperbound. No place, no date [New York, 1870?]. 1st ed. $25.

WILL, George F. *Notes on the Arikara Indians and Their Ceremonies.* 48 pp., paperbound. Denver, 1934. One of 75. $45.

WILLARD, John Ware. *A History of Simon Willard, Inventor and Clockmaker.* Boston, 1911. One of 500. $90, possibly more.

WILLEY, S. H. *An Historical Paper Relating to Santa Cruz.* 37 pp., paperbound. San Francisco, 1876. $45.

WILLIAMS, G. T. *Receipts and Shipments of Livestock at Union Stock Yards for 1890.* 40 pp. Chicago, 1891. $75.

WILLIAMS, Jesse. *A Description of the United States Lands of Iowa.* Folding map in color. New York, 1840. In cloth case, $175. Another, $100. [See *GIYA.*]

WILLIAMS, Joseph. *Narrative of a Tour from the State of Indiana to the Oregon Territory.* 48 pp., paperbound. Cincinnati, 1843. 1st ed. $2,000 and up. New York, 1921. One of 250. $25 to $30.

WILLIAMS, O. W. *In Old New Mexico, 1879-1880: Reminiscences of Judge O. W. Williams.* 48 pp., paperbound. No place, no date. $35.

WILLIAMS, R. H. *With the Border Ruffians.* New York, 1907. 1st ed. $35.

WILLIAMS, Samuel. *The Natural and Civil History of Vermont.* Folding map. Walpole, N.H. 1794. 1st ed. $25.

WILLIAMS, Samuel C. (ed.). *Adair's History of the American Indians.* Johnson City, 1930. (By James Adair.) $30.

WILLIAMSON, James J. *Mosby's Rangers*. New York, 1909. 2d ed. $30.

WILSON, John A. *Adventures of Alf Wilson*. Toledo, 1880. Worn, $25.

WILSON, John Albert. *History of Los Angeles County, California, with Illustrations Descriptive of Its Scenery*. Oakland, 1880. Waterstained, $250.

WILSON, Obed G. *My Adventures in the Sierras*. Franklin, Ohio, 1902. $37.50.

WILSON'S History of Hickory County, Missouri. Hermitage, Mo., no date. Spine chipped, $30.

WILTSEE, Ernest A. *Gold Rush Steamers*. San Francisco, 1938. One of 500. $50.

WINKFIELD, Unca Eliza. *The Female American*. Newburyport, no date [1794]. (By William Winkfield.) Minor defects, $27.50.

WISE, George. *Campaigns and Battles of the Army of Northern Virginia*. New York, 1916. Spine faded, $40.

WISLIZENUS, Frederick A. *A Journey to the Rocky Mountains in the Year 1839*. Folding map. St. Louis, 1912. One of 500, boards. $40. Others, $25 and $35.

WISLIZENUS, Frederick A. *Memoir of a Tour to Northern Mexico, Connected with Col. Doniphan's Expedition*. 3 folding maps. Washington, 1848. 1st ed. $25 (for copies in boards, new and old, and unbound).

WITHERS, Alexander S. *Chronicles of Border Warfare*. Clarksburg, Va., 1831. 1st ed., with 4 pp. table of contents. $100. Other copies, $52.50; chipped, flyleaf stained, $37.50. [Supersedes entry in *GIYA*.]

WOLFE, Thomas. *Of Time and the River*. New York, 1935. 1st ed. In dust jacket, $25. In dust jacket and inscribed by author, $50.

WONDERFUL Stories of Fuz-Buz the Fly and Mother Brabem the Spider. Philadelphia, 1867. (By S. Weir Mitchell.) 1st ed. One of 170 on large paper. Rubbed, stained, inner front hinge split, $92.50. 1st regular ed. $37.50.

WOOD, James H. *The War, Stonewall Jackson, His Campaigns and Battles, The Regiment, As I Saw Them.* Cumberland, Md., no date [about 1910]. Cover worn and spotted, $60.

WOOD, R. E. *Life and Confessions of James Gilbert Jenkins: the Murderer of 18 Men.* Paperbound. Napa City, Calif., 1864. $75. Another, $55.

WOOD, W. D. *Reminiscences of Reconstruction in Texas.* 58 pp., paperbound. No place [San Marcos], 1902. Front cover frayed at edges, $30.

WOODRUFF, W. E. *With the Light Guns in '61-'65.* Little Rock, 1903. Waterstained, $47.50. Another, rebound in buckram, $52.50.

WOODS, Daniel B. *Sixteen Months at the Gold Diggings.* New York, 1851. 1st ed., with 8 pp. ads. In slip case, $50. Another, no slip case, $45. Another, lacking front flyleaf, $30.

WOODSON, W. H. *History of Clay County, Missouri.* Topeka, 1920. $25.

WOODWARD, Augustus B. *Considerations of the Executive Government on the United States of America.* 80 pp., unbound. Flatbush, N.Y. 1809. $25.

WOODWORTH, Samuel. *The Champions of Freedom, or the Mysterious Chief.* 2 vols., boards. New York, 1816-1818. Spines chipped, title page of Vol. 1 mounted, $75.

WOOLF, Virginia. *Two Stories.* Paperbound. Richmond, 1917. 1st ed. $90.

WOOLMAN, John. *Considerations on Keeping Negroes.* Part 2. Paperbound. Philadelphia, 1762. In folding case, $85.

WOOLWORTH, James M. *Nebraska in 1857.* Colored folding map. Omaha, 1857. Rebacked, $175.

"WORLD'S" History of Cleveland ("The"). Cleveland, 1896. Binding somewhat loose, $25.

WRIGHT, E. W. (ed.). *Lewis and Dryden's Marine History of the Pacific Northwest.* Morocco. Portland, 1895. $90, $85, $60. Another, front hinges cracked, $50.

WRIGHT, Harry. *Harry Wright's Pocket Base Ball Score Book, No. 1.* Boston, 1876. $27.50.

WRIGHT, Capt. T. J. *History of the 8th Regiment, Kentucky Volunteer Infantry.* St. Joseph, 1880. Cover faded and worn, $35.

WROTH, Lawrence C. *The Early Cartography of the Pacific.* New York, 1934. One of 100. $25.

WYETH, John A. *Life of Gen. Nathan Bedford Forrest.* 55 plates and maps. New York, 1899. $35.

WYETH, John B. *Oregon, or a Short History of a Long Journey.* [and] John K. Townsend's *Journey Across the Rockies to the Columbia.* Cleveland, 1905. $30.

Y

YALE-COLLEGE. Subject to the General Assembly. Stitched, uncut. New Haven, 1784. (By Samuel N. Dana.) 1st ed. $35.

YE Preposterous Booke of Brasse, Which Includes Divers Strange & Surprising Vituscan Voyages, etc. 55 pp., gold metallic covers. No place [San Francisco], 1937. $25.

YEARY, Mamie. *Reminiscences of the Boys in Gray, 1861-1865.* Dallas, 1912. Rebound, $75.

YELLOWPLUSH Correspondence (The). Boards. Philadelphia, 1838. (By William Makepeace Thackeray.) 1st ed. $90.

YOAKUM, Henderson K. *History of Texas.* Folding document and maps. 2 vols. New York, 1856. $60.

YOUNG, Andrew W. *History of Chautauqua County, New York.* Buffalo, 1875. $25.

YOUNG, Brigham. *Governor's Message to the 1st General Assembly of the State of Deseret.* No place, no date [Great Salt Lake City, 1862]. $100.

YOUNG, Harry. *Hard Knocks.* 25 plates. Portland, 1915. 1st ed. $25. Chicago, 1915. $15.

YOUNG, R. M. *Argument of Attorney for the Occupants of Portage City Against the State of Wisconsin.* 62 pp., paperbound. No place, no date [Washingon, 1857]. $45.

YOUNGBLOOD, Charles L. *Adventures of . . . During Ten Years on the Plains.* Boonville, Ind., 1882. 1st ed. Autographed, $265.

Z

ZACCARELLI, John. *Zaccarelli's Pictorial Souvenir Book of the Golden Northland.* Oblong, paperbound. Dawson, no date [1908]. $25.

ZAMACOIS, Niceto de. *El Buscador de Oro en California.* 81 pp., paperbound. Mexico, 1855. $37.50.

ZAMORANO 80 (The). *A Selection of Distinguished California Books etc.* Los Angeles, 1945. One of 500, signed, $45, $55, $32.50.

ZAVALA, Lorenzo de. *Ensayo Historico de las Revoluciónes de Megico, Desde 1808 Hasta 1830.* 2 vols. Mexico, 1845. $90. [For 1st ed. of this, see *"De Zavala"* in *GIYA*.]

ZEVALLOS, P. Francisco. *Carta del Padre Provincial Francisco Zevallos Sobre la Apostólica Vida, y Virtudes del P. Fernando Konsag Insigne Missionero de la California.* 31 pp., vellum. Mexico, 1764. $600.